G000037965

ILLUSTRATED ENCYCLOPEDIA OF BIRDS

ILLUSTRATED ENCYCLOPEDIA OF BIRDS

HAMLYN

Photographic acknowledgements

Ardea Photographics, London – J. Carlson, 38; M. D. England, 26 bottom; Kenneth W. Fink, 41; W. R. Taylor, 30. **British Museum, London,** 13. **Bruce Coleman, Uxbridge** – 16 middle, 31, 58, 60, 89 top, 92, 149 top, 182 bottom, 183 top; Jen & Des Bartlett, 67 top, 74 top, 75 top left & bottom, 77, 94 bottom, 111, 132 top, 145 bottom, 147 top; Des Bartlett, 75 top right, 143 top; S. C. Bisserot 26 top; Mark Boutton, 98; E. Breeze-Jones, 104; John R. Brownlie, 160; Jane Burton, 16 bottom, 62 bottom; Bob & Clara Calhoun, 29 top, 114, 120, 151, 173 bottom; Bob Campbell, 87; Brian J. Coates, 140, 158, 174 bottom, 183 bottom; Alain Compost, 141; Stephen Dalton, 156 bottom, 162, 166; L. R. Dawson, 11; A. J. Deane, 84 bottom, 85 top, 101 top, 102, 119, 125, 126, 130, 137, 150, 152 bottom; Jack Dermid, 178 top; Ernest Duscher, 83 bottom, 179 top, 180 top; Francisco Erize 73 bottom, 80 top, 90 top, 143 bottom; M. P. L. Fogden, 146, 148 bottom; Jeff Foott, 109, 135 bottom; C. B. Frith, 108; Robert Gillmor 6/7, 135 top; Sven Gillsater, 25 bottom; Dennis Green, 144 top, 172 bottom; M. P. Harris, 74 bottom; Pekka Helo, 148 top, 175 top; D. Houston, 54, 78; Udo Hirsch, 81 bottom, 84 top, 86, 88, 107 top, 185 bottom; M. P. Kahl, 89 bottom, 121 bottom, 154 bottom; Stephen J. Krasemann, 175 bottom; Hugo A. Lambrechts, 145 top, 155 top; Gordon Langsbury, 91 bottom, 133 bottom, 169 top, 171 bottom, 184; Wayne Lankinen, 103, 144 bottom; Cyril Laubscher, 163 top; Leonard Lee Rue III, 17, 45, 80 bottom, 82 top, 93 bottom, 107 bottom, 113, 155 bottom, 157, 171 top; Antti Leinonen, 165; John Markham 161, 167 bottom, 172 top; Derek Middleton, 76 top, 129; Colin Molyneux, 90 bottom; R. K. Murton, 142 bottom, 149 bottom, 164, 169 bottom; Norman Myers, 97; Charles J. Ott, 18, 24, 61 top, 94 top; Alan Parker, 131; John Pearson, 59 top left; Roger T. Peterson, 154 top; Graham Pizzey 182 top; G. D. Plage, 28, 79, 110, 174 top; Dieter & Mary Plage, 101 bottom; S. C. Porter, 85 bottom, 132 middle, 138, 172 middle; S. Prato, 29 bottom; Mike Prior, 168; Masood Qureshi, 82 bottom; Hans Reinhard, 59 bottom, 117 bottom, 147 bottom, 163 bottom; H. Rivarola, 23 top; Alan Root, 121 top, 179 bottom; John Shaw, 177 bottom; Reinhard Siegel, 173 top; M. F. Soper, 73 top, 76 bottom, 128, 142 top; Lynn M. Stone, 127; Diane & Rick Sullivan, 81 top; Norman Tomalin, 95, 152 top; Simon Trevor, 99, 180 bottom; D. & K. Urry, 25 top, 69, 133 top; Peter Ward, 93 top, 105, 185 top; W. H. D. Wince, 118; Joseph van Wormer, 91 top, 106, 117 top, 122, 123, 134, 167 top, 177 top, 178 bottom; Rod Williams, 72, 156 top; Gunter Ziesler, 16 top, 23 bottom, 83 top, 96, 132 bottom, 139, 159. **Rian Davies, Wallington,** 136. **Ron Eastman,** 21. **P. J. Green, London,** 9. **Hamlyn Group Picture Library,** 34/35, 50, 70/71. **Brian Hawkes, Newnham,** 36, 55. **Eric Hosking, London,** 43, 59 top right. **Jacana Press Agency, Paris,** Montoya, 33; Nardin, 61 bottom, 62 top; Zeisler, 71. **S. D. MacDonald,** 37. **Natural History Photographic Agency, Hythe** – E. A. James, 42; Peter Johnson, 53; M. Savonius, 39; Philippa Scott, 22. **P. O. Swanberg, Scaraborsgatan,** 44. **Weha-Photo, Berne,** 63.

First published 1989 by The Hamlyn Publishing Group Limited,
a Division of the Octopus Publishing Group,
Michelin House, 81 Fulham Road,
London SW3 6RB

Some material in this book has previously appeared in other Hamlyn books.

ISBN 0 600 56692 7

Produced by Mandarin Offset
Printed in Hong Kong

Contents

Section One
Biology of Birds 6

Evolution and antiquity 8
Feathers 10
Structure and skeleton 12
Feeding and beak structure 15
Migration 18
Courtship and territory 22
Nests and eggs 26
Young birds 30
Extinction and conservation 32

Section Two
Bird Habitats of the World 34

Tundra 36
Northern forests 39
Temperate woodlands 42
Tropical forests 46
Temperate grasslands 50
Savanna 53
Deserts 57
Temperate wetlands 60
Tropical wetlands 63
The oceans 66

Section Three
Bird Families of the World 70

Ostriches 71
Rheas 72
Emus and cassowaries 72
Kiwis 72
Tinamous 73
Penguins 73
Divers and loons 74
Grebes 76
Albatrosses, shearwaters and petrels 77
Pelicans and allies 78
Herons, storks and allies 82
Ducks, geese and swans 89
Birds of prey 95
Gallinaceous birds 108
Cranes and rails 120
Waders and gulls 126
Sandgrouse and pigeons 136
Parrots and parakeets 139
Cuckoos and turacos 141
Owls 143
Nightjars and allies 147
Swifts and humming-birds 150
Colies 152
Trogons 152
Kingfishers, hoopoes, hornbills and allies 153
Woodpeckers and allies 155
Perching birds 157

Index 186

Section One

Biology of Birds

Birds are not only one of the most successful groups in the animal kingdom but they hold a special position in our awareness of the natural world. They are often the most obvious living creatures in a landscape (their apparent confidence borne of an ability to fly to safety) and their bright colours and melodic songs have long been admired by man. Yet it is only recently that we have begun to fully appreciate just how intricate their lives are.

The 8000 or so species of birds have evolved over millions of years and have adapted to many different modes of life. If one was to take a single feature which places the birds apart from all other animals it would be the development of feathers. These complex and delicate structures not only make flight possible but also serve many other functions, notably providing insulation from cold or wet and furnishing attractive or eye-catching plumages for use in courtship and territorial rituals.

As an introduction to birds, the first part of this book covers every aspect of their biology and behaviour from the skeleton and feathers to courtship and migration. The second part describes the various habitats of the world and the types of bird found in each, and the third part of the book provides a comprehensive directory of bird families of the world, from ostriches to crows, and illustrates the amazing diversity of these fascinating creatures.

Lesser Flamingoes feeding in the dawn mist at Lake Nakuru, Kenya. The population of Lesser Flamingo on this one lake has been estimated at over one million birds, out of a world population of five to six million.

Evolution and antiquity

Birds have lived on earth for far longer than man or any of the mammals. When giant dinosaurs roamed the world, there were already many kinds of birds inhabiting the forests, and wetlands and the marine environment. They included some types which we would recognise today, such as grebes, herons and waterfowl. In fact, it seems that birds are probably descended from small dinosaurs called coelurosaurs which ran standing up on their hind legs and balancing with their tails, much as birds do today. *Compsognathus (below)* is a typical coelurosaur.

The birds' reptilian ancestors were cold-blooded, active only when the heat of the sun had warmed up their bodies and becoming torpid at night or in cold weather. Obviously, any creature which could make itself less dependent on warm external temperatures could be active, hunting or breeding, when cold-blooded competitors were immobilised. That would mean evolving an insulating coat so that heat generated by the digestion of food could be kept in the body to fuel the muscles—in other words, becoming warm-blooded. It is possible that some coelurosaurs developed loose, overlapping scales which helped to insulate them, and in turn these scales evolved into feathers (which are a very efficient insulation). The new, warm-blooded creatures which possessed them eventually began to use their feathers for other purposes, growing wings and tails, and finally obtaining the power of true flight.

The fossil remains of the earliest bird-like creatures known to science—*Archaeopteryx* (the name means 'old wings')—were found in Germany in sediments which are about 150 million years old. Its pigeon-sized skeleton is much more like a reptile than like a modern bird: it has a jaw with teeth instead of a beak; there are claws on its fingers; it has a long bony tail and it lacks the strong breastbone which, in true birds, supports the powerful muscles needed for proper flight. But it does have long feathers on its forelimbs, like the primary wing feathers of modern birds, and all down its tail. Whether or not it could fly at all is anyone's guess—perhaps it only glided from tree to tree in calm air or just trotted along the ground using its wings as a sort of butterfly net to help it catch small insects to eat, with its feathery tail helping it to keep its balance. What is certain is that the few fossil skeletons of this sharp-toothed little monster from the swamps of prehistoric Bavaria are our main clue to the direct link between the reptiles and the familiar sparrows and starlings which live around us today.

Unfortunately, because birds are small and their bones are light, their remains are not often found as fossils, but from the discoveries that have been made we know that 100 million years ago true birds had evolved with their skeletons adapted for powered and controlled flight. By the Eocene period, 60 million years ago, many of the modern families of birds had already appeared as well as some extinct species, such as *Diatryma*—a fearsome, fast-running predator.

Evolution is not a process which is confined to the realms of prehistory, but rather something which continues to this very day. Charles Darwin, who through his theory of natural selection has helped us understand how evolution functions, was one of the first people to realise this and he travelled the world in order to formulate his ideas.

Darwin visited the Galapagos Islands, a chain of volcanic outcrops which lie over 500 miles off the coast of Ecuador in South America. Here he found extraordinary animals, such as giant tortoises and penguins, but it was the islands' finches that particularly fascinated him. Populations of finches from each of the islands were superficially similar and bore a striking similarity to a species from the mainland, but on closer examination, each was uniquely different. In particular, the bill-shapes varied considerably and Darwin proposed that although all the Galapagos' finches had a common ancestor, each island population had evolved in isolation to suit the exact environmental requirements of their own island.

The structural affinity between *Archaeopteryx* and its reptilian forbears is clearly apparent.

Darwin realised that every individual animal is slightly different from all others and that through a process known as 'natural selection', those best suited to the particular environment are more successful, their characters being inherited by the next generation. With modern advances in the field of genetics, we now know that genes, composed of a chemical known as deoxyribonucleic acid (DNA), are responsible for passing on the information.

Evidence of evolutionary change can even be seen in the birds that are more familiar to us all, such as crossbills which are compact little finches with bills whose tips cross at the end and which are used to prise out seeds from pine cones. The birds are widespread across much of the northern hemisphere but are largely sedentary and through geographical isolation, different races have developed in separate areas of North America. In Europe, the same is true of island populations on some of the Mediterranean islands, whilst in the caledonian pine forests of northern Scotland, the birds are considered to have become a separate species, distinguished by their larger bills.

Birds are one of the most successful groups of creatures ever to exist. Today, there are more than 8000 different species that live in extremely different environments all over the world. One and all, they owe their success to the long-extinct reptile which first grew feathers.

Archaeopteryx lithographica, the first bird, is known only from a few fossilised specimens found in the Jurassic limestone of Bavaria. The tail, bone structure and teeth resemble a small dinosaur, but the fine deposits have preserved the impression of the wing and tail feathers.

Feathers

Birds have a thin skin, consisting of two layers, the epidermis or outer layer, and the dermis or inner layer. Although the skin is thin, it produces feathers, beaks, claws and thin scales, but no cutaneous glands, except the uropygial gland at the base of the tail (Gk. *oura*, tail; *pyge*, rump), and not all birds have this.

Except in a few groups of birds, such as the ostriches, penguins and tinamous, feathers do not grow evenly over the entire surface of the body. When chickens and other fowl are ready for roasting one may see the areas from which the feathers were plucked forming well-defined tracts. In the higher orders, such as the perching birds, these tracts are even more sharply defined and follow patterns so uniform that they are given standard names. Preening birds are not only repairing individual feathers, but rearranging the plumage just as humans readjust their clothing after physical activity. Actually the feathers which cover the entire body so well grow from less than two-thirds of the skin area.

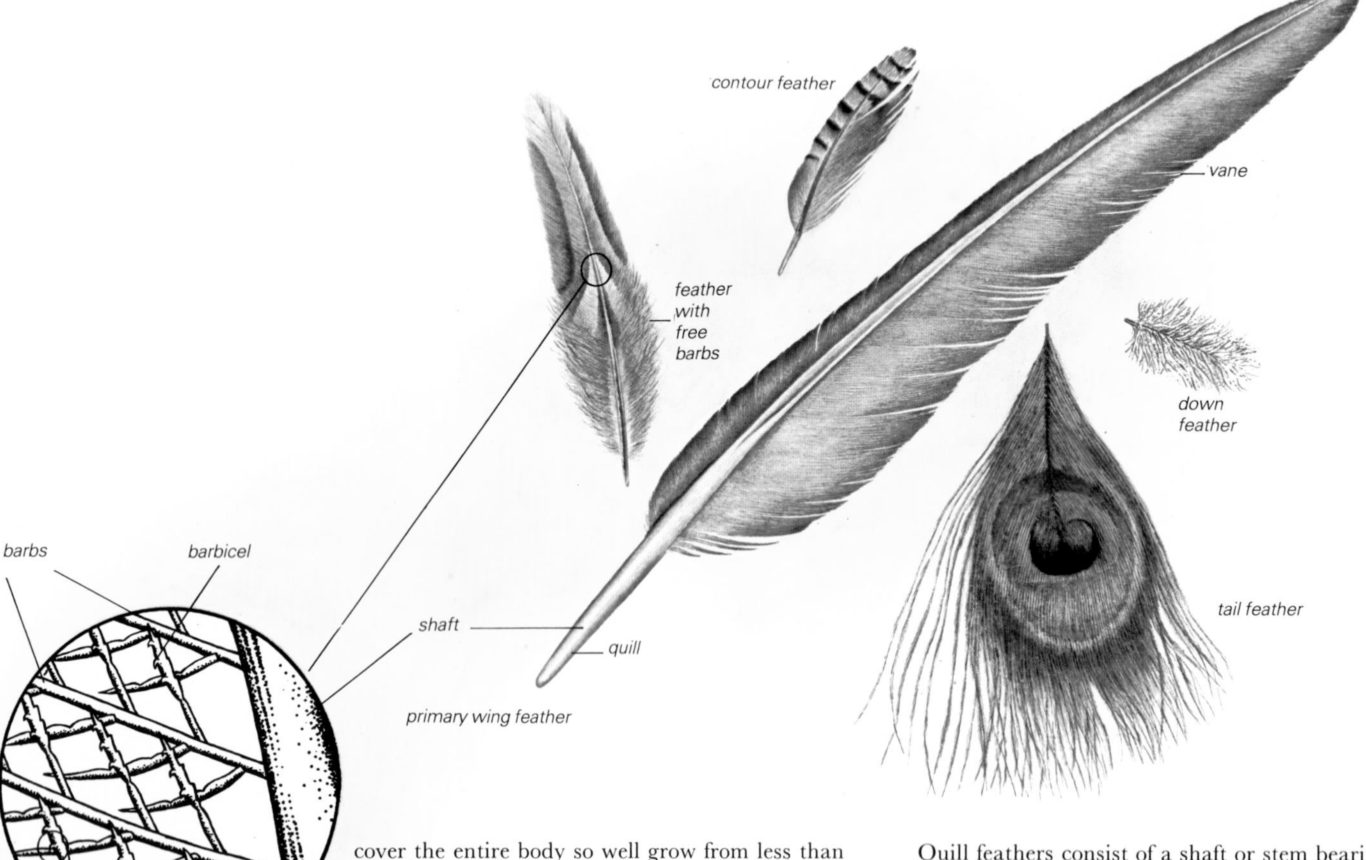

Birds have more than one type of feather reflecting their different functions. Their structures are also highly complex as can be seen in the detail shown left.

Usually there are several kinds of feathers making up the plumage of birds: the remiges, or large flight feathers of the wing; the rectrices, or large flight feathers of the tail, used for maintaining stability and for steering and braking; the tectrices, or contour feathers, which cover the body and coverts, which cover the bases of the flight feathers; the small, fine feathers which form the down; the filoplumes, or hair-like feathers, which occur on the body; and other modified feathers, such as the bristles fringing the mouth opening of most insectivorous birds.

The remiges, rectrices and contour feathers are all quill or vane feathers. The number and arrangement of the remiges and rectrices seldom vary within a species. The remiges are of three kinds: primary, attached to the 'hand' and forming the point of the wing; secondary, on the forearm; and tertiary, or scapular, from the forearm to the shoulder.

Quill feathers consist of a shaft or stem bearing a long vane down each side. The shaft has a hollow basal part, or calamus, embedded in the dermis, and a solid distal part, or rachis, supporting the vanes. Until the feather completes its growth the calamus contains blood vessels, which enter through the narrow basal opening, the inferior umbilicus. The blood flows only as far as the superior umbilicus, at the junction of the calamus and the rachis.

The vanes extend along opposite sides of the rachis. Each consists of a row of small branches, or barbs, which bear lateral branches, or barbules. The barbules of adjacent barbs overlap; those projecting towards the base of the feather lie on top and have a few small hooks, or barbicels, on their undersides. These lock on to corresponding notches on the underlying barbules of the previous barb, giving the feather cohesion as a unit and enabling the bird to fly. If the cohesion is disturbed it is rearranged by the bird preening the feather with its beak, using the oily secretion from the uropygial gland. Preening is vital to keep the feathers healthy.

Tectrices have the same structure as quills but are usually less rigid. In some species there is a miniature feather, or aftershaft, on the tectrices, which grows from the top of the calamus. It is almost identical in structure with the main part of the feather but lacks barbicels. In emus and cassowaries the aftershaft is as large as the main feather.

The down-feathers, which form the down of young birds and also persist in the adult under cover of the contour feathers, have at most a very short shaft from which spring long and fragile barbs, almost devoid of barbules. The filoplume grows on most parts of the body. It is small and superficially resembles mammalian hair.

Full-grown feathers, which are mainly dead material, are shed and renewed during the moult, usually once a year, but in some species there are two or more moults a year or one full moult in which all feathers are replaced and a partial moult. While this replacement is in progress some birds may become temporarily flightless.

The coloration of the feather is without doubt its most striking feature and is the result of structural (physical) or chemical (pigmentary) factors, or both. Structural colours are produced by the diffraction, reflection and refraction of light by systems of fine laminae, reticulations and prismatic formations in the feathers. They can always be distinguished from chemical colours because they disappear when the structures producing them are destroyed or altered, but remain unaffected by chemical solvents. Pigmentary colours, on the other hand, are produced by the presence of biochemical substances in the feathers, such as melanins, which are buff, red, brown or, more often, black; carotins which are yellow; and guanins which are white. Some birds appear to have black in the plumage which, as in the European Magpie, because of structural layering becomes iridescent green, blue or purple.

The feathers of a parrot of the genus *Ara* provide an example of structural and chemical colourings. If one of the red feathers is compressed it will retain its colour, because this is produced by pigments. Similar treatment, however, will turn one of the blue feathers brown, and a green feather yellow, because a structural colour is superimposed on the brown and yellow pigments. In this case the structural colour results from a superficial reflecting layer overlying a deeper prismatic layer.

There is usually a change of colour or shade of colour during the moult. So during its lifetime and through a single year a bird may show a succession of distinct plumages. First comes a simple pattern of the down in the young bird. This will be followed by the juvenile colour pattern, which may later give way to a winter dress. Next comes the summer or breeding coloration, followed by a new winter plumage, then again a breeding plumage, and so on. When male and female have different plumages, the young may resemble one or other of the parents (usually the female) or they may be intermediate between them, or unlike either for part of their early life.

Changes in colour through moult are gradual, for the feathers are replaced slowly, never all at one time. So there may be an almost imperceptible transition from winter to summer dress and vice versa. A good example of a gradual seasonal change is seen in the Ptarmigan and Willow Hen of northern latitudes. Both are white as snow in winter, white with brownish markings in spring, brownish in summer, and brown flecked with white in autumn. Some colour changes are not due to moult, but to feather wear. The tips of the feathers frequently differ in colour from the centre and when the tips are worn off the bird changes colour.

A hen Cuban Finch preens her mate: an important part of courtship.

A bathing Robin may look dejected, but clean plumage is essential for survival in cold weather.

Structure and skeleton

Birds' skeletons, respiratory and digestive systems and eyesight have all had to change greatly from their reptilian origins in order to create an efficient flying machine.

The flexible reptile skeleton has been largely fused together to form a strong box frame able to withstand the stresses caused by take-off and landing, by sudden changes of direction and by flying in turbulent air. To reduce their weight, birds' bones are hollow and, in some of the larger wing and leg bones, the interior is criss-crossed by many bracing struts: modern engineering practice shows that this sort of construction combines lightness with exceptional strength and flexibility, thus reducing the risk of breakage—a bird with a broken wing is soon a dead bird.

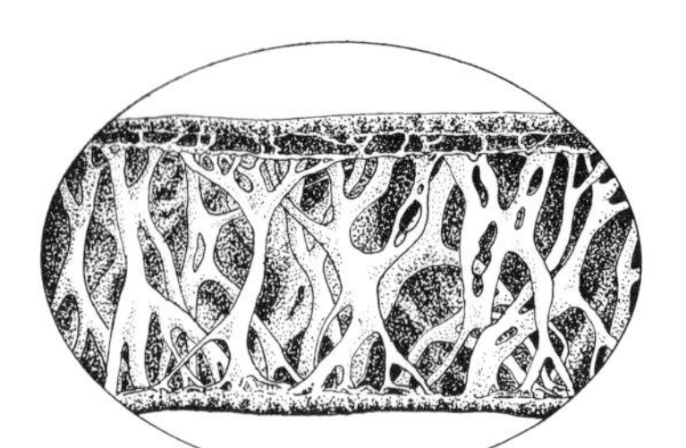

Internal struts give wing bones lightness and great strength.

Wings and flight

The exceptional feature of the bird skeleton is the modification of the forelimbs for flight. There are other adaptations also connected with flight. The shoulder girdle is particularly well developed and forms a rigid support for the wings. It also serves for the insertion of some of the wing muscles. The sternum or breastbone, which extends not only along the length of the thorax but most of the trunk as well, forms a wide plate with a substantial median projection, or keel. This keel gives anchorage to the large flight muscles. Extending laterally from the front of the sternum are two short and strong bones, the coracoids, which, along with the light but strong clavicles, form the pectoral girdle. In a sense, birds have two pairs of 'collarbones', the true collarbones, or clavicles, in front, and the coracoids lying behind them. From the top of each caracoid a scapula or shoulder-blade extends to the rear along the rib cage, further strengthening the whole structure to the stresses of winged flight. The shoulder socket, or glenoid cavity, is formed at the junction of the coracoid and scapula.

The wing is a modified arm, the three parts of which (upper arm, forearm, and hand) carry the remiges. The bases of these feathers are overlaid by rows of smaller feathers called wing coverts. The hand is considerably reduced and consists merely of three digits fused together in varying degrees. The first digit is reduced to two bones, the second to three, and the third to one. The bony structure of the bird's wing is therefore different from that of the bat with its four, elongated fingers, and from that of the flying reptiles of the Mesozoic era, which was supported by the arm-bones and one much elongated digit.

The movements of the wings of most birds are so rapid that they cannot be properly analysed or explained without the help of slow-motion film. This is particularly true of hummingbirds, so named from the humming sound produced by an

Birds have evolved into very efficient flying machines. To enable them to fly, their bones are constructed in a different way from other vertebrates, and the arrangement of the bones has produced a skeleton specially adapted for flight.

Cast of a pigeon's air sacs. Unique to birds, these aid respiration and cooling when muscles are working hard.

exceptionally rapid motion of the wings. Analysis of wing movements of the hummingbirds shows that the wings first extend upwards, are then brought forward (the feathers opening fanwise at the same time) and finish with a strong backward and downward beat. It is with this last movement that they obtain their thrust on the air and drive the bird forwards and upwards against the direction of the beat. Put another way, the bird loses height during the first phase and regains it during the third phase of wing action. The wing tips actually trace out figures of eight, the lower loop of the figure being smaller than the upper one. There are other patterns of wing movements during flight of different species groups. In general, when the wing is raised during flight each feather rotates on a plane like Venetian blinds, allowing the air to pass through and rotate closed for the down beat.

The speed, nature and type of flight of any bird depend on the form of the wing and the proportions of its various parts. In pointed wings the leading primary feather is usually longer than the others, which are progressively shorter. A pointed wing in which the 'arm' is short, as in swifts, is best adapted for speed and manœuvrability. A pointed wing coupled with a long 'arm', as in a goose, usually means a slow, powerful and sustained flight. Rounded wings, those with the middle primary feathers longer than the others, indicates slower but less sustained flight, as in the partridge. The unusually wide wingspan of eagles, albatrosses and frigate-birds enables them to make maximum use of winds and other air currents and glide for long periods of time without actually beating their wings. Vultures with their long but broad wings are able to ride rising air currents effortlessly. This is an example of economy of effort brought to an extremely high level of perfection.

In order to support the wing movements and to give the forward part of the body sufficient stability, the thorax has to be supple as well as strong. This is ensured by a number of special features. Some of the vertebrae (thoracic and lumbar) are fused (ankylosed) at their transverse and neural processes. The ribs are held firm and yet remain flexible by being braced at both the upper vertebral part and a lower sternal part. They are additionally strengthened by uncinate or hooked processes projecting backwards from each rib to overlap the rib immediately behind.

Any flying machine is easier to control if the bulk of the weight is at the centre of its body. So birds have had to make their heads as light as possible and they have done this by dispensing with teeth and all the associated heavy bones and muscles. Instead, they have a lightweight beak and they chew up their food internally. Swallowed whole or in large chunks, the food is first stored in the crop and then passed on to the gizzard. This is a tough, muscular bag which grinds up food items. Many kinds of bird deliberately swallow small pieces of grit which lodge in the gizzard and help the grinding process. One extra advantage of this system of digestion is that birds can take food from unsafe places, where they may be exposed to predators, gulping it down quickly to 'chew' it later in some places of safety.

Flight demands very good eyesight. Birds' eyes are large compared with those of most mammals. All birds need binocular vision ahead so that they can judge distances, since without it they would be unable to fly and land safely. For predatory birds

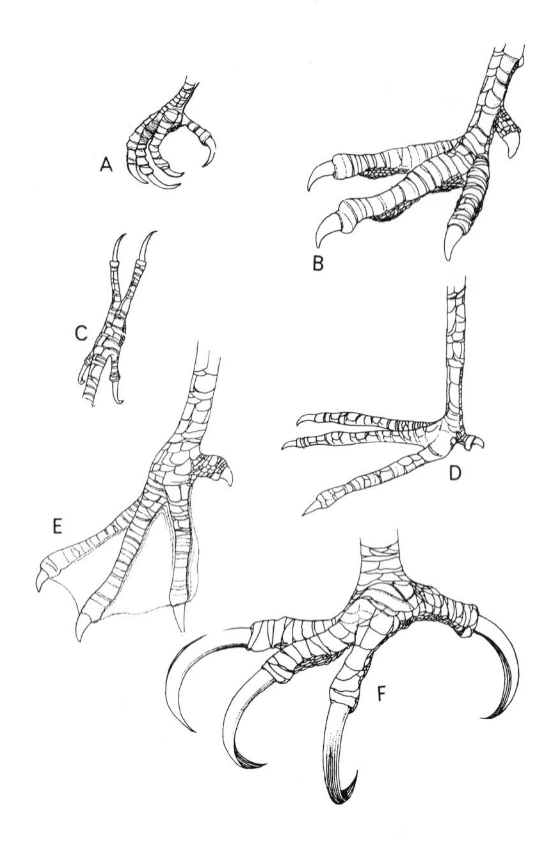

Birds' feet reflect adaptation to particular habits. The opposable hind toe of perching birds (A) is adapted for gripping a slender branch or twig, while climbing birds (C) have zygodactyl or yoke-shaped feet with sharp claws for clinging to the bark of trees. Predatory birds (F) have a wide grasp and curved talons. Walking birds (B) have heavy tarsi and toes with short, blunt claws. The elongated digits and claws of wading birds (D) give support on soft mud, but have little grasping power. In swimming birds (E) the feet are webbed and function like paddles.

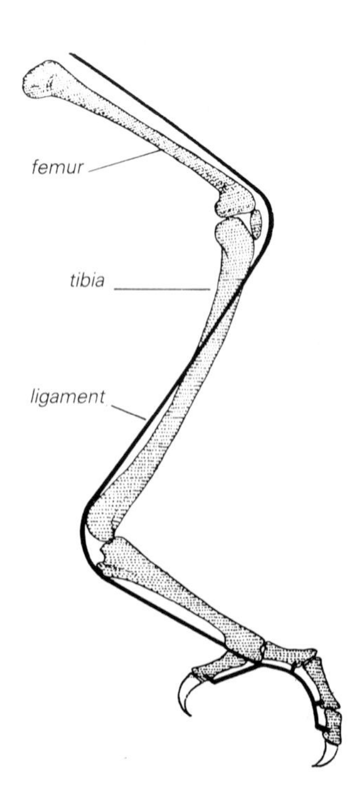

The special muscular arrangement that allows birds to cling to the branch of a tree for long periods without fatigue. The more sharply the bird bends its leg, the greater the pull on the long tendons controlling the toes.

binocular vision is also vital for catching prey. By contrast, birds which are hunted need good all-round vision so that they can instantly spot danger approaching from any direction. An excellent example is the woodcock, which probes for its food with its beak and so does not greatly need binocular vision but has complete all-round vision to spot a predator approaching from any direction.

Respiration and circulation

The trachea begins with a glottis without an epiglottis, and it has no larynx or voice box. Instead of a larynx near the upper end of the trachea, birds have a syrinx near the lower end. The syrinx serves the same general purpose as the larynx and is particularly well developed in singing birds. It is situated at the point where the trachea branches into two bronchi. Each main bronchus, the mesobronchus, runs through the lung and sends branches separately to the anterior and posterior airsacs. The airsacs also connect directly with the lungs and some connect with the airspaces in the pneumatic bones. The functioning of this complicated system serves to cause air to flow through the lungs in one direction during both inspiration and expiration. On inspiration, air passes through the lungs and posterior airsacs from the mesobronchi and through the lungs to the anterior airsacs. On exhalation, air passes from posterior airsacs through the lungs and back into the mesobronchus, where it mixes with air flowing out of the anterior airsacs. The hinged ribs allow large volume changes in the thorax. This system enables birds to extract oxygen more efficiently from thin air at great altitudes.

Flight uses energy, which in turn generates heat. Birds need very efficient respiration both to provide the oxygen necessary for converting stored fat into muscle power and to keep them cool. The airsacs connected to the lungs extend through the body and into the bones, and help particularly to keep the working muscles from overheating and seizing up.

The avian heart and associated arteries could be derived from one similar to that of the crocodile by the loss of the left aortic arch, which leads from the right ventricle and contains mixed blood. Birds have only the right aortic arch, which carries oxygenated blood from the left ventricle to the organs of the body. This is therefore a perfectly developed blood system and as it is linked with the airsac respiratory system it enables a bird to maintain a constant body temperature of between 43 °C and 44.5 °C, a great advance in comparison with reptiles and higher than that of mammals.

Legs

Birds, being winged, are necessarily bipedal, and consequently peculiar structural features are to be found in the legs. The first is that the pelvic girdle, which supports the entire weight of the body and must stand the stresses of landing from relatively high-speed flight, is elongated and fused with some of the vertebrae.

Secondly, the femora or thighbones are held in a nearly horizontal plane to bring the feet nearer the bird's centre of gravity while perching so that the bird does not fall forwards. The loss of height caused by the horizontal position of the thighbones is compensated for by the tibia or shinbone being elongated and fused with the fibula and some tarsal bones to form a long tibiotarsus, and yet a third segment is formed by the tarsometatarsus (commonly called the tarsus). The tarsus and metatarsus are distinct in the embryo but then fuse together to form this third section, on which there are scales instead of feathers.

A bird is digitigrade, that is, it stands only on its digits, heels raised off the ground. Normally there are four digits to the foot, three in front and one behind for most walking and perching birds, and two in front and two behind in many climbing birds. The toes of some species are adapted for walking on mud or floating aquatic vegetation; those of the Jacana, for example, are very long. The grebe's toes are edged with membranes, and in the Coot each toe is lobe-webbed, but most swimming birds have webs either between the three front digits, as in ducks, or even between all four, as in pelicans. Many running birds have only three toes on each foot, or two as in the Ostrich.

The claws at the end of the digits are also subject to modification. They are, for example, wide and flat in birds which scratch the soil, and serrated and sharply pointed in birds of prey.

A peculiar feature of birds is that they are able to cling to a branch for long periods of time without muscle fatigue. This is because the muscles which curl the toes and cause the feet to grasp the perch have long tendons; these run behind the tarsus, round the heel, and then close against the forward surface of the leg bones. So the more the bird bends its legs, as when it perches on a twig or branch, the greater the pull of the tendons on the toes and the firmer their grip on the branch (*see* diagram on left).

Feeding and beak structure

The bird's beak is formed by hard epidermal coverings, or rhamphothecae, over both the upper and lower jaws, and has a pair of nostrils often fringed with bristles. It serves many purposes, one of the most important being to obtain and grasp food. In consequence the form of the beak is to a large degree related to diet. Insectivorous birds may have small beaks for picking up their prey one at a time, or, as in swallows and swifts, widely gaping beaks to catch insects in flight. Others have stout beaks with which they bore holes in tree-trunks to secure their prey. Seed-eaters use their beaks to crack or remove husks from seeds, and consequently these are short, thick and strong. Birds of prey have a hook-tipped beak, often with a toothed edge. Wading birds are well adapted with long bills. Ducks and geese have broad, flat bills with transverse lamellae for straining food from water. Other highly specialised bills are seen in pelicans with their remarkable pouched beaks, crossbills with the tips of the beak crossed, and the hornbills and the toucans with their outsize bills.

The beak, then, is a useful identifying feature, but not necessarily a reliable guide to relationships. Where the several related species in a single group have adopted different diets their beaks differ in shape, as in the Darwin finches of the Galapagos. Conversely, unrelated species with the same type of diet have the same kind of beak, as in herons and storks. The tongue, also, is related to diet. There is the thick, fleshy tongue of the parrot, used in manipulating food in the beak, the long, extensile tongue of the woodpecker, and the grooved tongue of the hummingbird, which is forked near the tip.

The alimentary tract of a bird consists of a number of clearly distinct parts. The base of the gullet, or oesophagus, is often enlarged into a crop for food storage. In pigeons and turtle doves the crop secretes a milky substance used in feeding the young. The oesophagus ends at the glandular stomach, known as the proventriculus, which secretes the gastric juices. Beyond this is the heavy muscular gizzard, which crushes and grinds the food. Birds often swallow grit, which remains in the gizzard for a time and helps to grind up the food. Beyond the gizzard lies the small intestine, an organ of fairly uniform diameter, ending in the cloaca, as in reptiles and amphibians. The pancreas and the gall-bladder discharge digestive fluids into the forepart of the small intestine. The cloaca receives the discharge from the intestine as well as from the genital and urinary organs.

Modifications of parts of the alimentary tract can be correlated with the bird's diet. In seed-eaters the crop, gizzard and rectal caecae are more extensively developed than in flesh eaters, possibly because vegetable matter, particularly seeds, takes

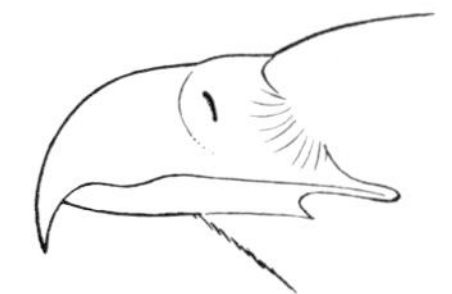

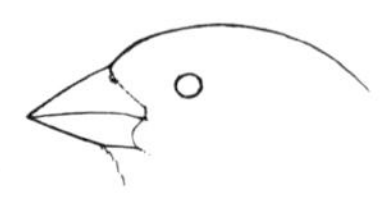

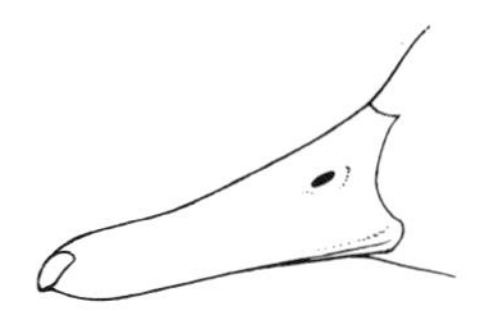

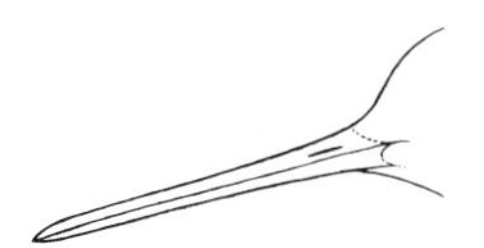

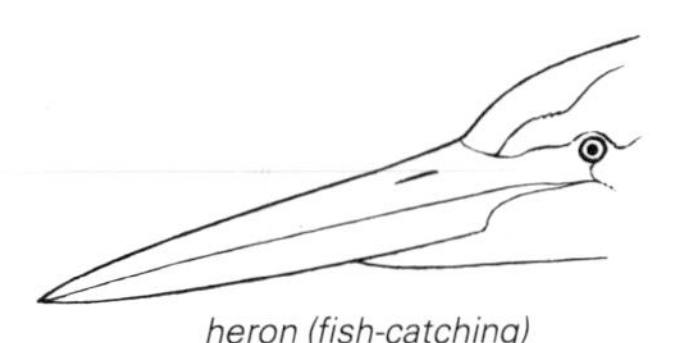

Bird beaks show enormous variation in both shape and size. At one extreme, birds of prey possess large, hook-tipped beaks for tearing flesh whereas waders' beaks are long and thin for probing mud.

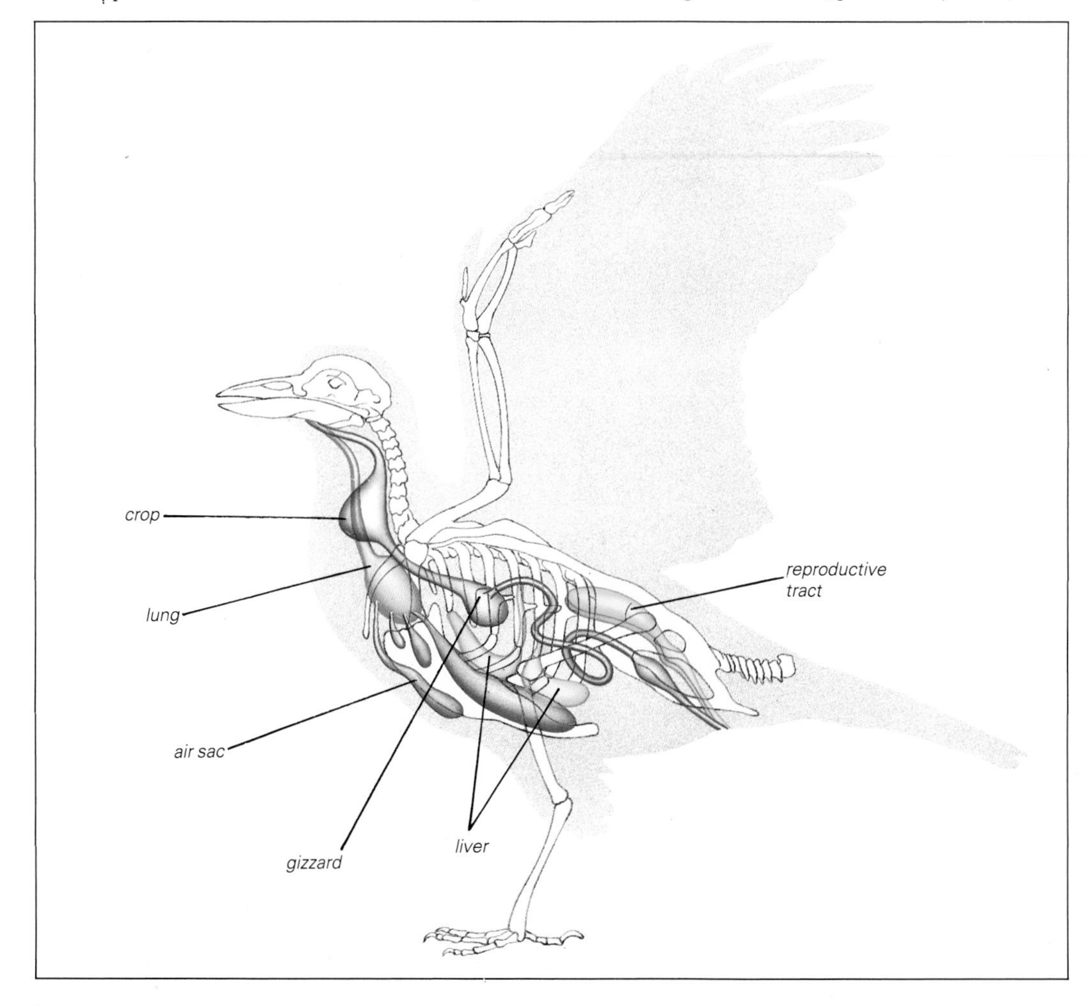

A diagram of a bird showing the internal organs. The complex digestive system and crop allows the bird to swallow its food rapidly, leaving the gizzard to break it down at a later stage.

Upper
Probably the most grotesque bird in the world is the Shoebill (*Balaeniceps rex*). It feeds on a variety of marsh animals in the papyrus swamps of the White Nile.

Middle
The Hawfinch (*Coccothraustes coccothraustes*), of Europe, is an extraordinarily shy bird and consequently seldom noticed by the casual observer. Its beak represents an extreme example of the cone-shaped beak typical of the finches and used for cracking hard seeds. A Hawfinch can even crack cherry stones.

Lower
A Golden Eagle (*Aquila chrysaetos*) calling. This bird shows the large, strong, sharply hooked beak needed by all the raptors and which, with the aid of their talons, they use to kill and dismember their prey.

longer to digest. Exceptions in this respect are pigeons which have short caecae and owls which have long ones, but this may perhaps be explained by a relatively recent change in diet.

The variety in birds' beaks

Birds' beaks come in all shapes and sizes, some small and delicate, others large and menacing. In almost all cases, the beak has evolved specifically to suit the method of feeding and by understanding how the structure and function of this essential tool are related, the keen-eyed observer can gain insight into a bird's diet and habits simply from its appearance.

Fish-eating birds

Divers or loons, and grebes are birds of coast and lake which spend almost all their time on the water. Understandably, their diet comprises almost entirely fish and members of both families have dagger-like beaks with which they catch their prey while diving underwater. Gannets and boobies have similarly powerful and pointed beaks, with slight serrations along their edges, but instead of diving from the surface of the water like grebes and loons, they plunge from great heights, thus taking their quarry unawares.

A third group of birds shares the same diet of fish and possesses a strikingly similar bill shape. Herons and egrets stab at their prey from the safety of comparatively shallow water relying on patience and good eyesight rather than active pursuit.

Anhingas or darters are curious birds, related to cormorants, which have an almost prehistoric appearance. Fish comprises their diet too but the bill is much more needle-like than other birds with a similar diet. Instead of catching the fish between the two mandibles, anhingas prefer to spear the unfortunate animal and when safely at the surface of the water, they toss it in the air in order to manoeuvre it for swallowing.

Pelicans

The beak of a pelican is its most striking feature. Below the long mandibles hangs a large pouch which can stretch when full of water and this is the key to the pelican's success when fishing. White pelicans often feed collectively and loose circles of birds can be seen driving fish towards the centre of the ring. When the prey has been concentrated, the birds simply scoop them up with their mouths wide open, the capacious pouch engulfing a huge volume of water together with the fish. The liquid is gradually forced out and the meal swallowed.

Brown pelicans, common along the Florida coastline, are unique amongst their family for they have abandoned the strategy of feeding on the surface of the water; instead, they dive from a great height. On contact with the water, the bill opens and the pouch expands to enclose both water and fish.

Tube-noses

Members of the albatross, shearwater and petrel family have uniquely shaped bills. Hooked at the tip to enable them to snatch and tear at food on the oceans' surface, the top of the bill has two long, open-ended tubes which give the birds their nickname of 'tube-noses'. This feature is often visible at some considerable distance and is thought to serve a function in the excretion of salt from the seawater they drink.

Filter-feeders

Many different birds filter small plants and animals from freshwater, seawater and the fluid, muddy margins to these habitats. The process involved for each bird is the same, namely to extract the food without ingesting vast volumes of liquid. However, the ways in which the bills have been modified for this purpose are varied and extraordinary, often to the point of being comical.

Roseate spoonbills are familiar birds from the wetlands of the southern United States, and their name is extremely appropriate; the long, flattened bill is enlarged at the tip giving the bird's bill the appearance of a spoon. The birds feed extremely vigorously, moving their bills from side-to-side through the water, while at the same time snapping the upper and lower mandibles together rapidly. This latter process draws in and forces out water at a considerable rate, and sieves on the inner surfaces prevent items of food leaving the mouth once ingested.

Ducks

Some species of ducks feed in a similar manner, and shelduck, teal, wigeon and shoveler are well-known 'dabbling' ducks. However, many of their relatives have very different diets and feed on much larger food items. Eider ducks have stout bills with which they tear mussels and clams off the seashore rocks, whilst mergansers and buffleheads, known collectively as 'sawbills' catch fish and to ensure their slippery quarry does not escape, have serrated bills.

Predators

Predatory birds generally have formidable beaks which are stout and hooked at the tip. This enables both owls and birds of prey to tear strips of flesh from the bodies of their prey and by so doing they can eat animals too large to swallow whole. A few species of raptor have abandoned the role which their bills once played, however, and the honey buzzard, for example, uses its beak to extract grubs from the hives of wild bees and wasps. The bill and diet of the snail kite is even more specialised: the upper mandible is extremely long and curved and is just right for 'winkling' a snail's body out of its shell.

Shorebirds

Waders or shorebirds are generally characterised by their comparatively long, slender bills. With these they probe the mud in search of invertebrates and not surprisingly, the tip of the bill, in particular, is sensitive to touch and taste. Most plovers have rather short bills, but those of godwits or the long-billed curlew are so long that they almost seem an incumberance.

Insect-eaters

Bee-eaters belong to a colourful family of birds found throughout Asia and Africa, and as their name suggest, they prefer to eat insects. At first sight, their long, needle-like bills would perhaps appear most suited to delicate feeding on the ground, but instead, the birds use them to catch insects on the wing with unerring accuracy. They are related to woodpeckers which also share a largely insectivorous diet and again have an appropriate name since they do indeed bore into rotting wood in search of beetle grubs and other insects. Because, the timber is often tough, their skulls are specially protected from the jarring that results from hammering wood.

Passerine birds

Passerines, or perching birds, are numerous and widespread through the world. The diversity of species is amazing and while the majority have thin, delicate bills for picking off insects, some of the variations in design are extraordinary.

Shrikes, which are active and fearless predators for their size, have evolved bills which are remarkably similar to those of birds of prey being stout and hooked at the tip. These are used to tear up the prey but because the birds lack the size and powerful feet of most raptors, they sometimes resort to impaling their prey on thorns to secure it.

The bills of finches are mostly used to crack seeds and nuts and their strength is most highly developed in the hawfinch (*see opposite*). Its massive bill can crack even the hardest nut, and this gives it an advantage over many other birds. Strength is not always the answer to feeding problems, ingenuity also being adopted as a strategy. Crossbills, whose bill-tips overlap, use these remarkable structures to extricate pine seeds from even the most unyielding of cones.

Swifts and nighthawks

Some birds have ceased to use their bills for precision feeding but instead use them, together with the mouth as a whole, as a kind of sieve. Swifts, for example, feed by flying through the skies, collecting the insects that get caught in their large gaping mouths. A fringe of feathers around the mouth helps encourage a through-flow of air and prevents insects from escaping.

Some insects, such as moths and many beetles, only take to the wing after dark and thus avoid swifts, but instead nighthawks and chuck-will's widows take to the air. In the tropics, their relatives, the potoos and frogmouths, are common and in keeping with the outsized proportions of the insects, have enormous mouths and gapes.

The American Avocet (*Recurvirostra americana*) breeds on the shores of marshes and lakes in the western half of the United States. It feeds in the usual manner of avocets by skimming the surface of water with its slender upturned bill and can be readily recognised by its brown neck and white bar on the wing.

Migration

Among the familiar sights of autumn in the northern hemisphere are the swallows preparing to fly south and the formations of wild ducks, geese, cranes, storks and other large migrant birds passing overhead. Few other living creatures make such long and regular migratory journeys. Recent scientific studies are beginning to reveal convincingly why birds migrate, how their journeys are made, how far they go, and what routes they take. The information on which these conclusions have been based has been obtained in a number of ways, one of them being bird ringing. Bird ringing, or banding as it is known in North America, provides information about the movements of birds, the routes used by migrants, and, on occasion, the approximate time they have been travelling, as well as the duration of their visits. The bird is either taken from the nest or is trapped, care being taken not to harm it, and a numbered band of monel or aluminium alloy is fixed around one of its legs.

In countries in the middle latitudes, and with temperate climates, there are three kinds of migratory birds: summer residents that breed in a particular area, such as Barn Swallows and Red-eyed Vireos; winter visitors that nest further north in summer, such as Snow Geese and the American Wigeon or Baldpate; and birds that pass over the country during their outward and return journeys, such as in Europe, cranes, and in America, the Sanderling that breeds in Alaska but stays in southern Argentina during the northern winter.

In all three types of migration breeding grounds are distinct from winter quarters. In tropical areas, however, there is no such distinction, as reproduction is not so restricted by factors of time and place. Migrations do occur here, but these are probably caused by the need to find food; the Sulphur-bellied Flycatcher (*Myiodynastes luteiventris*) of Central America, for example, flies further south.

Birds are normally selective in their food, and with their high degree of mobility they can fly to where the kind of food they require is available. Locust-eating birds will follow swarms of these insects, while birds of prey will appear in large numbers during the dry season when bush fires drive small animals out of their hiding places and make them easy victims. Intertropical hummingbirds can hardly be said to migrate, but they regularly fly several hundred kilometres in search of the nectar they require.

One of the most curious patterns of bird movement is that of the Pennant-winged Nightjar (*Macrodipteryx vexillarius*), which is insectivorous and catches flies while on the wing. The insects on which it feeds are particularly abundant during the rainy season, and the Nightjar follows a strict

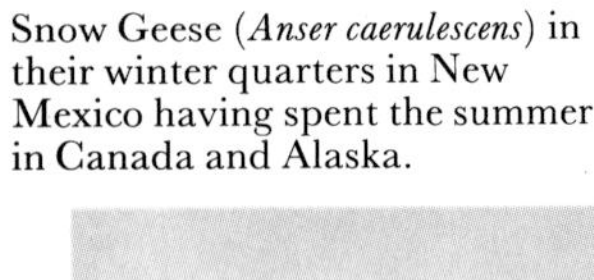

Snow Geese (*Anser caerulescens*) in their winter quarters in New Mexico having spent the summer in Canada and Alaska.

schedule of migration determined by these flies. This bird lives in the savanna regions of southern Africa during the spring rains, from September to December. Then from January to March it migrates northwards, passing over the equatorial forest and settling in the savanna country of northern Africa (Sudan), again during the season of spring rains from April to June. In July and August it crosses back over the forest zone and returns to its point of departure. Nesting takes place south of the equator and moulting occurs north of it.

As a general rule, species whose range of food is limited make the longest journeys. Of European migratory birds, the great majority are aquatic or insectivorous in habit. Aquatic birds leave shortly before the lower temperatures reduce the food supply in their normal habitats; similarly, insectivorous birds do not winter in regions where insect food is scarce. Grain-eating and omnivorous birds migrate only to a limited extent, while woodpeckers and similar birds which find their prey, winter and summer alike, in the trunks of trees are among the few that do not migrate.

However, the European Quail (*Coturnix coturnix*), which winters on the shores of the Mediterranean and even further south in Egypt and tropical Africa, is the only gallinaceous bird with a granivorous diet to undertake such lengthy migrations. It may be that whereas most species of quail are intertropical, the European one has extended its breeding grounds far to the north only to return each year to its ancestral feeding area.

Very different are those migrations which are usually called irruptions. These can hardly be explained by any of the foregoing hypotheses. They may occur at intervals of years, or of decades, and have no relation to breeding behaviour, for those birds subject to them breed at any time and anywhere.

Crossbills appear irregularly over a large part of the northern United States and western Europe, though normally they are seen only occasionally in certain mountain woods, their true habitat extending over the spruce zone of North America and coniferous forests of northern Europe. There they nest and feed on conifer seeds. What is remarkable is the Crossbill's ability to adapt itself to local foods quite different from those of its northern habitat. It has been observed feeding on grapes, sunflower seeds, apple pips and damaged fruit. Often many birds die in migration, but by the beginning of winter the survivors return to their habitual surroundings.

Methods of migration

Migratory birds do not all make their journeys in the same manner. Social birds, such as swallows, bee-eaters, and others which normally live together in flocks, retain their social instincts during migration, departing and travelling together. Similar social migratory tendencies are also exhibited by some birds that are solitary and aggressive during the breeding season; for example, most of the small singing birds of Europe, such as warblers, finches, robins, wrens, old-world flycatchers, and so on. When they migrate their aggressive instincts wane and they become gregarious, individuals of different species often congregating in one flock. The are other solitary birds, the Golden Oriole and many birds of prey

Above
Many species, such as the Indigo Bunting (*Passerina cyanea*), are nocturnal migrants: experiments show that they recognise constellations and use them for guidance.

Below
Experiments with birds transported away from their nests confirm their ability to return swiftly over unfamiliar terrain.

species	birds tested	distance transported (miles)	% returning	typical speed (miles/day)
Leach's Petrel	61	135-470	67	30
Manx Shearwater	42	265-415	90	200
Laysan Albatross	11	1665-4120	82	100
Gannet	18	213	63	100
Herring Gull	109	214-872	90	60
Common Tern	44	228-404	43	125
Swallow	21	240-310	52	150
Starling	68	200-440	46	25

B

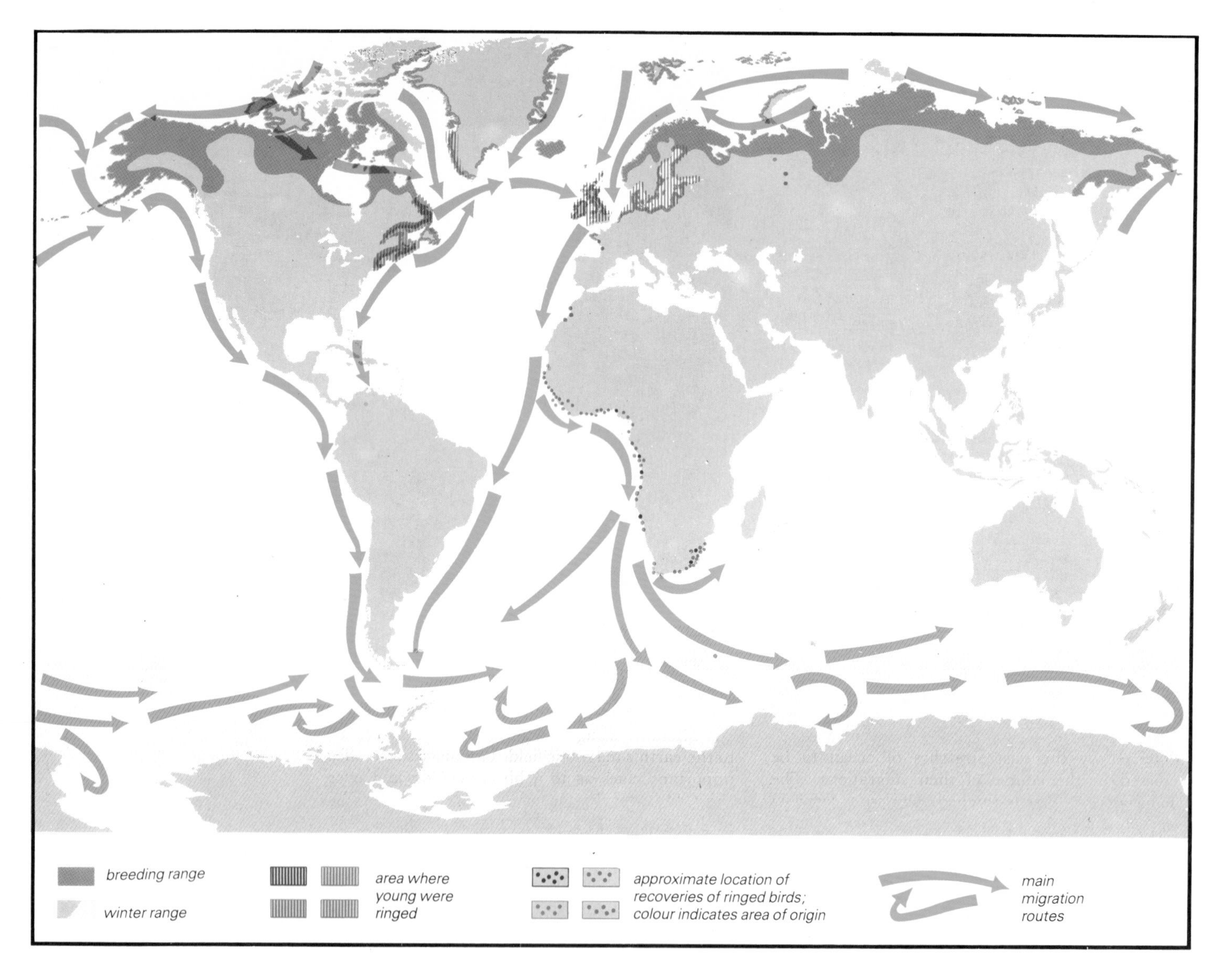

Arctic Terns (*Sterna paradisaea*) are amongst the furthest travelled of all birds, breeding in the north and 'wintering' in the Antarctic summer.

among them, which live and travel alone. Their movements are, more often than not, so isolated that they pass unnoticed, little more being observed than that they are here at one time of year and absent at another.

The method of flying may also vary a great deal with the species. Most of the small passerine birds travel in dense groups without any particular formation, but ducks, geese, cranes, storks and others fly high in skein, line or V-formations. There is a double advantage in this kind of formation flying; visibility is increased and flying made easier for the individual because there is continuous flight in a single direction. These flight patterns have the advantage of each participant being able to 'see' where it is going.

Passerine birds usually travel at night and rest by day, which tends to give them better protection against birds of prey. It is these night flyers that are sometimes attracted to lighthouses or beacons where many are killed as they dash themselves against the glass of the light. Wading birds and web-footed birds will travel by night or by day, and often cover long distances without a rest. Birds generally take off into the wind and, like gliders, take advantage of the air currents at different altitudes. They usually avoid severe atmospheric disturbances, although they may be caught up in cyclones or violent storms. Otherwise birds tend to keep the same compass course regardless of weather conditions. This may explain the presence each year in Great Britain of many American stragglers and vice versa.

Direct observation and radar tracking have both recently provided some detailed and exact information on the height and speed of bird flight. Flocks of geese, for example, have been seen flying at a height of 2500 metres during a storm, while others have been plotted by radar at a height of 1500 metres and over a distance of 128 kilometres. The flight of small passerine birds is influenced by the force and direction of the wind and altitude is usually less than 90 metres. The intensity of light, visibility, rain and the presence of trees will also influence the height. The average speed of flight during a migration may be high: radar plotting has shown that some geese fly at an average speed of thirty-eight kilometres an hour. As for length of flight, a finch has flown 600 kilometres in a day and a shrike 200 kilometres.

Flying is not the only means of locomotion during migration. Penguins from the Antarctic regions may occasionally swim long distances between their summer and winter quarters.

Migratory routes

There are two interesting features of migratory routes: direction and distance. The view that birds fly along straight lines, linking the equatorial regions with temperate and cold areas is an oversimplification.

Information provided by bird ringing or banding has proved that our knowledge of migration is still far from complete. The first factors to be taken into account are the great natural barriers which birds seek to avoid: oceans, seas, deserts and mountain chains. European passerine birds migrating to Africa tend to avoid long passages over the Mediterranean, preferring one of the shorter sea-routes from Spain to Morocco, from Italy and Sicily to Tunisia, and from Asia Minor to Egypt. North American migratory birds heading for South America fly either to Venezuela by way of the Isthmus of Panama or across Florida, Cuba and the Yucatan Peninsula, but seldom over the West Indies.

In the Mediterranean, migrating European robins, swallows, wagtails and starlings are quite commonly seen from ships and they will sometimes perch on board, even on rare occasions remaining for the entire crossing.

When passerines have a long sea crossing ahead, they might be expected to fly high. In fact this is seldom so. Individuals of all species often fly low over the water, zigzagging along with frequent changes of course, twisting and turning above the waves as they utilise up-currents of air.

Waterbirds, of course, do not appear to be deterred by the vast stretches of ocean to be crossed in the course of their migrations. The Tahitian or Bristle-thighed Curlew (*Numenius tahitiensis*) is a particularly good example, as it travels for thousands of kilometres across the Pacific between the various islands where it winters and Alaska where it nests.

Arctic Terns (*Sterna paradisea*) make some of the longest migratory journeys of all. They nest in northern Europe, Asia and Alaska, and then travel far down into the southern hemisphere to the Antarctic where they spend the southern summer. Often they will fly between 12,000 and 15,200 kilometres each way along the coasts or over the sea. Their migrations are thus the reverse of those of Wilson's Storm Petrel (*Oceanites oceanicus*), which nests in the southern hemisphere.

The migrations of the Arctic Tern provide an interesting comparison with those of the Great Shearwater (*Puffinus gravis*). From June to August, the northern summer, the tern nests and the shearwater resides without nesting in northern Europe. Between September and November both species migrate to the southern hemisphere, and during the southern summer from December to March it is the tern that is the resident and the shearwater that nests in southern Africa. Both then return north in April and May.

Bird navigation

The way in which pigeons and other birds navigate over long distances is not fully understood. Experiments indicate that birds can orientate and fly on a compass course by reference to the position of the sun and stars. They can also calculate their geographical location by reference to the height and movement of the celestial bodies and, by comparing these with the equivalent data for its destination, lay off a course for home. This is essentially how a human navigator operates.

Recent experiments have shown that some birds can orientate using a magnetic sense by reference to the earth's magnetic field. Landmarks also offer important clues as to a birds position and over short distances, homing pigeons learn to recognise local landmarks and so improve with training. There is growing evidence that smell, once considered a relatively unimportant sense in birds, has a far more widespread role. Leach's petrels use it to help locate their burrows after dark and homing pigeons are thought to recognise and track their home-loft by its smell.

The Bosphorus is an important land bridge used by birds of prey and storks migrating from Europe to Africa. Here, a large flock of storks circles over Istanbul.

Courtship and territory

Courtship

The songs and displays which are used to repel other males are also used to attract and court females. Unattached females seek out males who are advertising their availability and the rituals of courtship continue through the breeding season to help maintain a bond between the pair. The display of some male birds is quite spectacular. For example, the male Argus Pheasant clears a small arena in the depths of the Malaysian forests where he calls and then waits for a female. When she appears he performs a complicated and lengthy dance which culminates in his spreading his enormous wing feathers to form a saucer with a constellation of 'eye-spots'. This highly specialised display stimulates the female to a comparable degree of sexual activity and mating follows.

The Cock-of-the-rock, which inhabits Guyana and Brazil, has well-defined display grounds where each male displays in turn, in a form of acrobatics, which lasts until he is exhausted. As each performance ends and the next begins the females make a loud noise, as if applauding.

The birds-of-paradise of New Guinea, the most spectacular of all birds, participate in group-dancing displays in the trees, each species having its own individual pattern of behaviour. The display includes dances, the spreading of gorgeous plumes, whistles and calls, all combining to give a most spectacular effect. In some instances the display ends with the male hanging upside-down from a branch with all his plumes spread. In all species the movements and postures of the males result in the brilliant plumage being shown to produce the maximum effect.

In the Ruff, a bird related to the plovers, courtship takes place on a small stretch of high ground in marshy grassland, where the males await the females. When one appears the males erect their ruff feathers and lower their heads, displaying to the full their splendidly coloured 'ruffs'. This type of performance by a number of rather highly ornamented males in a small area of court is known as a lek display, but the area is called a hill. The females then choose their mates from among the males on display.

Another feature of bird courtship is concerned with the special coloration of the mouth; orange-yellow in the Kittiwake, bluish mauve in the Fulmar and so on. When face to face, male and female will open their beaks to display these colours. The beak is also used to caress the

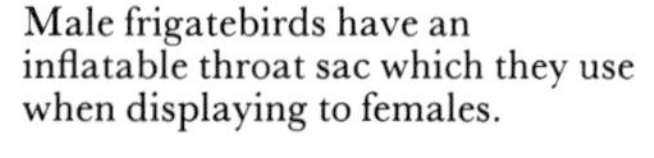
Male frigatebirds have an inflatable throat sac which they use when displaying to females.

The plumage of the male Mandarin Duck (*Aix galericulata*) is the most ornate of the duck family. In its breeding display the drake Mandarin makes much use of its plumage, a noticeable feature being the way the chestnut back feathers are depressed as part of the courtship pattern. The female's dull plumage helps to conceal her from predators, which biologically is most desirable since she carries the burden of producing the next generation.

feathers of the mate, and at times to impart a beak-to-beak 'kiss'. Some birds, such as Cassowaries, have brightly coloured throat pouches, and when a male Frigatebird displays his inflated pouch the female becomes submissive.

Territory and fighting

It has always been assumed that the males fight for possession of the females, that in a polygamous species the male fights to keep unsuccessful males from the harem, and that in a monogamous species two males will fight for the lady's favours. This idea is wrong. Careful study has shown that most of the fighting—if not all—is over a territory. The female may happen to be near, but it would be wrong to assume that the two males are fighting for her. In one of the few instances in which a definitive study has been made of this—a study of blackbirds—it was seen that males fight not only for territory but whenever they meet during the days preceding the actual breeding season. In all instances where breeding behaviour has been closely studied, whether among birds or mammals, it has been shown or suggested that fighting between males is for territory, not for a female, or for dominance in a hierarchy.

The fiercest fights are those of the gallinaceous birds, particularly the Phasianidae, the domestic cock, pheasant cock and Peacock. The fighting instinct is a secondary sexual character of the male, closely linked with the secretion of a hormone by the testes and accompanied by a striking splendour of plumage. The males of the Javan Peacock and of various pheasants (Silver, Reeves's and Copper) fight so ferociously, almost like fighting cocks, in fact. Fighting and courtship are closely allied, and it is not uncommon to find that the male's first approach to a female, a prospective mate, entering his territory is aggressive. But as the female's response is one of submissiveness his aggressive display quickly dies down.

Fights between males are not always a matter of actual physical combat. Sexual rivalry more often expresses itself in a threat display, a mock attack accompanied by the erection of the crest and other feathers, all of which is governed by an innate and inflexible code of behaviour. The male hoopoes, with their wings a dazzling contrast of black and white, will display in flight for hours while exhibiting little more than a virtuosity in their flying skill. Two Partridge cocks meeting in a furrow will alternately pursue and withdraw, carefully leaving a space between them so that there is no risk of their actually coming to blows. Male Blackcaps will chase one another furiously in and out of bushes, but in fact they go no further than uttering a full-throated song punctuated by sharp cries of anger. When two male Green Woodpeckers meet

Black-headed Gulls (*Larus ridibundus*) mating.

In many species, like the Goldfinch (*Carduelis carduelis*), the male feeds his mate to help her gain condition for egg-laying.

The Spruce Grouse (*Dendrophagus canadensis*) is fairly common across Canada and into Alaska, a very tame and non-social grouse living in coniferous forests. It is monogamous.

they go into a head-shaking display, though they have beaks as sharp as chisels and can chip the bark off an oak tree. Birds of prey will often do no more than make a show of coming to grips in mid-air, though they are well equipped to kill. Other species will stage a kind of tournament. On the plains where the Little Bustard lives innumerable narrow paths lead across the fields to a small corner where all the young shoots will be trampled down. This is the arena where all the males in the immediate neighbourhood meet, often staying for hours at a time, strutting and threatening, and bounding up and down in the air. Finally all return to their favourite haunts, leaving only a few feathers to mark the scene of their rivalry.

Song

A song consists of a series or pattern of notes and like the calls may perform a variety of functions. The commonest kind of song is that which serves to proclaim territory and to warn off another bird of the same sex. Where this kind of song is employed sometimes the female also sings, as in the European Robin and the Mockingbird. Usually territorial song has a dual function, for it serves also to attract a mate. In the Brown Towhee, however, it seems to be solely for the purpose of attracting a breeding partner, since mated males do not sing. Song may have yet another function: to co-ordinate the activities of individuals; a singing male is advertising his physiological readiness to mate and thus attracting most readily the females in the same condition. A mated pair often sing during courtship. Other songs may be to produce a gaping of the young nestlings. It is possible that some songs are sung in the absence of other stimuli; that is, when the bird has nothing much to do. Finally, the elaboration of song among birds such as some of the thrushes and Old World warblers is so great, often beyond what biological necessity seems to require, that the possibility of birds singing for pleasure cannot be ruled out. However, this view is hotly contended by many biologists who insist that song always serves a function.

Breeding habits

Many seabirds, geese, swans and birds of prey mate for life. Courtship in these species may be prolonged but, once a bond has been formed, the pair is usually parted only by death and only the minimum of courtship is needed after the first breeding season. There may be instances of birds mating for life in species other than those mentioned but it is difficult to be sure without intensive study of individual species. Certainly pairs are known to have remained together for several years and parrots, which have reached a high level of social development, probably pair for life.

More commonly, birds come together for one breeding season only. It is usual to find all members of a species taking their partners more or less at the same time. At the end of the breeding season the pairs break up. The following year each bird probably takes a different partner.

Ostriches are polygamous. The male mates with several females who lay their eggs in a communal nest but only the male and one of the females incubate the eggs and guard the chicks.

In the painted snipes (*Rostratula*), small wading birds from the humid regions of Africa, Australia, southern South America and tropical Asia, in the button-quail (family Turnicidae) of India, Malaysia, southern Europe and China, and the Northern Jacana (*Jacana spinosa*) of Central America, there is a remarkable reversal of normal sexual behaviour found in other bird species. In these, the female is polyandrous and courts several males, leaving them thereafter to brood the eggs and care for the young.

In fact, neither monogamy nor polygamy, nor any intermediate condition, is likely to prove invariable in any species. Just as in a monogamous human society there is bigamy, occasional polygamy, desertion, divorce and broken marriage, so in the avian world there are departures from normal state of affairs. This has been proved in certain instances of ringed wild birds kept under constant observation, and these precise records are backed by numerous well-documented instances of circumstantial evidence. It is not even true that conjugal infidelity results when the physiological condition of a pair fails to coincide because one of the pair is at a higher state of sexual activity than another.

Lesser Black-backed Gull (*Larus fuscus*) giving the 'mew call'. This is a long-drawn note made with the neck stretched forward, usually with the bill directed downwards and widely opened. It is a plaintive call and is associated with breeding activity, indicating a friendly attitude towards mate and, later, young, and is in no sense aggressive.

Albatrosses breed colonially on remote islands. Here Waved Albatrosses (*Diomedea irrorata*), are engaged in courtship display on Hood Island in the Galapagos. The courtship display consists of calling to each other, rubbing bills and also displaying their magnificent wings.

Nests and eggs

Nest building

A bird's nest is more than just a shelter for eggs and young. Birds are almost the only oviparous vertebrates with a constant and relatively high body temperature. The nest therefore enables them to provide the vital physiological requirement of a fairly uniform temperature in which their eggs will hatch and their young thrive. Birds must incubate their eggs and this can be done most efficiently in a nest. Nearly every species specialises in some form of nest construction, some elaborate, some simple. Some birds, such as King and Emperor Penguins, however, do not build a nest, but keep the egg warm by resting it on their feet and covering it with a fold of skin developed specially on the lower abdomen.

Casual nests

Certain owls, such as the Little Owl and the Long-eared Owl, together with parrots, doves and hoopoes, simply choose a ready-made cavity to use as a nest: a hollow in a tree or a rock, or the eaves of a roof all give suitable shelter.

Converted nests

These are nests located in the hollow of a tree or of a rock, sometimes even on an overhanging rock or the fork of a branch. Some birds add only some branches to improvise a nest in one of these places. The eyries of some eagles are typical of the simplest form of converted nest. Other types are better fitted out, such as those of wood pigeons, sparrowhawks, storks, magpies and crows. Here

Eider Ducks (*Somateria mollisima*) line their nests with copious soft down which helps to keep the eggs warm in sub-arctic conditions.

The Fairy Tern (*Sterna nereis*), breeding in the still, warm airs of tropical Pacific islands, builds no nest at all but simply balances its single egg on a bare branch.

the bird gathers together branches, twigs, strips of bark, leaves, lichens, a little clay, hair and feathers, and then builds a strong nest which sometimes lasts for several years and may even attract the attention of the 'nest stealers'.

Hollowed-out nests

These are made by digging and range from a simple shallow depression in the surface of the ground to a tunnel dug in a bank or cliff. The Skylark nests in the fields in a hollow dug by the female alone and lined with blades of grass, dry stalks and pieces of root. Partridges, quail and all similar ground-nesting birds do much the same. Ostriches and other ratites, such as rheas, emus and cassowaries, also lay their eggs in bare hollows in the ground dug by the males.

The Kingfisher's nest consists of a tunnel, a metre long and about six centimetres in diameter, cut in a river bank. At the far end it widens out into a dry nest-chamber, the floor of which becomes strewn with fish bones and other remains of food. Bee-eaters are also skilful miners, the nest tunnels being as much as two metres long.

Woodpeckers, parrots, hornbills and similar birds make hollows in trees, though they sometimes save themselves effort by taking over a ready-made hole. A Green Woodpecker's nest has an opening some eight centimetres in diameter and is about forty centimetres deep. The maximum diameter of the nesting chamber is twelve centimetres, leaving only enough room for the female and her eggs during incubation. The inner surface of the chamber is perfectly smooth and the bottom is covered with small wood chips.

Some hornbills have the strange habit of imprisoning the female and her eggs by blocking up the nest opening with mud, which not only protects the eggs but prevents the female leaving during the incubation period. The male brings her food and then goes on to feed the young.

Plaster nests

Some swallows and martins make their nests in or close to human habitation, preferring eaves, stables and barns, window recesses or chimneys. Whatever the site, it is invariably sheltered from rain, which would soon reduce the mud nest to a sodden and shapeless mass. Some 500 journeys over a period of eight days or so are needed to fetch and carry material for the construction of the swallow's nest.

The Red-rumped Swallow makes a nest of mud plastered to a vertical rock face, terminating in a spout, which hangs down and looks rather like the neck of a bottle with its opening on the underside.

The Brazilian Ovenbird's nest is spherical or muff-shaped, made of clay, completely smooth inside and out, and attached to a branch of a tree. A side opening leads to the brood chamber, which is concealed from the outside by a partition.

Woven nests

These are perhaps the most complex of all nests, and the behaviour patterns attending their construction are equally complex. They are remarkable achievements when it is remembered that the bird's only tool is its beak. Nests have to be strongly built and firmly secured if they are to hold a family of restless chicks and survive the wind, the swaying of the bough on which they are built, and the rain. A variety of materials is used: blades of grass, dry leaves, lichens, mosses, fur, feathers, horsehair, strands of wool and even spiders' webs. These are all skilfully woven together and held in position with a mixture of mud and saliva. The thickness of the walls appears to be correlated with the weight of the chicks to be reared.

The Mallee Fowl of Southern Australia builds 'compost heaps' which provide the heat for incubating its eggs.

The African Village Weaver (*Ploceus cucullatus*) constructs a nest of palm fibres, first forming a ring and then enlarging it by stages. Suspended from a drooping branch, and with the entrance hole beneath, it is largely inaccessible to predators.

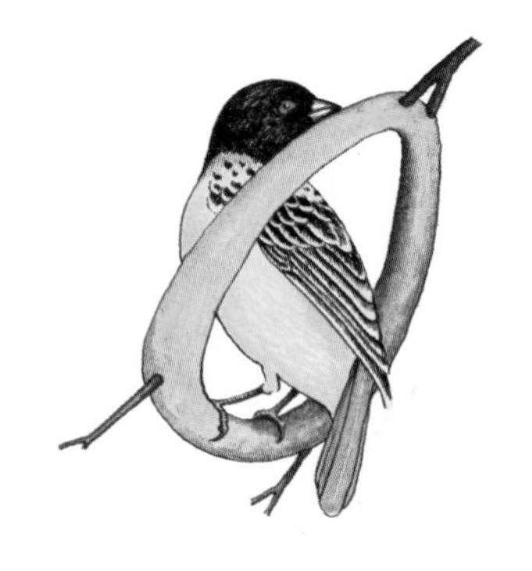

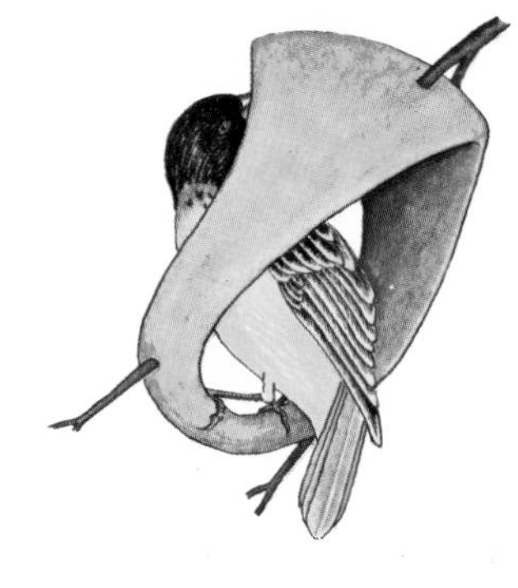

The wall is generally made up of three layers, the outer layer being the thickest, while the inner one is made of the finest materials which may help to conserve the heat from the female's body. A typical nest is a small, hemispherical basket; there are others shaped like a hammock, a muff, or a bottle, or moulded to fit their surroundings.

The nests of the Weaver-bird, the Baltimore Oriole and the Penduline Tit are different from others, being completely closed and slung from a branch. The opening is at the outer end of a sleeve-like extension at the bottom or the side of the nest. The walls, which surround an inner chamber sheltering the eggs, are made of intricately interwoven vegetable fibres.

Other types of nests

The Tailor-bird, which lives in Asia, southern Europe and North Africa, builds the walls of its nest from leaves cleverly sewn together. It is usually the male bird that undertakes this laborious work, first making a series of holes in the leaves with his beak and then threading vegetable fibres through them, finally overcasting the seams exactly.

The Edible-nest Swiftlets of the Indo-Australasian archipelago make their nests out of mosses, agar-rich seaweeds, and a few of their feathers. They cement these materials together with their own saliva, which is both copious and glutinous, solidifying on contact with the air. The nests can be made into soup, considered a delicacy.

Social nests

Weaver-birds often build their nests close together in a tree. The Sociable Weavers of South Africa go much further and have a collective nesting structure built around a tree trunk, the individual nests being part of a large formation built by a group of birds. From the outside this collective nest, which houses many hundreds of birds, looks like a conical roof several metres in circumference. The entrances to the individual nests are under the edge of the roof.

Eggs and development

Usually the size of the egg is proportional to the size of the bird producing it. That of a humming-bird is little more than 0.8 centimetres long, while an Ostrich, the largest of modern birds, lays an egg measuring as much as thirteen by fifteen centimetres and with a volume equal to that of about two dozen hen's eggs. The average size of a hen's egg is six by four centimetres and weighs fifty-five grams. Generally the eggs of precocial species are larger than those of altricial ones.

As for shape, eggs may be grouped into four main categories: almost spherical (some penguins, owls and the Honey Buzzard); oval or ellipsoidal (Peregrine Falcon, gulls, grebes and Golden Oriole); slightly enlarged at one end (most birds); and pyriform or pointed at one end and rounded at the other (auks, puffins, plovers).

Shells may be porcellaneous and highly glossy (tinamous), smooth and glossy (passerine and galliform birds), smooth and matt (birds of prey and waders), coarse and granular (ostriches), oily-looking (ducks), or covered with a chalky layer (pelicans). There is also wide variety in the coloration. About a quarter of all bird species lay white eggs; the rest lay coloured eggs, which may be spotted to a varying degree.

Large birds of prey, like these African Fish Eagles (*Haliaeetus vocifer*), construct huge, conspicuous nests, relying partly on inaccessibility and partly on their own size to give them protection.

Coloration is sometimes said to be mimetic. This is true in some cases though not in others. The eggs of birds nesting in dark places are white; but so too are many others which lie in open nests or in nests on the ground, but they are usually close-brooded, as by the pigeons. The Magpie and the starling, in contrast, have closed nests and lay coloured eggs. Cuckoo's eggs show some degree of mimicry, the colour and appearance often resembling those in the nest in which they are laid.

The number of eggs varies considerably from one species to another and is very probably related to the availability of food for rearing the brood after hatching, to the mortality rate of the species, and to the size of the brood patch. Many birds lay only one egg in a clutch, most pigeons lay two, herons three to five, the Great Tit five to ten, and the European Partridge ten to sixteen.

Structure and chemical composition

The egg of a bird is contained within a calcareous shell which may vary from thin and fragile if the nest is downy to thick and robust if the nest is either on the ground or crudely constructed. The shell of a hen's egg is between two- and three-tenths of a millimetre thick and consists of ninety-eight per cent calcium carbonate and phosphate and two per cent organic matter. The shell is pierced by countless small pores through which the embryo obtains the air it needs.

Lining the inner surface of the shell is the shell-membrane which consists of an inner and an outer layer, between which air is accumulated at one end, this air-filled cavity being known as the air cell. Its extent, seen by holding the egg up to the light, is an indication of the age of the egg.

Immediately inside the shell-membrane lies the albumen or white of the egg, which makes up nearly half the total weight. It is a watery, viscous solution of albuminous substances containing mineral salts as well as amino-acids, two of which (lysine and tryptophane) are especially important as growth factors.

The yolk is suspended within the albumen and is, strictly speaking, the egg or ovum, that is, the part which enters the oviduct from the ovary. It is enclosed in a thin membrane and is held in position in the centre of the egg by two twisted threads of albumen, the chalazae. It is made up of two parts: the germinal disc, which is the only living part and which gives rise to the embryo; and the yolk or vitellus, a collection of protein substances destined to nourish the embryo.

Incubation and embryonic development

There are two aspects to incubation: sitting and the development of the egg. In general the former is essential to the latter because the egg must be kept at a fairly constant temperature to allow the embryo to develop normally.

Sitting may begin immediately after the first egg is laid or it may be delayed until the last one is laid (as in most passerines). Usually it is the female that incubates the eggs, but the male may relieve her or even be responsible for most of the incubation. The period of incubation varies largely with the size of the bird, the European Cuckoo taking about eleven days, the Bullfinch fourteen days, the Barn Swallow fifteen days, the Domestic Fowl twenty-one days, the Californian Condor fifty-five days, and the Emu fifty-eight days.

Above
Woodpeckers like this Lewis' Woodpecker (*Melanerpes lewis*) from North America make their nests in holes in trees. Some species enlarge existing holes while others excavate new sites.

Below
A hen's egg opened up to reveal a fifteen-day-old embryo chick. The yolk-sac still occupies most of the cavity of the egg and the system of blood-vessels which transfer nutrients from it to the developing chick can be seen clearly.

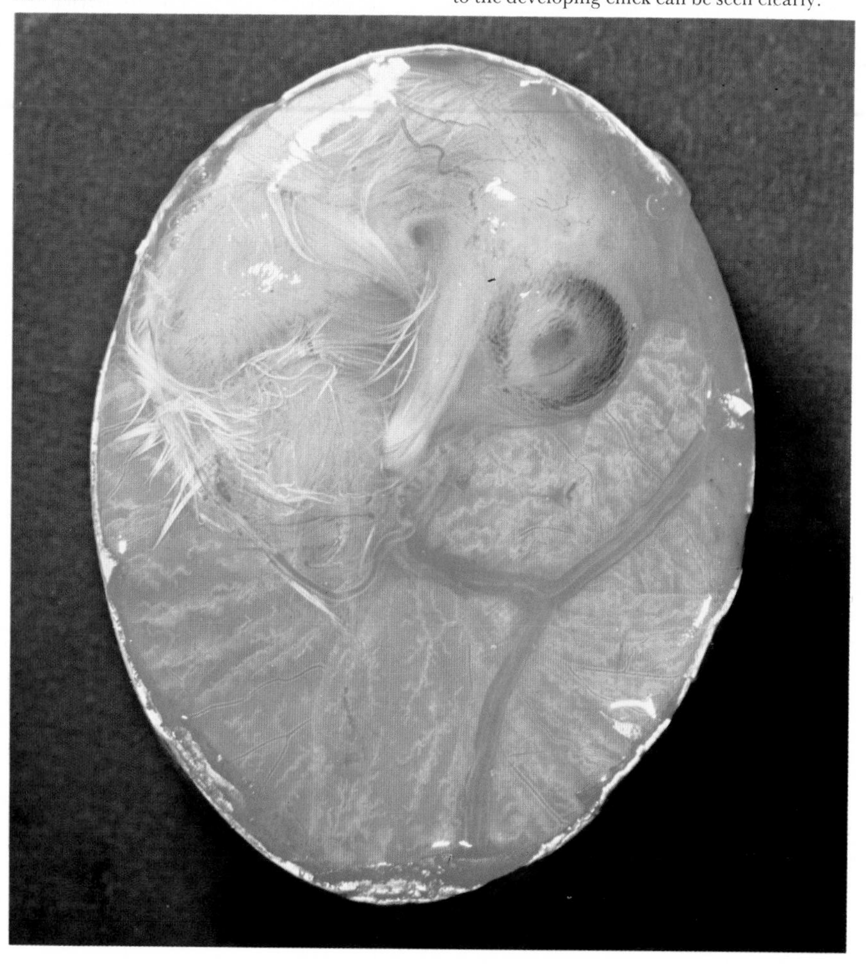

Young birds

The young of birds which nest in relative safety off the ground, hatch naked, blind and helpless, and are called altricial: their parents carry food to them not only until they can flutter away from the nest but also thereafter for several days for most small birds and for weeks with some large ones.

Ground-nesting birds are very vulnerable to predators. The chicks of wildfowl, waders and most other similar species hatch clothed in warm, camouflaged down and are able to feed themselves; they are called precocial. As soon as possible, they are led away from the nest by the adults, whose job it is to provide shelter at night and in rain by brooding the young, and to provide

The Australian Striped Honeyeater (*Plectorhyncha lanceolata*) raises three or four chicks in the safety of a purse-shaped nest suspended near the end of a drooping branch.

warning of danger, when the chicks will crouch motionless while their parents attempt to drive or draw the predator away. By contrast, birds which nest on the ground in large colonies, such as gulls and terns, often have enough mass 'air power' to be able to attack and drive off marauders, so the young do not need to leave the nest until they are well grown.

The time it takes to care for the young until they become independent limits the number of offspring which can be produced each year. A few birds, including cuckoos in Europe, cowbirds in America and wydahs in Africa, evade this constraint by laying their eggs in other species' nests. Thus, they can concentrate all their energies on egg production and produce more young than if they had to rear the chicks themselves.

The life-history of the European Cuckoo is extraordinary and fascinating. Once she has mated, the female cuckoo selects a suitable nest belonging to a Reed Warbler, Dunnock or Sedge Warbler, and lays her egg amongst the clutch of the owner. On occasions, female cuckoos have been known to remove some of the host eggs but this is normally left to the offspring.

Young cuckoos often hatch slightly earlier than the host bird's eggs. As soon as they are strong enough they heave the other eggs, or even the young birds if they have hatched, out of the nest. Having reduced at a stroke the competition for food, the cuckoo develops at an amazing rate and before long it dwarfs its unwitting, surrogate parents. The wide, orange-coloured gape, common to many young birds, is almost irresistable cue for the parent birds and by the time the cuckoo has fledged, they are exhausted.

Puffins and Razorbills feed their youngsters on fish. As the offspring grow, the parents gradually increase the size of the fish and skilfully judge the size that can be handled. Gannets also feed their young on fish but swallow them at sea and have to regurgitate them back on land. This process often requires a little encouragement on the part of the youngster and frenzied bill-tapping is an essential precondition for regurgitation.

All these different systems of rearing young have the same purpose—ensuring the survival of the young. The majority of young birds die in their first winter before they have become experienced. As they grow older, so their chances of survival increase but, even so, few small birds live beyond the age of three years. In order to ensure their survival, these birds have to produce large numbers of young and may produce two broods in one season. At the other extreme, many larger birds are very long lived once they reach maturity. They may not begin to breed until they are about four years old or more and then perhaps rear one chick a year for twenty years.

In practice, there are many breeding failures. The Great Tits might lose all their young to a marauding weasel, or have them drowned in the nest hole by torrential rain, so that the exceptionally good years when twenty young leave the nest, are balanced by others when none are produced. Large birds too have breeding failures due to predators, bad weather or accident. But these individual tragedies do not have an effect on the numbers of a species provided that, by the end of its life, each adult has produced just one survivor to replace it in the breeding population.

Goshawks (*Accipiter gentilis*) have small broods, cared for by both parents, which improves the survival rate of the young.

Young Cuckoo (*Cuculus Canorus*) being fed by a Reed Warbler (*Acrocephalus scirpaceus*).

Extinction and conservation

Once occurring in immense flocks in North America, Eskimo Curlews (*Numenius borealis*) were killed in great numbers for sport and food in the last century. Only a few exist today.

Birds, like all other living creatures, live in a competitive world. Individuals within a species compete for food and for mates and those best suited to the demands of their environment survive to breed successfully. Different species also tend to compete with each other where the requirements for food or nesting habitat overlap.

Head-on competition may be fatal for the losers, and so instead species avoid this by becoming more specialised—exploiting their environment in different ways. At the same time, healthy species expand by producing more young than needed to replace normal adult mortality. This surplus enables them quickly to take advantage of any increase in available food resources, resulting either from the decline of a near competitor or from some external circumstances affecting the habitat on which they depend.

Because natural conditions are never static there is always an ebb and flow in the affairs of species. In the long-term whole continents split and re-form; mountains erode and new peaks arise elsewhere; climate changes. Relatively quickly, forest may replace grassland or a lake silt up and become a reedbed. The effect on species depends on both the extent and the rate of change. If conditions change gradually over a long period, a species may be able to evolve with them. This is because each generation is made up of individuals with different qualities. Thus if, for example, the climate cools very slowly those individuals which are most cold tolerant will tend to survive better and contribute most young to the next generation. It in turn will contain some individuals even more cold tolerant than their parents. Slowly, over many generations—perhaps hundreds or thousands of years—the species will change its character, adapting itself to a changing environment until perhaps it no longer remotely resembles its original ancestors. This is known as evolutionary extinction.

If change is rapid, then a species may be unable to respond to it quickly enough. A rapid cooling of climate could outstrip the ability of a species to withstand the cold, and all its members would die. This is known as terminal extinction.

Man influences birds and their environment in a variety of ways, both directly and indirectly. Sometimes birds are killed using weapons and traps while the effects of pollution, although often unseen and insidious, are no less damaging.

In North America, the Passenger Pigeon, whose populations once numbered tens of millions of birds, was exterminated in the name of 'sport' in the space of a few decades. Island birds, which are often flightless and hence more vulnerable to ground predators, have all too often suffered the same fate and the Dodo which once roamed Mauritius is a classic example.

Even the power of flight has not protected some species from the devastating effects of mankind. Cahows, which are elegant seabird members of the petrel family, once lived in their millions on Bermuda. Nesting in rock crevices, both the adult birds and their downy young are extremely vulnerable and after their discovery in 1603, man soon plundered and decimated their numbers. DDT, a pesticide which thins the egg shell, and rats, caused the population to fall to the brink of extinction by the 1960's but through active conservation and creation of safe nest-sites, there may yet be hope for the Cahow.

Seabirds are also seriously under threat from the commercialisation of the oceans. Unscrupulous skippers and accidental collisions all too often cause spillages of oil and other chemicals. Auks, seaduck and loons are particularly vulnerable since they spend much of their lives on the surface of the sea. Contact with oil renders their feathers useless both for flight and as insulation, and they quickly lose their waterproof qualities. A natural response on the part of an oiled bird is to try to clean itself by preening but this only hastens its demise since ingested oil destroys the lining of the intestine.

Over the centuries, man has deliberately and unwittingly introduced alien animals to many parts of the world: sheep and cattle, for example, are widespread as sources of meat, wool and milk. However, some of the other visitors are less welcome and goats and rats, for example, have

Right
A flightless seabird, the Great Auk was exploited by mariners as a source of fresh meat and huge numbers were boiled down to produce lamp oil. The last individual was killed in 1844.

Opposite
Birds of prey have suffered heavily in developed countries from deliberate human persecution and loss of habitat. A number are endangered including the Californian Condor (*Vultur californianus*).

taken a heavy toll on vegetation and ground-nesting island birds all over the world.

In New Zealand, man introduced a whole range of small mammals which soon became abundant in their new home. In order to control them, someone had the bright idea of introducing stoats which are one of their natural predators. Unfortunately, in addition to thriving on the small mammals, the stoats soon turned their attentions to New Zealand's native birds. Because of their large size, Takahes, which are members of the gallinule family, were not attacked, but their eggs and young were easy prey and the species was soon on the verge of extinction.

The pet trade also takes a heavy toll on many endangered birds, it being an unfortunate reality that the scarcer the species, the higher the price it commands and the greater its collector value. Parrots and macaws, which are generally difficult to rear in captivity and which can seldom be trained as adults are often acquired by raiding the nests. This in itself is a destructive process since it often involves felling the complete tree in which the parrot has nested. Hopefully, rigorous enforcement of existing and future legislation may put a stop to illegal aspects of this trade.

The story of man's association with birds is not all gloom, however. Thanks to his ingenuity, and genuine concern on the part of many individuals and governments, positive steps are being taken in many countries to preserve and encourage the wildlife. Unfortunately, for some species this has come too late and many will probably go extinct in our lifetime. For example, the Californian Condor, whose numbers have declined sharply over the last century due to changes in land use and other factors, now no longer survives in the wild. A captive population is all that is left of this most majestic of raptors, but if successful breeding programmes create a large enough group, perhaps the skies of southern California may again be graced by its immense wingspan.

The story of the White-tailed Eagle is a little more encouraging. Once persecuted by farmers and landowners and badly affected by pesticides, these impressive birds have been re-introduced into many of their former haunts and Scotland now has regular breeding pairs. The tale of Gurney's Pitta is even more remarkable. Considered extinct for over 50 years, this colourful and secretive bird once haunted the lowland rain forests of Thailand. In 1986, the hard work of a dedicated birdwatcher, convinced of its continued existence, paid off and a small colony was rediscovered.

Without doubt, in the course of avian history a huge number of bird species have become extinct naturally. Now man is the main cause of terminal extinction. Some birds have been exterminated by over-exploitation for food. More have been wiped out as a result of the introduction of alien predators against which they have no defence. The greatest losses have been due to the destruction of habitat: the felling of forests, the drainage of wetlands, the ploughing of the prairies. Only in the last few decades have we begun to seek to ensure the conservation of endangered species, and it will need major changes in land use policy and a very different attitude worldwide to our natural environment if the hundreds of different species now at risk are to be saved.

Section Two

Bird Habitats of the World

The first problem that faces all creatures is how to stay alive. All living things at all times are under the pressures put on them by the habitats in which they live and by the other creatures with which they compete. Birds have been in the past, and remain, a very successful group of creatures in exploiting the world's habitats. They occupy an enormous variety of environments. Thus some drink nectar in the constant summer of the tropical forests while others incubate their eggs in the continuous darkness and horrifying cold of an Antarctic mid-winter; some soar without apparent effort in the thin high air above mountain peaks but others pursue their prey for long minutes deep beneath the cold water of the oceans.

The ability to migrate has enabled birds to exploit habitats that provide suitable food sources for only part of the year. Indeed, some species will occupy several different habitats in a single year. To see how birds relate to their environment and to each other in them, the following pages describe the major habitats of the world. From tundra to desert and tropical forest to ocean, the environment and most important bird families found there, are fully covered.

Coot (*Fulica atra*) with a chick riding on its back amongst yellow water lillies in a secluded pond in western Europe. Coot have evolved partially webbed feet which enable them not only to swim and dive but also to move about freely on land.

Tundra

The Snow Bunting (*Plectrophenax nivalis*) is one of the few small birds to occur in the tundra since they generally find it harder to resist cold conditions than do larger species.

For the brief arctic summer, the tundra is thronged with birdlife. Countless thousands of shorebirds nest amongst the mosses and lichens together with ducks, geese and swans.

The tundra is a vast and treeless habitat mainly stretching across the north of America, Europe and Asia that presents birds with enormous challenges and great opportunities. In winter in the north, snow covers the frozen ground and the days are very short. In summer, there is almost constant daylight, the soil surface becomes marshy and sprinkled with thousands of pools. There is a rich growth of ground vegetation, insects become abundant and small mammals breed rapidly: the potential food supply is, briefly, generous.

Because the winter conditions are so severe, few creatures can live here throughout the year. This gives an advantage to migratory birds because they can move into the habitat to exploit its riches during the short summer with little competition. Wildfowl and waders in particular find it ideal.

The tundra breeding season is brief and no time must be wasted. Many wildfowl complete their courtship in their wintering areas so that nest construction and egg laying can begin quickly when the birds reach their breeding grounds. The demands of migration may be considerable; on arrival, birds must concentrate on feeding busily to quickly regain their condition. With Red-necked Phalaropes, incubation and care of the young is entirely the responsibility of the males: possibly after the females have migrated from the equatorial oceans where they winter, and then produced eggs, they are incapable of undergoing the prolonged semi-starvation of incubation.

Snowy Owl populations fluctuate greatly with the fortunes of the lemmings on which they largely prey. When these are abundant the owls rear large broods—more than the habitat can possibly support in winter. Then, many of the birds are obliged to move south, well outside their normal range. Such occasional 'irruptions' are a feature of the lives of many tundra and boreal forest residents.

Snowy Owls are not the only tundra birds to rely upon lemmings for food. Elegant Long-tailed Skuas also benefit from the abundant food supply in years when these endearing rodents are numerous. In poor years, however, they may not even attempt to breed. Skilled fliers, they can hover briefly, their long tail-streamers floating in the breeze, when they spot the scurrying of a lemming below. Their elegant plumage belies their fierce disposition and prey is quickly dispatched using their powerful, hook-tipped beak. Unlike the owls, Long-tailed Skuas are not year-round residents but only visit the tundra for the brief months of summer. By August, most adult birds have begun to depart and spend the winter far out to sea in the tropical oceans.

Arctic Skuas, relatives of the Long-tailed Skua, also breed in loose colonies on the tundra but instead of lemmings, their diet comprises young birds and food stolen from other birds. The colonies are often in the vicinity of Arctic Tern nest-sites for the good reason that the skuas are pirates, chasing and attacking the smaller birds, forcing them to drop or regurgitate their last meal.

During the height of summer, insect life in the form of mosquitoes, midges and horse flies is abundant as any visiting birdwatcher will testify. The larvae of the creatures abound in the mosaic of pools and lakes which dot the tundra landscape and provide a never-ending feast for many birds. Snow and Lapland Buntings, who nest amongst the boulders and tangled, dwarf vegetation, feed on the adult insects whilst many of the breeding shorebirds prefer midge and mosquito larvae.

Amongst the lichen-covered boulders and compact mosses of the Scandinavian tundra, Dotterel nest. Their indifference to the presence of man has earned them the nick-name 'moss-fool' and they can be difficult to spot as they creep quietly along. Curiously, it is the female and not the male Dotterel which has the brighter markings and in a most unusual arrangement for a bird, it is she who courts the male and he who incubates the eggs.

This curious role-reversal is also shared by a few other, equally charming, shorebirds which breed in the high arctic tundra of North America. Red-necked Phalaropes are buoyant little birds who resemble miniature gulls as they bob and spin on the surface of the water. Their lobed feet help them swim as they twist and turn, darting at insects beneath the surface. Female Grey Phalaropes are even more spectacularly marked than Red-necked Phalaropes, having bright red plumage with distinct black-and-white facial markings. They nest at even higher latitudes than their relatives and, in years where spring is late in coming, they may not breed at all.

Across the vast tracts of Canadian and Siberian tundra, countless thousands of other shorebirds nest. More familiar to most people as winter residents of the seashore, Black-bellied Plovers, Ruddy Turnstone, Least Sandpipers and Semi-palmated Sandpipers are common. Both adults and young birds provide easy pickings for the tundra's most dramatic bird, the Gyr Falcon. Of the two colour varieties that occur, the pure-white form is by far the most stunning and although from a distance the bird may resemble a pale rock, once in the air there is no mistaking it. The size of

Snowy Owls (*Nytaea scandiaca*) are one of the few bird species able to live on the tundra for all of the year. Their insulating plumage gives them good protection against extreme cold.

A Rock Ptarmigan (*Lagopus mutus*) crouches on its nest amongst the tundra mosses. Its mottled plumage renders it extremely inconspicuous.

Breeding distribution of the Red-necked Phalarope (*Phalaropus lobatus*)

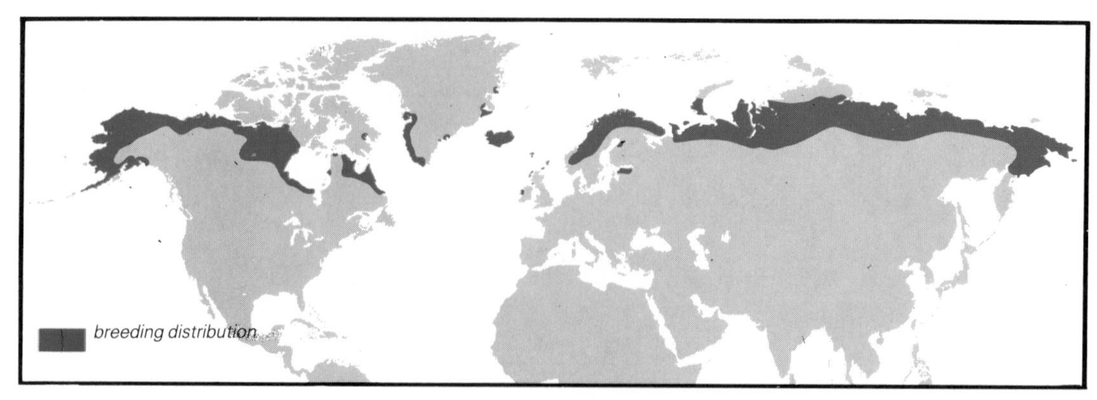

a Herring Gull, Gyr Falcons relentlessly pursue quarry as large as Rock Ptarmigan but will often settle for much smaller shorebirds.

Rocky outcrops provide nest sites for Rough-legged Buzzards, broad-winged birds of prey whose dark carpal wing-patches and white rump are distinctive identification features. Catholic in their choice of food, lemmings, shorebirds, young wildfowl and even carrion all feature in the diet. As winter approaches, Rough-legged Buzzards move south towards the tree line.

During the summer months, the tundra vegetation is a rich variety of colours, shapes and textures. Mottled grey-brown lichens cloak the boulders and blend in with green mosses and dwarf shrubs which provide luxuriant growth in an otherwise hostile environment. Stare at this landscape for long enough and one of the boulders may start to move. In all likelihood this will not be a hallucination but a Rock Ptarmigan betraying its fabulous camouflage by its movements. As soon as it stops moving it becomes invisible again, its mottled brown, white and grey plumage being a perfect match for the surroundings.

Mottled plumage is fine during the summer months when rocks and mosses make up the surface of the landscape but come the winter months a carpet of pure-white snow blankets the tundra. To overcome the disadvantage of contrasting colours, the Rock Ptarmigan moults its summer coat for pure white feathers which help it avoid the unwelcome eyes of predators.

Many tundra species, like the Red-necked Phalarope (*Phalaropus lobatus*) have very widespread distributions throughout the circumpolar habitat. Unusually, it is the male that incubates the nest.

Northern forests

South of the tundra, mean temperatures are generally warmer, the summer is a little longer and the winter gales less fierce. Here, trees can begin to survive—scattered and stunted willows and spruce on the fringes of the open tundra lands giving way to taller timber and finally to dense coniferous forest.

Because the northern forest varies little from one area to another, a number of bird species or closely related groups are distributed throughout the entire 8000 mile extent of the zone across Europe, Asia and America. For example, because there are coniferous trees throughout these forests, all three continents contain crossbills, which feed by prising up the scales of cones with their crossed mandibles to get at the tiny, nutritious seeds within. Different crossbill species have evolved different-sized beaks suitable for different sorts of cones. Thus, the crossbill group can exploit the seeds of many different types of conifer, the competition between the different species is minimised.

Crossbills must breed to take advantage of the time when cones are ripe and opening naturally, making seeds easy to gather. As this often occurs in mid-winter, the young birds must be able to tolerate temperatures far below freezing. Where most naked nestlings would die in minutes, young crossbills merely become torpid while their parents are away from the nest collecting food: when the adults return to brood them, they quickly recover and feed.

With a similar distribution to the Crossbill, the Two-barred Crossbill is also found throughout the coniferous forests of Scandinavia to Siberia and across North America north of the Great Lakes. It has conspicuous, white wing bars which make it easy to distinguish. Having a relatively small beak, it must tackle smaller pine cones than its relative and shows a marked preference for Norway spruce and hemlock.

Like the Crossbill, it too breeds early in the year, making a neat nest of twigs close to the trunk of a tree. Young Two-barred Crossbills are similarly resistant to cold and like other finches are fed a diet of regurgitated seeds. Later in the year, their diet is not entirely confined to seeds and the birds take a heavy toll of insects such as caterpillars and sawfly grubs as well as berries.

Pine Grosbeaks are superficially similar to crossbills, to which they are related, although they lack the crossed-tips to the bills. They too have a worldwide distribution throughout the pine forests

Coniferous trees comprise the northern, evergreen forests of America, Europe and Asia. Their dense foliage provides shelter from the elements and seeds and insects are a rich source of food.

Feeding on insects and fruit, Waxwings (*Bombycilla garrulus*) have no regular winter migration pattern but merely move as far south as is necessary to find adequate supplies of food.

Right
Crossbills (*Loxia curvirostra*) are adapted to feeding on conifer seeds grasping the cones with strong feet while they prise the scales open with their beaks.

of the northern latitudes and are a familiar sight perched high in conifers in Canada and the mountains of New England. Like many birds of boreal forests, harsh winters often drive them south in search of food and in some years they may turn up as far south as southern New England and Pennsylvania.

The large size and striking salmon-pink or green colouring of the Pine Grosbeak make it a distinctive bird and thanks to its bold nature it often sits in the open providing the birdwatcher with excellent views. The large and powerful bill can easily crush seeds and large flocks can denude a tree in a matter of hours.

Cedar and Bohemian waxwings are also residents of the northern forests, feeding largely on insects and berries. During the winter months, when insects are at their least numerous, the waxwings rely almost entirely on berries and in years with a poor supply, they are often forced to disperse south over a wide area in search of new food sources. By the late winter, they are often forced to use berry-bushes in people's gardens and since they are often confiding birds, their soft pink plumage and crest can be seen to good effect.

Although the environment is inhospitable during the winter months, especially for insectivorous birds, the summers, on the other hand, provide an absolute bonanza. Consequently, large numbers of migrant birds which have spent the winter months in Central or South America, or Africa, return to the forests in April and May. Temperatures are mild, and caterpillars, plant-lice, bugs and beetles abound amongst the foliage of the trees and the dense ground cover.

As if to herald the arrival of these migrants, the first warblers to return immediately burst into song and to identify individual species amongst the medley of sound can sometimes tax even the most experienced of birdwatchers. Perhaps the most musical of these songsters is the Canada Warbler, which to many people's eyes is also one of the most attractive species with its yellow and blue-grey plumage and neat eye-ring. However, American Redstarts and Magnolia, Yellow-rumped, Blackburnian and Nashville Warblers offer plenty of colourful alternatives.

The forests of northern Europe lack the variety of species of warbler which grace the boreal forests of North America. However, the presence of Fieldfares and Redwings, both members of the thrush family, make up for this. Insects, berries and fruits comprise their diet and so, consequently, each fall they migrate south and east from Scandinavia travelling as far afield as Great Britain and France.

The woodland floor of the northern forests of America are a rich tangle of vegetation. Dense mats of lichens and mosses carpet the ground, dotted with the white flowers and bunches of red berries of Canadian bunchberry. In glades and clearings, lush bushes of blueberry and myrtle grow vigorously and the supply of fresh shoots and energy-rich berries provide rich pickings for Spruce Grouse. These beautifully marked gamebirds, have a delicately mottled plumage which blends in perfectly with the dappled light that filters through the leaves. Unless they betray their presence by movement, their camouflage renders them almost impossible to spot.

Spruce Grouse are year-round residents of the boreal forests and in winter share the habitat with the Gray Jays. These engaging little birds show little fear of man, and are familiar to anyone who has camped in the northern forests. They fearlessly investigate visitors to their territory in case there is food to be had and this natural curiosity combined

with their ingenuity, enable them to turn to new sources of food when times are hard. Almost anything edible will be taken, from berries to shoots, and carrion to eggs and nestlings.

Nesting amongst the northern forests, a variety of birds of prey take a toll of the small birds and mammals that dwell there. Sparrowhawks in the forests of northern Europe and the similar Sharp-shinned Hawk of North America are dashing little raptors who specialise in catching birds such as sparrows and grosbeaks on the wing. Stealth and surprise are the secrets of their success as they weave quietly through the branches, taking their prey unawares.

Sharp-shinned Hawks build nests of twigs and leaves close to the trunks of trees and sometimes take over abandoned nests of other species. In early spring, they circle high above the woods in display and often share the skies with Red-tailed Hawks. Egg-laying is timed so that the chicks hatch just as the young of their prey are fledging, thus providing the hawks with the best opportunities for feeding their hungry brood.

The most impressive raptor of the northern forests is undoubtedly the Goshawk, a crow-sized bird whose active flight and large size enables it to take quarry as big as Spruce Grouse or Snowshoe Hare. If disturbed near the nest, its loud shrieking calls are far-carrying and it fearlessly defends its brood against intruders.

At dusk and after dark, a different range of avian predators takes to the wing. The excellent vision and hearing of owls, combined with their silent flight enable them to capture nocturnal mammals and roosting birds with ease. Largest of these is the Great Horned Owl which is widespread throughout much of the United States. However, other species have distributions which are more restricted to the coniferous forests of northern latitudes.

Hawk Owls are one of the most northerly nesting species, often being found at the very fringes of the tree line in northern Canada, Scandinavia and Siberia. Living at such high latitudes where, during the summer months, daylight is almost perpetual, the normally nocturnal owls are forced to hunt during the day. This behaviour, which is unusual for an owl, combined with their tolerance of man and habit of perching prominently, make them easy to spot.

During the daytime, the diminutive form of the Boreal Owl is sometimes seen hunched amongst the branches as it roosts until dusk. Songbirds sometimes mob them but show greater respect for resident Great Gray Owls. This is one of the largest and most aggressive species found in the woods which shows little hesitation in attacking man if he strays too near to a nest.

Insects become plentiful in the forest in summer, when the warblers migrate into the habitat to breed, but in winter few insectivorous species remain. Those that do stay commonly form mixed flocks and seek food together. This habit may give them increased protection from birds of prey, because a flock is a little easier to find in a forest than a single bird but it has many more watchful eyes, so its members can each spend more time looking for food and less watching for danger than if they searched separately.

As an insurance against the inevitable shortage of food in winter, many titmice or chickadees habitually store surplus food during the summer, tucking insects, spiders and seeds away in crevices where they may chance upon them while searching through the trees in winter. There is no evidence that titmice actually remember where they have hidden individual food items but it is certainly the case that some other forest residents which cache food do know just where they have put it. Nutcrackers can find their food stores even under snow.

Collaboration and foresight are usually considered to be amongst the special qualities of mankind. But birds evolved these abilities long before man, and using them, can survive under conditions which even he finds almost intolerable.

Coniferous forest habitats occur in many mountain ranges south of the true northern forests. Steller's Jay (*Cyanocitta stelleri*) occurs in such forests along the length of the Rockies as far south as Panama.

Temperate woodlands

In the temperate zones of the world, woodlands occur wherever there is adequate rainfall. In any such wood there are many different tree species and a wide variety of ground vegetation, shrubs and flowering plants, which in turn support innumerable insects, small mammals and other creatures. This means that there are an enormous number of different ways for birds to exploit the habitat, each species occupying a particular 'niche' which minimises competition.

Stroll through a temperate woodland during the summer and it will not take long to appreciate that every niche here is occupied. In a North American wood, Ruby-crowned and Golden-crowned Kinglets flit through the leaf canopy in search of insects whilst chickadees inspect every bud and twig on the lower branches. Bark and rotting wood are rich sources of insect life and Red-breasted Nuthatches and Yellow-bellied Sapsuckers probe and chisel away at the surface to reveal them whilst Brown Creepers search more diligently. Even the woodland floor is not neglected by some species of forest birds and small parties of Bobwhite Quails scurry through the undergrowth whilst Veerys and Wood Thrushes flick over leaves in search of invertebrates.

Throughout the temperate woodlands of North America, the extraordinary variety of warblers (family Parulidae) is the highlight for many birdwatchers. Up to twenty species, including American Redstart, Yellow Warbler, Parula Warbler, Black-throated Green Warbler and Ovenbird may occur in the same wood, all having migrated from their wintering grounds in South America for the duration of the breeding season.

The variety of warblers can be quite bewildering, especially at the end of the summer when the birds are no longer singing. To add to the confusion, some of the adults will have begun to acquire winter plumage and their numbers are supplemented by juveniles. Hummingbirds, on the other hand, are much more easy to identify at any season and Ruby-throated Hummingbirds on the east coast and Rufous Hummingbirds on the west coast, are frequent visitors to woodland glades. Here they seek out flowering plants and their nectar, and their inquisitive natures often lead them to 'buzz' human visitors out of curiosity.

A variety of birds of prey also frequent the woodlands of temperate North America. The rounded wings and long tail of Cooper's Hawk are distinctive and are suited to its hunting method

Temperate woodland offers a wealth of different niches to birds, from the leaf canopy to the woodland floor. Insect life abounds and in the fall, seeds and fruits are numerous.

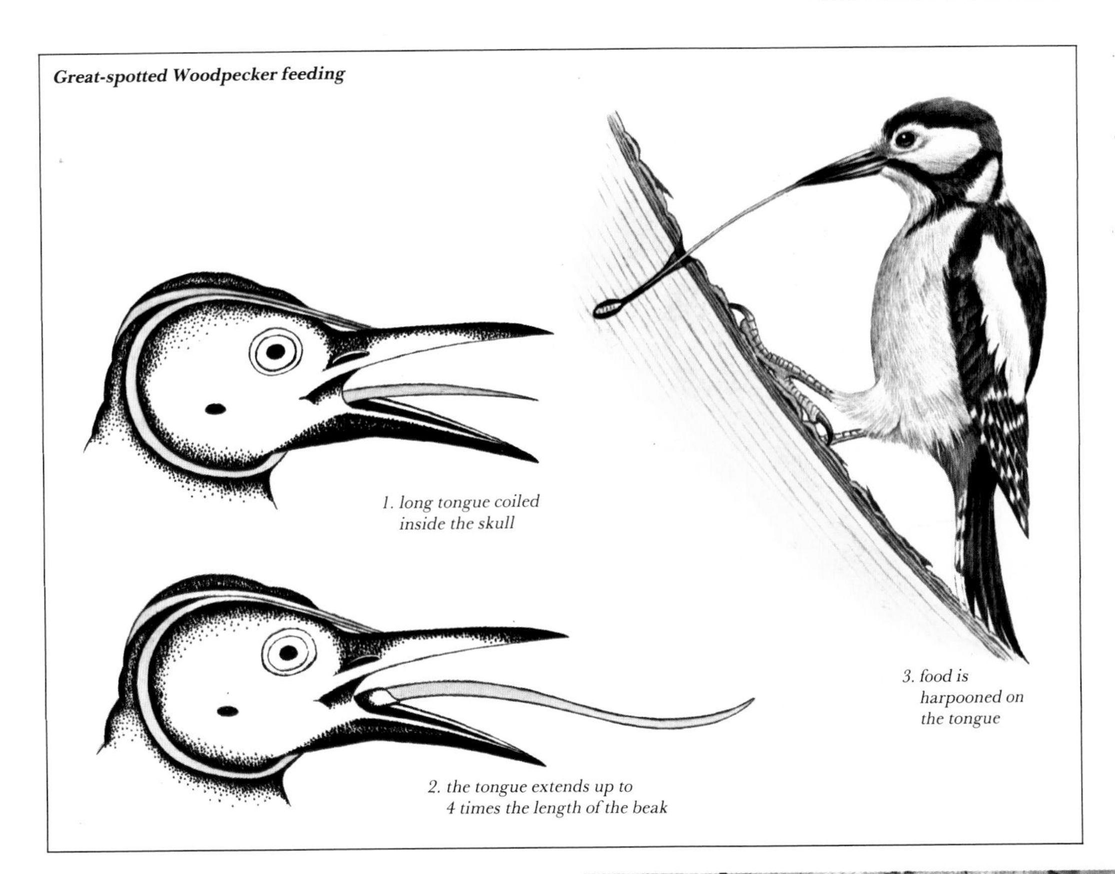

The woodpecker's tongue is especially elastic and can reach up to four times the length of its beak, probing holes for insect grubs and other food.

The Wryneck (*Jynx torquilla*) is a 'primitive' woodpecker, nesting in natural cavities and feeding largely on ants.

as it dashes through the branches, catching prey by surprise. Broad-winged Hawks and Red-shouldered Hawks are larger raptors who use their greater wing area to rise on thermals above the wood. Both species nest in secluded tree tops and depart the woods in fall to spend the winters in southern United States or South America.

In summer, a wood in Europe is full of insect-eating birds, including some which are normally seed-eaters but rear their young on insects. A number, such as the Wood Warbler, feed only in the canopy, fluttering amongst the topmost leaves. Blue Tits are particularly agile, hanging head downwards to pry into bunches of foliage that even Wood Warblers find hard to reach. Amongst the stouter twigs and branches, larger birds such as the Chaffinch move more sedately, perhaps stretching for a choice caterpillar but rarely getting off balance. By contrast, the Treecreeper never ventures into the canopy at all, but instead runs mouselike up the trunk and main branches to pry into cavities with a long, curved bill. Other species, like the Garden Warbler, feed mostly in the understorey of bushes and young trees. Wrens forage even closer to the ground amongst the herbage and fallen boughs while Robins prefer to seek food on the ground itself amongst the litter of dead leaves. Spotted Flycatchers take most of their food on the wing, flitting out from their perches to snap up passing flies.

As in American woodlands, competition for nest sites is similarly reduced by different preferences. The Chaffinch lodges its nest at the fork of a branch, the Garden Warbler low down in dense shrubbery, Wood Warblers on the ground itself. Blue Tits prefer holes in trees, ideally one with a tiny entrance through which only they can squeeze. Treecreepers look for sites behind loose bark. Flycatchers will nest in much more open cavities, perhaps where a bough has torn off, while the Wren might site its mossy nest in the rotting end of the fallen bough itself. Robins particularly like holes or places behind ivy.

Because the habitat is so varied, it can support many more species in summer than northern forests do. However, though winter cold is less severe in temperate woods, food does become scarce which means that many insectivorous species must migrate south in autumn. Whether migrant or resident, many of these birds—especially the young inexperienced ones—will die before the following spring when the survivors come to breed again in the greenwood.

A feature of temperate woodlands are woodpeckers which have developed a range of adaptations enabling them to exploit a niche largely unavailable to other birds—the trunks and underside of the branches of trees. This has enabled them to spread widely throughout the world, though they have not yet colonised Australasia and Madagascar. There are about two-hundred species of which the vast majority are true woodpeckers. Two are the wrynecks, regarded as primitive species that do not have woodpecking adaptations, and eight are the tiny piculets which have characteristics intermediate between the other two groups.

All true woodpeckers have a similar basic structure. Their chisel beaks can cut into wood and are mounted on a skull which is especially constructed to withstand the stresses of hammering, while the whole unit is powered by strong muscles. To provide a firm working platform, a woodpecker hangs on the trunk of the tree, sharp claws gripping the bark (with two toes forward and two back), and props itself on its tail (the centre shafts of the feathers being strong enough to support it). From this position it can hammer powerfully to break into the galleries of wood-boring insects. The woodpecker's tongue is mounted on a structure of elastic tissue and flexible bone which passes in two strips around the back of the bird's skull and over the top of the head, and is anchored at the right nostril. This produces a spring-like device, enabling the bird to probe with its tongue along insect galleries for up to four times the length of its beak (13 cm or more depending on the species). Backward-pointing barbs at its tip harpoon the prey and pull it out as the tongue springs back.

One group of North American woodpeckers, the sapsuckers, specialises in feeding on the sap which exudes from the holes that it drills. Other species, including the European Green Woodpecker, feed mainly on the ground, and especially at ants nests where their long sticky tongues are ideal for probing the galleries. In winter, when the ants retreat underground, Green Woodpeckers will break down the nests to reach them.

As well as insects, many species take tree seeds such as acorns and cones, wedging them into clefts or crannies so that they can be hammered open.

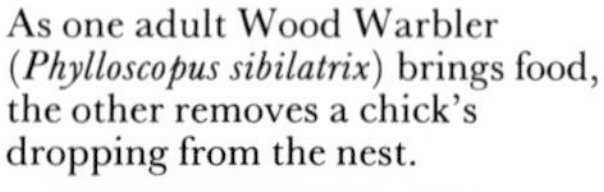

As one adult Wood Warbler (*Phylloscopus sibilatrix*) brings food, the other removes a chick's dropping from the nest.

The North American Acorn Woodpecker deliberately excavates little cavities in which to store its favourite food for use during times of shortage.

Woodpeckers use their wood-boring skill to excavate nesting holes and, incidentally, provide a useful service to other woodland hole nesting birds which will use these sites in subsequent years.

Some species use their hammering as a form of song. Selection of a resonating branch ensures that their 'drumming' is amplified and carries over long distances.

When darkness falls, most birds in the wood are already at their roosts, sheltering from predators, wind and rain. Owls, on the other hand, are wakeful. Stretching wings and legs after a day of inactivity, they prepare for the night's hunting. The largest of them, the Great Horned Owl, stands 76 cm tall and has a 1.5 m wingspan; they may tackle and kill creatures a good deal larger than themselves including foxes, young deer and other birds of prey. The smallest is the Elf Owl, a 15 cm tall insect hunter. Between the two extremes there are about 130 other kinds of owl, preying on mammals, birds, fish and crustaceans, worms and insects—in fact, owls take every sort of live prey, hunt in every type of habitat and have colonised every continent except Antarctica.

Nocturnal activity demands special powers of sight and hearing. It has been suggested that an owl's eyesight is up to 100 times as light sensitive as man's. During daylight, they protect their eyes from damage by expanding the coloured iris and closing the pupil. Even the most nocturnal of them can move about by day if disturbed, while most species hunt regularly in the half light of dawn and dusk, and a few have become wholly diurnal.

An owl's hearing is exceedingly acute. The ear openings are located on the sides of the face, sometimes forming a semi-circle reaching from above each eye to below it. Concealed within the 'facial disc' of flattened feathers, which may itself act like a radar disc to catch faint sounds, the ears are fitted with movable flaps to help sound location. In many species the ear aperture on one side of the face is higher than on the other. This gives owls great accuracy in judging the location of sounds rising from below them—the usual location of prey.

The 'ear tufts' have nothing to do with hearing. Varying subtly from species to species in their particular size and location, they create a distinctive head silhouette. Meeting in the dark, quick identification at a safe distance is important when the other bird could be your mate, a potential competitor for living space or even an enemy capable of killing you.

Small birds recognise all owls as dangerous. If they find one at roost by day, they will gather round and mob it by calling loudly. The effect is to ensure that no bird in the neighbourhood is unaware of the potential danger that threatens them all by night.

The North American Screech Owl (*Otus asio*) will take any kind of prey small enough to overpower. In the split second before capture, the wings are spread and pushed forward to brake the bird's momentum, its eyes focus precisely on the prey and the feet—themselves sound-muffled by furry feathers—are extended. Owls can swivel one toe around, changing the three-forward and one-back arrangement best for perching to a two-forward and two-back grasp ideal for killing prey by squeezing with the feet and driving in the dagger-like talons.

Tropical forests

Many tropical forest birds, such as the South American Quetzal (*Pharomachrus mocino*), have brightly coloured or bizarre plumages. Growing these absorbs a significant part of the bird's energy resources, which is probably why species in less stable habitats, and particularly migrants, cannot afford such elaborate ornamentation.

Tropical forests grow where temperatures remain high throughout the year and there is generous rainfall, creating an extended and continuous growing season. This has three very important effects for birds. First, the forests are incredibly diverse in character and, because of the great number of specialised niches available, able to support a great diversity of birds. A count in Ecuador found two-hundred different species occurring in one five-hectare plot. Secondly, in turn this means that no individual species can be particularly common in one place—a striking contrast with boreal forests where there are many fewer species, each with an extensive range.

The third major effect of the continuous growing season and the constant availability of food is that there is no need for birds to be migrants—the forest is fully occupied all year by resident birds.

Insects, fruit and nectar are the main food sources for the birds in these forests. Fruit grows mainly in the canopy where parrots, toucans, fruit pigeons and others feed on it, moving around from one part of the forest to another as different crops ripen. This soft food requires no particular beak adaptations and birds with very different bills feed on it. However, it has been suggested that the large beaks of toucans enable these heavy birds to reach out for fruit growing on branches too slender to take their weight. Fruit pigeons have very wide gapes and can gulp down whole fruit up to 5 cm across.

Birds, such as hummingbirds, which feed on nectar, usually have specially adapted tongues, which are either long and grooved or brush-like, enabling them to suck or lap up the liquid without fouling their plumage.

With no major seasonal temperature change, breeding is usually synchronised with the wet season when forest productivity is at its highest. Clutch size in most tropical birds is only two eggs, comparing oddly with the much larger broods of birds of colder habitats. It is possible that, living sedentary lives in stable and rich habitats, tropical forest birds are longer lived than many other species, thus needing to produce fewer young to maintain their numbers.

Parrots are found in tropical and subtropical forests all over the world. Some species have colonised savannas and grasslands, and a few occur in temperate habitats, several Australian species surviving even where winter snow occurs.

In total there are about 330 species variously known as parrots, parakeets, macaws and lovebirds. All have hooked powerful beaks, suited to feeding on hard-shelled seeds and nuts which are held against the curve of the upper mandible and husked or cracked by pressure from the lower one. However, the family is also fond of fruit and some species have evolved brush-like structures on their tongues to feed on pollen or nectar. Many species also take insects.

Their feet, like those of woodpeckers, have two toes pointing forwards and two backwards, giving them a very strong grasp. Using their beaks like a third foot, they are agile if careful climbers and well able to reach food hanging at the tips of swaying boughs. Some species also have the habit, unique amongst birds, of picking up food in one foot to eat it—an important skill for dealing with awkward items like large fruit or nuts in the swaying treetops.

However, not all species are tree-living; some spend most of their time on the ground, picking up the seeds of shrubs and grasses, while two species are almost flightless.

Most parrots are monogamous and pair for life. Even though they spend most of their time in family groups or large flocks, pairs remain close together all year round and will often sit side by side, preening each other when not feeding.

There are nine lovebird species in Africa, some inhabiting tropical forests, others savanna woodland and lightly timbered grassland. When collecting nest material, some lovebird species tuck strips of vegetation into their body plumage rather than carrying it in their beaks. No other bird is known to do this.

Hummingbirds' beaks have evolved to fit the trumpets of different types of flowers. The birds have extremely long tongues with which they can lap the nectar. Many species also catch insects in flight.

Macaws are a Southern American group. The Hyacinth Macaw (*Anodorhynchus hyacinthus; above*) is the largest parrot, at 1 m long. Once widespread, the Scarlet Macaw (*Ara macao; below*) has declined greatly because of destruction of habitat and collection for the pet trade.

Nests are made in holes, but few species actually originate their own sites: most simply enlarge a natural cavity or an old woodpecker hole. Some, such as the Patagonian Conure, dig burrows in the ground or under rocks. The American Monk Parrot is exceptional, gathering twigs and branches to build a huge communal nest, each pair having its own apartment in the structure.

At first when the young hatch, the female remains with them almost constantly, relying on the male to bring food to her with which in turn she feeds the young. Birds which rear their young on insects deliver them whole by the beakful, but seed-eaters which rear their young on the same diet, as do parrots, swallow the food and partially digest it before regurgitating it into their chicks' beaks. This technique makes it easier to carry such food in quantity and render it readily digestible by the young.

For a wide variety of flowering plants growing in the tropical forests of central and South America, hummingbirds fulfil the role of insects, carrying pollen from one to another so that seed will set. In exchange, the flowers secrete nectar on which the hummingbirds themselves depend. Hummingbird flowers are usually brightly coloured—often red and without perfume as they make no use of insects. They have long or curved trumpets, matching the beak shapes of different species of hummingbird. This means that hummingbirds tend to feed at the sort of flower which best 'fits' their beaks, and this is necessary because otherwise pollen would be wasted and flowers would fail to produce seed and soon di out, with disastrous consequences for hummingbirds.

For hummingbirds to feed at flowers they have evolved a way of flying unique amongst birds. Each wingtip follows a flattened figure-of-eight path through the air, providing lift and propulsion on not only the downstroke, as for ordinary birds, but also on the upstroke. This gives them incredible manoeuvrability—they can stop dead in mid-air, hover and even fly backwards. Normally the wings beat at 20–80 times a second, depending on the species, and they may reach two-hundred beats a second when a bird is flying at top speed.

Not surprisingly, hummingbirds use energy very quickly and, though nectar is very rich, they must feed every ten minutes or so throughout the day. For their size, hummingbirds have relatively the largest hearts of any warm-blooded creature, and they pump at five-hundred or more beats per minute, transferring fuel from digestive system to muscles.

They are mostly tiny birds. The smallest, the Cuban Bee Hummingbird, has a body only 15 mm long, though tail and beak make its overall length 55 mm. The smaller any creature is, the more problem it has in maintaining its body temperatures in cold conditions, and hummingbirds are no exception. If they attempted to maintain normal body temperature of 40°C (104°F) at night they would burn off their fuel reserves and die. Therefore they have to become torpid, slowing the heart beat almost to a stop and allowing their temperatures to fall—an ability shared by very few other bird species.

The tropical rainforests of New Guinea and its adjacent islands are home to most of the forty species of birds of paradise, although a few have reached northern Australia. Male birds of paradise are some of the most spectacularly plumaged birds in the world and they have evolved remarkably elaborate displays in order to show themselves to best advantage.

Tropical forests experience little change in temperature from season to season and little difference in the amount of food available to living creatures.

This means that in many tropical forest birds, the females are capable of rearing the young without help from the males who can afford to devote their energies to competing with each other for mates. Since the most attractive and vigorous males will be the ones which get the most females, they will pass on their talents to their offspring and gradually plumage and display will become more and more elaborate. Birds of paradise provide an extreme example of this evolutionary trend.

Living in dense forest, some species display in the tree-tops where there is ample sunlight to show off their plumage. Others display on the forest floor, choosing sunlit glades where they will clear away leaf litter and perhaps even peck off any overhanging foliage to ensure that nothing obstructs the spotlight of sunbeam in which they will sing, dance and posture. Favoured sites are used year round by the males, some of which display alone, while other species gather in groups.

Male bower birds are, if anything, more remarkable than birds of paradise. Instead of evolving remarkable plumage, they actually build elaborate structures on which to base courtship. There are nineteen species in New Guinea and Australia, and different species construct different styles of bower. Some consist of heaped up cones of twigs joined by a display perch, while others make parallel walls of tall twigs to form an avenue. Bowers are ornamented with collected objects, some species favouring lichens or flowers, others selecting items of one colour only or painting the walls with a pulp of berry juice. One species, the Australian Satin Bower Bird, is reputed occasionally to use a piece of bark as a brush to spread its paint.

Like birds of paradise, male bower birds take no part in domestic affairs once mating has been accomplished.

Male birds of paradise have developed elaborate plumages and individual displays. Perhaps the most bizarre is the Blue Bird of Paradise (*Paradisaea rudolphi*) which hangs upside down, singing and swinging itself to and fro.

Temperate grasslands

The Partridge (*Perdix perdix*) is locally common in grasslands throughout Europe.

Although the landscape of temperate grassland is comparatively featureless, a surprising variety of birds have adapted to the terrain.

Where rainfall is too limited to support forests, the habitats are dominated by grasses or by dwarf shrubs such as heather or sage brush. Trees do grow, but they tend to be stunted or scattered except along river valleys where they can draw on the higher water table in the ground. Generally, summers are hot and the winters are cold. Rainfall occurs mainly in spring and is followed by a flush of new plant growth and a consequent increase in food, mostly in the form of small seeds or ground-living insects and other invertebrates. The rains can be very heavy while they last, flooding low-lying ground to create temporary wetland habitats. At this season, many birds migrate into the temperate grasslands, including waterfowl which will breed in the marshes before they dry out.

The lack of trees over huge areas has major effects on the birds' breeding habits. Nests on the ground are particularly vulnerable, not only to predators but to the feet of grazing herbivores, and in many species the young leave their nests as soon as they are hatched in order to reduce the risk of total loss. Birds of prey, which mostly favour tree or cliff sites for breeding, are less common in areas far from such sites but some, such as the Steppe Eagle, will build on the ground.

Birds of prey, being large and conspicuous, can advertise their ownership of a territory by display flights but small birds must sing to make their presence known. And since singing from the ground does not carry far, larks and others ascend into the sky and sing from on high.

Species whose young are not adapted to leave the nest immediately after hatching seek nesting sites which are well concealed and sheltered from sun or rain. Burrows are attractive for this reason. The American Burrowing Owl digs its own or lives in holes made by mammals such as prairie dogs. Bee eaters, which feed on large insects caught in flight, excavate tunnels in steep banks and are often found along rivers, where suitable soft earth banks occur most frequently.

Of the seventeen species of grouse found in the world, many are found in grassland and most occur in North America. They are primarily vegetarians eating shoots, buds, seeds and berries. The majority are exclusively ground dwellers but the woodland grouse species do venture into the trees to feed. Grouse prefer to walk or run rather than fly. Their reaction to the approach of large birds of prey such as the Golden Eagle or Peregrine Falcon is to crouch and hide but if forced to

take to the air by danger on the ground, their stubby, rounded wings give them a good sprint capability over short distances.

Most species have communal mating displays. The males meet at traditional 'leks' where they display to each other, dominant birds winning central places and mating with most of the females, who are solely responsible for nest building, incubation and care of the young. While the females of these species have camouflaged plumage, the males are usually strikingly coloured, with extra adornments such as plumes or inflatable throat sacs. In monogamous species, where males assist in rearing the young, both sexes have plumages which blend in with their habitats.

As its name suggests, the Prairie Chicken is a resident of the once vast prairies of North America. Males in courtship display are an amazing sight as they strut around their communal lek with protruding neck feathers and inflated orange throat-sacs. Females are more sombrely marked which greatly improves their camouflage when sitting on the nest. Built amongst tussocks of grass, this consists merely of a shallow depression in the ground but for all its rudimentary construction, it is almost impossible to detect except by chance disturbance of the bird.

European grasslands are the haunt of Partridges, Quail and Corncrake, all of which are declining in numbers due to changes in land usage as well as persecution. During the summer months, the lush growth of grass keeps them hidden from predators but by the same token, they cannot easily keep in visual contact with other birds of the same species nor monitor their territory. To help overcome this, rival males advertise their presence by loud and repetitive calls, that of the Corncrake being described as 'crek-crek' and that of the Quail as 'wet-my-lips'. As soon as an intruder strays into an occupied territory, the resident male soon tracks down the source of the sound. For the bird in question, this task seems easy but to human ears, to pin-point its direction of origin is almost impossible.

Although not related to gamebirds, Great Bustards, which still roam the vast grassland 'steppes' of eastern Europe and Russia, have a similar lifestyle. Unusually for a bird, they take several years to reach their full size, during which time the males gradually acquire more and more elaborate throat markings. When fully grown they are one of the largest birds in the world still capable of active flight and a flock of these magnificent creatures in the air is a memorable sight.

Despite their size, bustards are extremely wary birds and will only inhabit areas where there is a clear horizon and intrusion by man is only an infrequent occurrence. In places where they do survive in any numbers, such as Poland, Hungary and eastern Austria, large flocks gather together in spring, the males fluffing up their feathers and arching their tails and wings in a most curious effect which almost completely covers the head. Hen birds find this sight irresistable and dominant males often attract several females.

Many temperate grassland birds are badly affected by severe winter weather and species such as Corncrake and Quail migrate south each autumn before its onset. Although they are hardier birds, Great Bustards are still forced to vacate the breeding grounds if deep snow or permanant frost cover the land. They head east or south until they reach milder conditions.

A Martial Eagle (*Polemaetus bellicosus*) striking at a Guinea-fowl.

The Sandhill Crane of North America is likewise an extremely wary bird, as it has been persecuted by man over the years. Due to its long legs and tall body it stands head and shoulders above the prairie grassland and keeps a constant look-out for danger. Once widespread across the continent, the Sandhill Crane is now reduced to a few pockets of grassland, from Canada south to northern California.

A similar tale of severe reduction in numbers has also befallen the Upland Sandpiper. Once persecuted in the same, relentless way which exterminated the passenger pigeon, guns and traps accounting for huge numbers on migration, the populations are only now beginning to increase. Like many prairie birds, they now face a new threat from changing agricultural practices as more and more land is intensively farmed. Lacking the stature of cranes and bustards, Upland Sandpipers are hidden from view as they walk amongst

Flock Pigeons (*Phaps histrionica*), like many other Australian grass species, are nomadic and move around in large groups following the infrequent rains to feed on young leaves and seeds.

Marsh Hawks (*Circus cyaneus*) hunt grassland and marsh habitat, flying slowly at low altitude, ready to pounce on any crouching small mammal or bird.

the grasslands. However, their aerial song-flights afford good views of the bird for the birdwatcher and the sound is memorable. They also have a liking for perching on fenceposts in order to survey the land round about.

European grasslands are the haunt of larks and pipits. The Skylark is probably the most widespread and common species and its beautiful trilling song, delivered on the wing, is one of the most evocative sounds of the British countryside. The nest is carefully hidden in a specially excavated pit, lined with grasses and mosses, and is extremely difficult to find. Like many birds that nest on the ground, the female Skylark is well camouflaged, sits tight on the nest so as not to give away the presence of the brood and is very difficult to flush.

The song of the Meadowlark is as familiar to the American ear as the Skylark is in Europe. Despite its name, this elegant bird, with canary-yellow breast, is more closely related to orioles and grackles than to larks and two distinct species occur, one in the east and the other in the west. Its flute-like song can be heard from April until November and is sometimes delivered in song-flight but often from a prominent perch, such as a bush or a post. In the carefully concealed nest, the young are fed on grassland insects and, after fledging, they join the adults in flying south to escape the harsh winters.

Often sharing the same grassy fields as Meadowlarks, Bobolinks are generally considered to be even finer songsters which sing both from the air and from a perch nearer the ground. Conspicuous in its black and white livery, the male Bobolink is one of the most distinctive birds of the American grasslands, but not so the female. She has a more sombre brown plumage, streaked with black, and to a casual observer might be confused with one of the many species of American sparrows which breed in this habitat. Most of these are rather secretive birds and a thorough knowledge of the songs and calls greatly assists in their identification.

Before the age of intensive agriculture, when man first began to clear the forests of North America for housing and small scale farming, birds like the Bobolink and Meadowlark would have benefitted. The feeding area would have been dramatically increased together with the density of seed-producing weeds.

All these small songbirds have to keep a wary eye open for predators. Snakes and predatory mammals take a heavy toll of eggs and nestlings and the threats are not all confined to ground level. High above, Red-tailed Hawks and Turkey Vultures scan the grasslands of the southern United States, and American kestrels often use man-made perches, such as telegraph wires and pylons, to give a better view of the ground below.

European grasslands are the haunt of the European Kestrel which, like its American cousin, feeds on small mammals and birds. Because ready-made perches are few and far between, kestrels use their aerial skills and hover overhead, plumetting to the ground if they detect the slightest movement in the vegetation below.

Across the grasslands of America, and particularly in the vicinity of water, elegant Marsh Hawks float through the air, their black-tipped wings and white rumps contrasting with the grey or brown plumage. Systematically quartering the ground below, the broad wings enable them to fly at slow speeds and by flying into the wind they reduce the speed even further. At dusk, Barn Owls and Short-eared Owls cover the same ground, using their enhanced eyesight and hearing.

Throughout the habitats of the world, birds have shown themselves capable of coping with extremes of temperature or food shortage. This adaptability is often a particularly noticeable feature of temperate grassland species which, where necessary, have adapted their behaviour and evolved means of getting around the problems caused by lack of cover and suitable nest sites.

Eastern Meadowlarks (*Sturnella magna*) and Western Meadowlarks (*S. neglecta*) look remarkably similar and occur together in places, yet no interbreeding occurs. The spectrograms show song to be the main isolating mechanism.

Eastern Meadowlark

frequency

time

Western Meadowlark

frequency

time

distribution of the Eastern Meadowlark

distribution of the Western Meadowlark

Savanna

Savanna grasslands occur on a large scale in tropical and sub-tropical zones where, though the temperature remains fairly high all year, rain falls only in summer. Forming a transition between forest at one extreme and desert at the other, savannas may carry large numbers of well-spaced trees or, in the dryer areas, only small and scattered thorn bushes.

The food resources are less restricted than in temperate grasslands, partly because of the greater tree cover and partly because reptiles are common. Many birds of prey catch snakes and seem to have no trouble dealing with venomous species. This is less surprising than it seems: clearly birds of prey must be able to despatch all sorts of quarry without being bitten or injured, or they would risk incapacitation and possibly death every time they make a kill.

Not surprisingly, raptors are generally common in savanna habitats. In addition to hunting reptiles and mammals on the ground, many species hunt in the air, falcons chasing other birds and large flying insects. When termites are mating and huge nuptial swarms leave the nest mounds, many birds gather to feed on them, including even eagles which find the huge numbers of termites ample compensation for their small size.

Most extraordinary of all the raptors found on the savannas of East Africa is the Secretary Bird, so-named because the arrangement of spiky feathers on the head, which form a loose crest when the bird is alarmed, reminded people of a Victorian secretary with quill pens tucked behind his ear. As it struts lazily through the long grass it keeps a sharp look-out for snakes and lizards which it will pursue at great speed if it needs to. The long legs and powerful feet come in useful when despatching a venomous snake and a single, powerful thump is often enough to disable even a large reptile.

In order to avoid injury or even death from the bite of a venomous snake, other birds of prey rely on surprise attacks which kill the prey in an instant. Martial Eagles and Black-chested Harrier Eagles do just this, patiently waiting perched in a tree and scanning the ground with their excellent vision. As soon as a potential meal is spotted, they glide down and deliver a crushing blow with their powerful talons.

Where there are large grazing herbivores, there are large numbers of insects which lay eggs in their

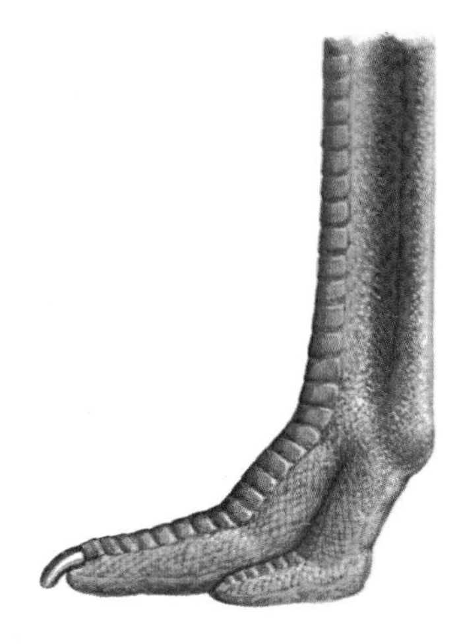

Ostrich (*Struthio camelus*) feet are highly adapted for running, being more like a hoof than a bird's foot.

Savanna grassland offers a greater variety of niches than temperate grassland. Consequently, many more species of bird are found here.

Weaver birds build intricately woven and often spectacular nests in the acacia trees which dot the landscape of the African savanna.

droppings or on the animals themselves. Flycatchers, such as the South American Cattle Tyrant, will move with the grazing animals, often riding on their backs, to catch insects that are associated with them or are disturbed from the grass by their feet. Cattle Egrets feed on insects, lizards and frogs flushed by grazing animals and will also pick parasites from the animals themselves so that the relationship is of mutual benefit. The spread of stock farming has provided them with a new opportunity and in the last forty years they have spread from their original range in Africa and Asia to North and South America, Indonesia, Australia and New Zealand.

Perhaps the most familiar of birds to freely associate with other animals are the oxpeckers, of

Two of Australia's ratites, or flightless birds: the Emu (*Dromarius novaehollandiae*) and the Cassowary (*Casuarius casuarius*). Unlike other ratites, the Cassowary prefers forest habitats.

which two species commonly occur in East Africa. Relatives of starlings, these industrious birds clamber around over the hides of grazing animals such as buffalo, elephant, rhino and giraffe. The hosts often appear to appreciate the attentions of the oxpeckers who pick off ticks, flies and other insects with their brightly coloured beaks. No part of the animal's body is neglected and the insides of the ears, the neck and around the eyes are given special attention.

Surprising though it may seem, many species of kingfisher throughout the world have abandoned their close associations with water and feed on the dry, open savannas. In Africa, the Woodland Kingfisher is often found miles from the nearest river, but in Australia, the Kookaburra has taken this to the extreme. The largest kingfisher species in the world, the Kookaburra habitually hunts for insects and snakes through open brush country and open savanna-type grassland, seldom, if ever, turning its attentions to water.

Parties of Guinea-fowl are a familiar sight on the savannas of Africa as they walk in long processions through the grass. Their diet is rather omnivorous and they will take everything from insects to seeds and fruits, pecking at almost anything that looks edible. Although they pay regular visits to water-holes in order to drink, Guinea-fowl keep their feathers in prime condition by taking dust-baths.

Low acacia bushes provide excellent perches for birds of prey to survey the land for both danger and food. Elegant Black-winged Kites shimmer in the heat-haze, dropping to the ground for a grasshopper or lizard. Pygmy Falcons, diminutive raptors who occupy the vacated nests of certain species of weaver birds, are also insectivorous but are dwarfed in size by Lilac-breasted Rollers who feed on similarly sized prey.

Look-out perches are the key to a successful hunting strategy in such a flat and featureless landscape and Carmine Bee-eaters have adopted a curious, but nonetheless successful method: they frequently ride on the backs of Kori Bustards which patrol the savannas of Africa. This has an added advantage for the bee-eater because the bustard often inadvertantly disturbs insects for it to catch. On the savannas of Africa, Kori Bustards are second only, in terms of size, to Ostriches and have the distinction of being the largest species of bird capable of active flight.

Although lacking the immense stature of bustards, the Ground Hornbill, another savanna-dweller from Africa, is no less imposing. Dressed in regal, black plumage it possesses extraordinary facial wattles and a long beak. Small parties of birds plod through the grass, snatching at lizards and insects which are sometimes tossed into the air before being consumed.

As flightless birds, Ostriches, and their relatives which are found throughout the savanna-type grasslands of the world, are amongst the most bizarre of creatures to be found anywhere on the planet, running instead of flying to escape danger.

The disadvantage of flight is that it limits the ability of birds to grow very large. Those which have done so have lost, or perhaps never possessed, the power to fly. Five bird families, known as the ratites, have flat breast-bones unsuitable for supporting wing muscles: ostrich, rheas, cassowaries, emu and kiwis.

The ostrich is the largest living bird in the world. Males may stand up to 2.75 m tall and weigh up to 154 kg. Living in the open savanna and semi-desert regions of Africa, their great height enables them to spot approaching predators at long range and to make off at speeds of up to 70 kph. Their muscular legs are bare so that they do not overheat when running fast, and their feet have only two toes, more like the hoof of an antelope than the foot of a normal bird.

An adult male ostrich will mate with three or more hens. One of these has a superior status in the group and it is she, not the male, who decides which subordinate hens may join. All the hens lay their eggs in one nest after which the subordinate females are driven off. Then male and female share incubation of the clutch, which may amount to as many as twenty-five eggs. The extra eggs are tolerated and cared for by the pair because they

The long-legged Secretary Bird (*Sagittarius serpentarius*) is a specialist predator of the African savanna—here it is killing a python.

The African oxpeckers, distantly related to starlings, feed exclusively on the external parasites of large herbivores, including domestic species, and are built rather like woodpeckers with sharp claws to hang on and a stiffened tail to give support.

add protection to their own eggs. The hen, being relatively camouflaged, sits by day and the male sits by night. The young birds can run and fend for themselves from birth: at a month old they can reach speeds of 50 kph though they are not fully grown until 18 months. It is normal for family parties to join up and for some adults to leave their young when this happens, so that dozens of immature birds of all ages and sizes may be in the care of just a couple of adults.

The grasslands of Australia support the emu and those of South America have two species of rhea. Australia also holds a giant forest bird—the cassowary; a second species occurs in New Guinea and a third in New Britain. All three species have horny 'helmets' supposedly as a protection against injury when running through undergrowth and low branches. These aggressive and powerful birds can inflict severe injuries by kicking and have killed a number of humans.

Formerly, New Zealand held a remarkable family of huge flightless birds, the moas, but these were exterminated by the Maoris after their arrival there about a thousand years ago. Today, New Zealand's only surviving ratites are the chicken-sized kiwis, which are nocturnal inhabitants of the evergreen forests.

The savanna grasslands of the world not only support vast numbers of resident species of bird but are also a major wintering ground for migrants from temperate woodlands and grasslands. They arrive in the habitat during the rainy season when sufficient surplus food is available to support them in addition to the breeding populations of resident birds. Once the food resources start to decline these birds will be on the way north again, back on their own breeding grounds.

Often, these migrants have flown vast distances from northern Europe, America and Asia in order to avoid the harsh winters on their breeding grounds. This frequently involves crossing the equator as, for example, in the case of Upland and Baird's Sandpipers, which fly from North America to winter on the grasslands of South America, and Caspian Plovers, European Bee-eaters and Rollers which depart Europe for Africa.

Even during the rainy season, the pattern of rainfall is often unpredictable and local so that migrant birds, newly arrived to the savannas, are sometimes faced with further flights to find areas of recent precipitation where plant growth is lush and insect life more abundant. The same problem is faced by many of the resident species and flocks of Red-billed Quelea and Waxbills are highly mobile. Many resident birds, such as the Zebra Finch of Australia, even nest and rear young on an irregular basis, and only when the climatic conditions exactly suit them.

The Australian Kookaburra (*Dacelo novaeguineae*) is a species of kingfisher which feeds by pouncing on small mammals and reptiles.

Tropical grasslands produce vast crops of seeds which are the food for many species of small birds such as these African waxbill species and the Australian parson finch.

1 The Parson Finch (*Poephilia cincta*), Australia.
2-8 Varieties of waxbill:
2 Red-eared, or Common, Waxbill (*Estrilda troglodytes*), Central Africa;
3 Golden-breasted (*Estrilda subflavia*), West Africa;
4 Yellow-bellied (*Estrilda melanotis quartinia*), West Africa;
5 Orange-cheeked (*Estrilda melpoda*), West Africa;
6 Crimson-rumped (*Estrilda rhodopyga*), East Africa;
7 St Helena (*Estrilda astrild*), Central Africa;
8 Black-cheeked (*Estrilda erythronotos*); South-western Africa.

Deserts

Deserts cover a fifth of the world's land surface, occurring in Africa, Asia, both the Americas and Australia. Rainfall is rare, but when it comes may be torrential. Daytime temperatures are high and the ground surface can become fiercely hot, but at night, temperatures plummet. Vegetation is sparse or absent except along the beds of seasonal rivers or around oases.

Despite its apparent inhospitability, a variety of birds live in the desert. Here, as in other habitats, the insulating qualities of feathers help them to cope with extremes of temperature. At night, they can fluff up their plumage so that it holds still air and enables them to keep warm; in the daytime they can slick it down so that the insulating pockets of air are squeezed out and their bodies can radiate excess heat. Desert species tend to be smaller than their counterparts in warmer habitats, following the rule that smaller creatures radiate warmth more than larger ones. If they are in danger of overheating, they pant, in the same way as dogs, so that air flowing over the moist throat surfaces causes evaporation and consequent cooling.

Lappet-faced Vultures (*Aegypius tracheliotus; right*) feed mainly on muscle torn from large carcasses. Egyptian Vultures (*Neophron percnopterus; left*) pick fragments from the bones and can scavenge successfully at rubbish heaps.

Inhospitable to all but the hardiest of creatures, deserts harbour a unique range of birds.

Dehydration is perhaps a bigger problem than heat itself. Water is hard to obtain and cooling by panting uses up body fluids. However, some desert species are so well adapted that they can lose up to half their weight through dehydration and still recover once they drink. The problem is greatest for seed-eaters because their food is so dry. Sandgrouse will make daily round trips of up to 100 km to drink. By bathing and saturating their belly feathers, the males can carry back adequate supplies of water for their young, which sip it out of their parents' plumage. Other seed-eaters feed their young on insects, which contain adequate moisture.

In many areas of the Sahara desert of North Africa there are seasonal rivers which flood after cloudbursts. Despite the fact that they flow only briefly and infrequently, the waters carve little valleys and recognisable stream beds. Although for most of the year these 'wadis' or 'oueds', as they are known, are dry, the residual moisture encourages comparatively greater plant growth and in some wadis there may even be permanant underground streams. Seeds and insects are easier to come by in the river beds and sandgrouse, Cream-coloured Coursers, Desert Larks and Hoopoe Larks all congregate here.

Each spring and autumn, millions of migrant birds pass over the Sahara on their way to and from their breeding grounds in northern Europe and their wintering quarters in southern Africa. Not surprisingly, they too recognise these wadis as welcome rest-stops on their long journeys but of greater value to these long distance travellers are the oases of permanant water which, at the right time of year, can hold thousands of swallows, bee-eaters, wagtails and many others.

Although water is a scarce and precious resource to desert birds, shade too is extremely important. This is never more clearly demonstrated than in the Mojave desert in southern California where Joshua trees dot the landscape above an altitude of 1000 metres above sea-level. So named because they reminded westward-trekking Mormons of Joshua at prayer, these trees play a key role in the ecology of the desert. Not only do they provide welcome shade on the ground during the heat of the day for many birds, but their branches are used as roosts, and twenty-five species have been found to nest in the boughs.

A North American species, the Mourning Dove (*Zenaida macroura*) can tolerate severe dehydration. Seed-eaters themselves, like other pigeons they feed their chicks by regurgitating a liquid 'milk' which ensures that the chicks do not lack moisture.

Being a species of yucca, Joshua trees produce striking flowers which, after dark, provide an important meal for yucca moths.

Every creature dies eventually, usually by falling prey to some other animal, but sometimes simply of disease or old age. In deserts, where food is at such a premium, death seldom goes unnoticed and a number of birds such as ravens and eagles are not slow to feed on carcasses or the remains of kills made by other creatures. One group of birds, the vultures, specialises in feeding exclusively on carrion.

Because vultures do not kill their own food, depending instead on the misfortunes of others to provide them with their meals, they cannot rely on being able to eat every day. Consequently, they are all fairly large to be able to live off their own fat reserves for days at a time. They have also evolved a very economical way of flying, which they share with other large birds of prey. Having large, broad wings they are able to float on the rising air currents, or thermals, which occur when the sun warms the land surface and causes the air above it to heat and rise up. Upcurrents which can be used by vultures also occur in mountainous areas where wind strikes the rising ground and is forced upwards. As a result, vultures are largely confined to the hot plains of Africa, southern Asia and the southern USA, though a few species live in southern Europe and along the mountain backbone of the Americas.

Soaring vultures keep a close eye on their neighbours and, if one sees another descend to the ground, it will swiftly glide over to investigate. Very quickly, birds from a wide area will arrive on the scene.

Many desert birds are powerful runners. For example, the Roadrunner, a North American cuckoo that preys on reptiles and invertebrates, is a bantam-sized bird that can run at up to 30 kph. It has a long tail which acts as a rudder to give it considerable manoeuvrability so that it can evade most ground predators without deigning to fly. Nonetheless, for most desert birds, good flying abilities are essential so that they can reach the thinly scattered resources of food, shelter and water.

Breeding is related to rainfall rather than seasons. When rains do come, many species pair and begin nestbuilding within hours; no time can be lost if the young are to hatch while plants and insect life are still briefly abundant.

Although superficially inhospitable and uninviting to the human eye, deserts exert a unique kind of fascination which cannot fail to entrance visitors. The wildlife, and in particular the birds, are fascinating and superbly adapted to life in such a harsh and arid environment, and their continued survival is a constant marvel.

Above left
Few birds use tools, but some Egyptian Vultures (*Neophron percnopterus*) learn to break ostrich eggs by dropping stones on them.

Above right
Desert Larks (*Ammomanes deserti*) of North Africa and the Middle East have well camouflaged plumage.

Below
The Ostrich (*Struthio camelus*) is the largest living bird. Now extinct in Asia, it is only common in parts of Africa and Arabia.

Temperate wetlands

Wetlands are often very productive habitats with abundant plants, small invertebrates and fish—a rich opportunity for any land creature which can adapt to life in the water. The main problem to overcome is how to avoid getting cold, particularly in temperate and tundra wetlands where water temperatures are low. Generally, mammals were slow to colonise wetlands because their fur gave them little protection against wetting and hence becoming chilled. By contrast, birds were ready equipped with a fairly waterproof outer coat of feathers. Even now, the plumage of waterfowl is not very different from that of land birds; the former merely have a denser coat of down to give better insulation against cold, and a smoother and tighter-fitting coat of contour feathers.

By the time a few mammals had evolved a system of trapping air in their pelts, so as to

Temperate wetlands support huge numbers of wildfowl and wading birds including shorebirds and herons. Particularly striking is the Black-winged Stilt (*Himantopus himantopus*) whose legs, in relation to the size of its body, are the longest of any bird.

waterproof themselves, birds had already moved into most of the different wetland feeding niches and mammals have been unable to oust them.

Though there are many wetland bird species, most of them, whatever their evolutionary origins, conform to one of the two shapes—duck or wader.

The 'duck' shape of divers, grebes, wildfowl (and many seabirds too) is suited to swimming on or under the water. The body is streamlined. The feet of many species are webbed: when the bird brings its foot forward, the toes come together so that the webs fold and the foot turns back to be pulled through the water with minimal resistance; on the backstroke, the whole foot unfolds and becomes a rigid paddle pushing against the water. The toes of coot are not joined by webs but have lobed sides. These are less efficient for swimming but are better than webs on land, where coots sometimes feed.

The legs of most waterbirds are placed well to the rear of the body because this gives them efficient propulsion in swimming. The disadvantage is that it tends to make them ungainly and slow-moving on land. To avoid this difficulty, birds such as waders and herons (which feed in the shallows and need to be able to move easily on land as well as in water) have developed long legs so that they do not have to swim at all. Their feet are usually long-toed to support them on soft ground, while their long legs and beaks enable them to catch creatures below the surface of the water or mud.

All curlews have long bills but it is especially long in the Long-billed Curlew (*Numenius americanus*), which lives in the western half of the United States and winters in Mexico. The length of the bill does, however, vary greatly. In other respects this is a typical curlew living on marshes and mudflats and nesting in meadows and pastureland.

The Grey Heron (*Ardea cinerea*) of Europe and Asia is one of sixty-three species worldwide that feed on fish, frogs, small mammals and birds at the water margin.

Few small birds enter the water because their size makes it difficult for them to keep warm. One exception is the Kingfisher (*Alcedo atthis*), which plunges briefly beneath the surface to grab unwary fish. Other members of the kingfisher family catch small reptiles by dropping from their perches, so it is easy to see how kingfishers extended this habit to catch fish.

Moorhen (*Gallinula chloropus*), working at its nest. An interesting feature of Moorhen behaviour is the way the birds contrive to keep the top of the nest and its contents above water level. In the event of flooding a pair will quickly gather more nesting material to build up the nest.

Longest legged of all birds in relation to the size of its body is the Black-winged Stilt whose black and white plumage contrasts markedly with its bright red legs. Together with several closely allied species of stilts, it is found all around the world in temperate wetlands, often in the company of another elegant wader with pied plumage, the Avocet.

At first glance, it might be supposed that these two wading birds would compete for food, but the shape of their bills and their feeding methods go some way to excluding this possibility. The needle-like bill of the stilt is used to dart at prey and pick it up with the precision of a pair of forceps, whilst the upturned bill of the Avocet is vigorously swept from side to side while at the same time the mandibles are rapidly opened and closed. By this means it sieves small food particles from the shallow, muddy margins of pools, marshes and estuaries.

The bills of other waders come in all shapes and sizes. These vary from the extremely long bills of Hudsonian Godwits and Long-billed Curlews, which probe deep into the mud for invertebrates, to the short-stubby bills of plovers which are used to pick items of food from the surface of the soil, and the unusual such as the Spoonbill Sandpiper. In proportion to the size of its body, the bill of the Snipe is extremely long and the tip is extremely sensitive and flexible. It probes the mud like a sewing machine and if it senses a worm, the unfortunate animal is grasped securely with the tip of the bill and extracted.

Relatively few species of bird find temperate wetlands a suitable habitat throughout the year and many are only temporary visitors during a particular season. Swans, geese and many species of wildfowl are lured to the wetlands of southern Europe and the United States to escape the freezing temperatures further north and on their departure in spring, their numbers are replaced by migrants from the south who find the wetlands ideal for breeding.

Some species breed around the margins of wetland areas, Yellow Wagtails and Snipe nesting amongst the lush waterside vegetation. Many others use the security that the water provides as an added security against predators. Purple Herons and Marsh Harriers build platform nests deep in the flooded reedbeds that they frequent whilst Reed Warblers construct neatly-woven basket nests high amongst the growing stems of the reeds themselves.

Black-winged Stilts build neat little platform nests far out in the marsh where only their long legs can reach while some birds, such as grebes, even go to the length of building floating nests in the middle of the water. In addition to being out of the reach of land predators, these rise and fall with the water level and hence do not get inundated in an unseasonal flood. Many species of kingfishers, on the other hand, protect their brood by excavating long burrows in the overhanging banks of the rivers which comprise their territories.

Though temperate wetlands are colder and may freeze in winter, the opportunities they offer for feeding are much like those of wetlands in warmer countries. As a result, species of waterfowl and wading birds which have broadly similar adaptations are found worldwide, from tundra pools to tropical swamps.

Tropical wetlands

The world's tropical wetlands are even richer than the temperate wetlands. Their warmth and the long growing season support luxuriant plant life and great numbers of invertebrates, such as crustaceans and insect larvae. The plants and invertebrates provide food for myriads of fish, all three in turn supporting a diversity of birds.

One feature of tropical waters is that during the heat of the day many fish rise to bask just below the surface. The skimmer takes advantage of this habit. Its beak is much longer in the lower mandible than the upper one, a unique feature amongst birds. It flies low across the water with its bill wide open, the lower half cutting the surface in a long line. Each time it touches a fish, the bird snaps its head up to flip the fish out of the water and swallow it. The jacanas feed very differently. They have extraordinarily long toes and claws to support them as they run over lily pads where they seek invertebrates and tiny frogs. The African Jacana sometimes carries its chicks beneath its wings.

Pelicans use the huge sac which hangs from the lower mandible as a kind of net to capture their food. Some, such as the White Pelican, fish cooperatively. A group of five or more birds will swim along in horseshoe formation, herding fish in front of them: then all the birds plunge in their beaks together, scooping at the gathered shoal before it can escape; the water is swilled from the beak, leaving the fish in the pouch to be eaten.

Despite their size—the Greater Flamingo stands nearly 1.5 m tall—all four flamingo species feed only on tiny creatures. They feed with their head partly or wholly underwater and the beak upside down. By waggling the tongue to and fro, water swooshes in and out between the mandibles. Fine sieves or filters inside the bill trap small food items which are then swallowed. Greater and Lesser Flamingoes sometimes occur together, but they do not compete for food. Greater Flamingoes have fairly coarse filters in their beaks and take mainly insect larvae and other small animals which they find in the mud. This means that they can only feed where the water is shallow enough for them to reach the bottom by wading or by swimming and upending. In contrast, Lesser Flamingoes have finer filters and feed on algae which float in profusion throughout the waters so that they can feed in any situation.

The flamingoes' feeding habits allow them to exploit a kind of wetland which few other creatures can tolerate—the great salt lakes which are so alkaline that no plants or fish can live in them, but are rich in tiny shrimps. Here flamingoes find not only food but safety for breeding, building their

Tropical wetlands, like the lakes in Kenya's rift valley, support vast numbers of resident and migrant birds. Vast numbers of flamingoes can be seen along the lake shore in this picture.

Many large wetland species, like the Scarlet Ibis, (*Eudocimus ruber*) nest colonially in trees to obtain security from predators.

Three species of skimmer occur in tropical wetlands: the Black Skimmer (*Rhynchops nigra; top*) in the Americas, the African Skimmer (*Rhynchops flavirostris; centre*) and the Indian Skimmer (*Rhynchops albicollis; bottom*).

nests of mud and stones in colonies which, in Africa, may be up to a million birds strong. As summer goes on, the shallow waters around the colony slowly dry up, so that when the young birds leave their nests they must travel far to feed themselves. As they cannot yet fly, they must walk all the way. On the Etosha Pan in South West Africa, a group of over 20,000 Lesser Flamingo chicks were observed to walk 80 km in a month to reach water and throughout their journey they were fed by their parents, which flew back and forth shuttling food supplies to them—a stunning example of the bond between parent birds and their young.

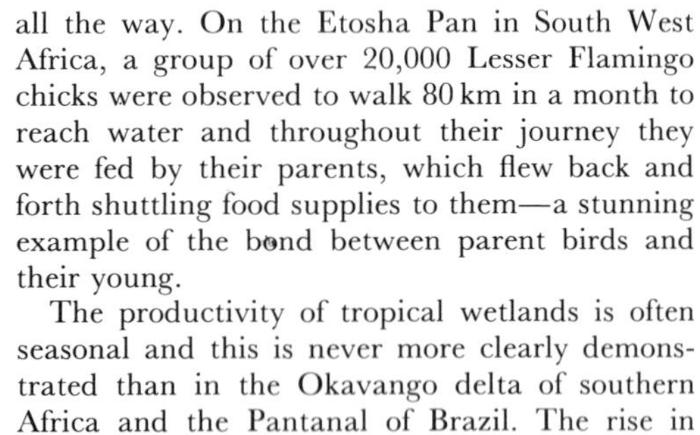

The productivity of tropical wetlands is often seasonal and this is never more clearly demonstrated than in the Okavango delta of southern Africa and the Pantanal of Brazil. The rise in water level is very often not due to local rainfall but rather to precipitation far away. In the case of the marshes adjoining the tributaries of the Amazon basin, it is rainfall in the Andes, over a thousand miles away, that is the cause of the rising waters. In the Amazon basin, the wetlands which appear seasonally cover a vast area of thousands of square kilometres, offering a huge area to be exploited by any birds adapted to a wetland existence.

The swollen waters bring a sudden input of nutrients to the tropical wetlands causing a vast increase in the numbers of microscopic plants and animals which live in the waters and this, in turn, encourages the fish and amphibians that dwell there. At this time of year, the wetland birds thrive on the seemingly limitless supply of food and as the waters gradually recede, the fish become concentrated, and feeding becomes easier and easier.

The birds that are attracted to these tropical wetlands are similar in appearance throughout the world. Great and Cattle Egrets are ubiquitous while similar species of cormorant occur globally and the massive Jabiru Stork of South America appears to fill the same niche as the Saddle-billed Stork of Africa.

The fishing technique employed by most species of herons is stealth and patience; they rely on the prey to swim within range of their dagger-like bills. However, amongst the abundance of drying pools, stocked with fish, many species throw caution to the wind and abandon this method for the more active approach of most egrets. As the

The African Jacana (*Actophilornis africana*) or lily-trotter carrying its young under its wing.

dry season progresses, the pools become smaller and smaller until finally there is no escape for the fish.

Black herons, however, seldom do this but prefer to rely on their unique and fascinating feeding method which has earned them the name 'umbrella bird'. They spread their wings outwards and forwards to form a circular parasol over their heads. This has the effect of reducing the glare caused by the blazing tropical sun and it has the added advantage of luring potential victims to the shade it creates.

In addition to the feeding methods of the herons, many different fishing techniques are employed by other birds of the tropical wetlands. Cormorants, anhingas and finfoots swim and dive, their sleek bodies gracefully gliding through the waters. Fish eagles, on the other hand, prefer to limit their contact with the water and skilfully skim over the water's surface, snatching a fish with their powerful talons. Very often they do not even get their feathers wet, but not so the kingfishers which haunt the margins of the pools.

Often with extremely colourful and iridescent plumage, kingfishers vary in size from the diminutive Malachite Kingfisher of Africa and the Pygmy Kingfisher of South America to the crow-sized Ringed Kingfisher of South America and the aptly named Giant Kingfisher of Africa. Each one catches different size fish and therefore does not compete for food, but all feed by plunge-diving into the water.

Many species of bird time their breeding period to coincide with the season of maximum food abundance in the tropical wetlands. Herons and storks build their nests of twigs and branches in loose colonies amongst trees and bushes close to the water, whilst African Fish Eagles also build their eyries within a short distance of the water. However, some species with equally well-defined breeding seasons, prefer to avoid the wettest times of year. For example, Egyptian Plovers and African Skimmers, which nest on exposed river sandbanks, do so after the seasonal floods have receded.

Tropical wetlands not only provide a haven for resident birds, but are also the wintering grounds for countless migrants from northern latitudes. Bharatpur in northern India, for example, hosts tens of thousands of wildfowl from October until March, which supplement the numbers of year-round resident egrets, herons and storks. However, the reserve is probably best known as the world's most important wintering ground for the endangered Siberian White Crane which arrive there every November.

The rift valley lakes of Kenya and Tanzania support staggering numbers of migrants including waders, such as Marsh and Wood Sandpiper, Marsh terns and hirundines, in addition to the phenomenal numbers of flamingoes, pelicans and egrets. It is sometimes difficult to believe these lakes can support so many birds.

Like all pelicans, the White (*right*) and Pink-backed (*Pelecanus rufescens; left*) pelicans use their huge beaks as nets to scoop up fish.

The oceans

The Cape Cormorant (*Phalacrocorax capensis; left*) of South Africa and the Guanay Cormorant (*Phalacrocorax bougainvillii; right*) of South America are both important producers of guano—the accumulated droppings of huge seabird colonies which are a valuable fertiliser.

Two-thirds of the earth's surface is covered by the seas. The most productive areas are the polar waters and off the west coasts of South Africa and South America, because in these areas winds and currents cause nutrient-rich water to well up from the ocean bed. This supports an abundance of plankton which in turn is preyed on by fish, squid, seals and whales, and great numbers of birds. By contrast, tropical oceans hold little marine life and birds are sparse except around islands.

Most seabirds spend much time on or under the water and must be well insulated with fat and waterproof plumage. Flight requires a light body structure and this also gives buoyancy which is a disadvantage to diving birds. They tend to have heavier bones and smaller air sacs than normal. The Galapagos Cormorant has abandoned the power of flight so as to be able to reduce its buoyancy. It floats with its back awash and can dive with little effort. Other cormorants deliberately wet their plumages to aid diving and when they come ashore must stand with their wings held out to dry.

Cormorants use their feet for propulsion under water. However, most seabirds which actively pursue their prey beneath the surface swim with their wings, which must be fairly short and paddle-like. This in turn affects their flying ability so that, though they can get along quite rapidly with a direct, whirring flight low over the surface, they lack manoeuvrability and agility in the air.

Many species feed by plunging from the air after fish which they can see just beneath the surface. Gannets and boobies have strengthened skulls and foreparts to absorb the shock of impact. They keep their wings spread for course correction until the last moment, folding them back to the shape of a paper dart as they hit the surface. To protect their eyes underwater, they close the nictitating membrane; this is a special inner eyelid which all birds possess and use to clean their eyes or to protect them from damage. In diving birds, the membrane has a clear central lens so that in effect they wear goggles while underwater.

Birds cannot penetrate deep beneath the oceans and the range of niches for them to exploit is far fewer than on land. As a result, there are less than three-hundred seabird species in the world, compared with over eight-thousand three-hundred land birds. However, several seabird species are far more numerous than any land birds because their habitat is so enormous: the Wilson's Storm Petrel, a south Atlantic species, is probably the world's most numerous wild bird.

About a hundred species of seabird, collectively known as tubenoses, have beaks which are made of distinct plates with the nostrils encased in large tubes. The purpose of this feature is unclear. It may assist in scenting food, as some species feed on the sea's surface at night, or it may be a device for sensing tiny changes in air pressure and so help birds which habitually fly amongst the waves.

Either way, it proves the relationship between birds as different in size and way of life as the albatrosses and diving petrels—birds which have evolved very different adaptations in order to exploit different opportunities at sea.

By becoming large, the albatrosses have gained certain advantages. They can take bigger food than most other seabirds so they avoid some competition. They are fairly safe from predators and, being long-lived, they need to produce only a few young to maintain their numbers. However, they have been able to grow so large only by evolving a method of flight which uses very little energy but which has made them dependent on strong winds. This means that albatrosses are largely confined to the southern oceans where winds blow almost constantly. Most species have been unable to cross the calm tropical seas and colonise the northern oceans.

The smaller shearwaters, so named for the habit in some species of flying low between the wave tops, depend less on constant wind and so are a far more widespread group. The disadvantage of smaller size is that they are very vulnerable to predators when on land. As a result, most of the smaller tubenoses nest in burrows or rock crevices on islands where there are no predatory mammals and, by coming and going only at night, also avoid attacks from gulls and skuas.

At the other extreme from albatrosses, the diving petrels of the Antarctic seas are small birds with short stubby wings which they use for swimming. They must whirr their wings rapidly to fly at all and, during the moult, they become entirely flightless when replacing their wing feathers.

Penguins have abandoned flight altogether. By becoming heavy for their size and adapting their wings into powerful paddles, they have developed the ability to swim far faster and dive much deeper than any other birds. There are thirteen species, some living in the relatively warm seas off Australia and New Zealand, South Africa and South America but others flourishing in the icy waters of Antarctica.

The largest of all is the Emperor Penguin, standing 1 m tall and weighing about 40 kg. For insulation and for protection against injury on the edge of the ice as they come ashore, their bodies are covered by a thick layer of fat and they are clad in a dense, oily plumage. They can swim at over

The Wandering Albatross (*Diomedea exulans*) has a 3.5 m wingspan. Young Wanderers do not breed until about seven, when they will return to the colony in which they were born.

All penguins nest in colonies. These are Magellanic Penguins (*Spheniscus magellanicus*), a South American species.

There are three species of fulmar. Each has a slightly different beak.

Opposite
A member of the auk family, the Puffin (*Fratercula arctica*) is found in the North Atlantic. It spends most of its life at sea but comes to land to breed.

Below
The Brown Booby (*Sula leucogaster*) and Masked Booby (*Sula dactylatra*) both feed by plunge diving. They replace Gannets in tropical waters.

40 kph, dive to at least 250 m below the sea's surface and remain underwater for over fifteen minutes at a time.

Emperors are so big and their chicks take so long to grow to full size that they must start breeding in autumn for their young to be ready to leave them by the following summer, the season when the weather is most mild and food plentiful. When their mating season arrives, the adults leave the sea and travel across the ice. The birds gather together in huge colonies of many thousand strong. By now it is June, the Antarctic winter. The female lays one egg, which the male at once takes into his care, balancing it on top of his webbed feet and squatting down so that it is warmly wrapped in the soft fold of feathers.

The males incubate their eggs through winter blizzards when temperatures drop to −60°C (−76°F). At last the eggs hatch and at about the same time the females return, to regurgitate food for the newborn chicks. Now it is the males' turn to go to sea and feed for the first time in four months.

As spring advances, the sea-ice slowly melts and the adults have less far to travel between the chicks and the fishing grounds, feeding frequency increases and by mid-summer the young birds are full-grown, to be taken to sea and left to fend for themselves at the ideal time of year.

The better adapted that birds are to life on the oceans, the less suited they are to life on land. Some are far from agile in flight and most are ungainly or slow on the ground, so they are potentially very vulnerable to predators when forced to come ashore to breed. Their choice of nesting places and their behaviour on land are dominated by this danger.

A few tropical and temperate species nest in large trees but most species live in regions where cold and high winds prevent the growth of tall vegetation near the coast. Forced to nest on the ground, some breed only on islands free from predatory mammals while others choose cliff edges which are practically inaccessible except to other birds. However, many seabirds including the larger gulls and skuas are themselves active predators so that some smaller species, including Puffins, nest underground in burrows or crevices. A few, such as shearwaters, also come and go only at night when their enemies are unable to hunt. By contrast, terns rely on the massed 'air power' of their colony to attack and drive off predators. So also do gulls, although each pair must also guard its eggs and chicks from its neighbours.

Skuas and frigate birds regularly practise piracy, harrying birds bringing food to their young until they drop it. Even large birds are not safe—skuas will catch flying gannets by the wingtip so that they 'stumble' in flight and reluctantly disgorge their catch of fish. This hazard does not affect the tubenoses because they convert their food into a rich oil with which to feed the young.

Since they do not feed in individual territories around their nests, seabirds can breed close together and this partly compensates for the shortage of safe nesting areas. Even so, some species will tolerate closer spacing than others. Gannets and Kittiwakes spread themselves out so that each pair is just out of pecking distance of its neighbour: by contrast, Guillemots happily stand packed close together on their breeding ledges. Because each species has individual preferences for spacing and site, seabird colonies often contain a wide variety of species, each occupying a different situation. In large colonies many thousands of seabirds of many kinds may use every available nook, cranny, ledge and flat surface. For a few weeks the air is filled with birds, but once the breeding season is over most will disperse to sea and the colony will be deserted for another year.

Section Three

Bird Families of the World

As has been shown, birds come in all shapes, sizes and colours. The following is a directory of the bird families of the world, giving examples, number of species in each and their major characteristics.

Ostriches (Order Struthioniformes)

Ostriches are the largest of living birds, some males weighing as much as 155 kilograms and standing 244 centimetres. Weight, small wing area, and inadequate wing feathers and flight muscles combine to make them flightless. It is not unusual, however, for Ostriches to run at speeds of forty to sixty kilometres an hour. Normally they run with folded wings, but these can be used to help the birds to turn or brake.

The Ostrich's wings are very small, and the feathers soft, with pendant barbs and short barbules that have no interlocking mechanism. A line of wing quills of this composition runs along the margins of the wings and there are three superimposed layers of wing coverts. A singular feature is that two of the wing fingers end in claws or spurs that can be used in attack. The rest of the plumage exhibits the same softness and structure as the wings. There are no rectrices, their place being taken by elongated tail coverts. The legs are long, strong and almost without feathers. There are only two toes, of unequal length, and the larger one ends in a nail. This is the greatest reduction in the number of toes exhibited by any bird. The Ostrich has a long neck, much of it bare of feathers, and a small, flat head terminating in a rounded beak with a huge gape. The eyes are large, and the upper lid has lashes.

Only one species of Ostrich survives and this is found in Africa and Arabia. Its great stature, its gait and the fact that it lives in the desert, explain why in ancient times it was compared to that other desert animal, the camel. Hence its specific name *Struthio camelus* (ostrich camel).

There are several races of Ostrich which interbreed in captivity and produce fertile crosses. In Africa there is a Northern and a Southern Ostrich, the first is found in Algeria, Tunisia and the Sudan, the second in the Transvaal, Natal and Cape Province. The differences between them are pronounced. The Northern Ostrich is larger and has a bare patch on the top of its head, which appears when the chicks are two months old. The skin of the hen bird is bright yellow and that of the cock scarlet, while the skin of the Southern Ostrich is light grey and dark blue in hen and cock respectively.

The plumage of these two races is very similar. Young birds and hens have grey-brown body plumage, turning to black at the tail and near the wings; the tail and wing feathers are a dirty white. The cocks have magnificent plumage, ebony black on the body, with pure white wing quills and huge tail coverts.

The Ostrich inhabits desert and savanna, though never straying very far from water, of which it needs about seven litres a day. It is omnivorous, but mainly vegetarian. In captivity its stomach sometimes contains an extraordinary variety of objects, because of its habit of picking up and swallowing bright or metallic objects. It is gregarious and lives in large flocks, often in company with antelopes and zebras.

Gulls on a cliff face in the evening sunlight.

The Double-wattled Cassowary (*Casuarius casuarius*) of Australia and New Guinea. The female lays two to three eggs and leaves the male to incubate them and care for the young. Living in the jungle, the prominent growth of bone may help to protect the Cassowary's head as it moves swiftly through the dense thorny undergrowth.

Opposite
The Gentoo Penguin (*Pygoscelis papua*) breeds in large colonies on the South Shetlands and other antarctic islands. This picture shows the ease with which a penguin moves in water emphasising its complete adaptation to swimming. Two eggs are usually laid in a nest on the ground and hatch after an incubation of seventy-two days.

Ostriches breed in the spring and are polygamous. Mating takes place after an elaborate courtship display. The cock makes the nest, a mere scrape in the sand about ninety centimetres across and thirty centimetres deep. The hens lay their eggs in the shared nest and both cock and the senior hen sit in turn until the eggs hatch. The eggs are about fifteen centimetres long and twelve centimetres in diameter. Each weighs about 1,200 grams and has a thick, tough, ivory coloured shell. Incubation takes from forty-two to forty-eight days. The baby Ostrich is precocial and at birth is about the size of a Domestic Hen. The cock and hen look after and protect the chicks.

Rheas (Order Rheiformes)

There are two species in this order, the Commom Rhea (*Rhea americana*) and Darwin's Rhea (*Pterocnemia pennata*).

The Common Rhea lives in flocks on the pampas and savannas, feeding on vegetable matter or small mammals, according to the season. Sometimes it joins a herd of cattle, feeding with them on clover and lucerne. It is neither as large as the Ostrich (the cock's maximum height is 170 centimetres) nor so striking. The plumage of both cock and hen is blackish on the head and on the top of the neck, yellow and ashen grey on the body, and dirty white on the belly. The neck is partly feathered, and in this respect it differs from that of the Ostrich. Each foot has three clawed toes webbed at the base.

In spring the cocks become very aggressive as they select and segregate their harems of three to seven hens. Courtship is brief. The cock digs the nest and sits on the eggs. There may be as many as fifty eggs laid by several females, lemon yellow when first laid and weighing as much as 800 grams. Incubation takes forty days.

Emus and cassowaries (Order Casuariformes)

Two families make up the order, the emu (family Dromaiidae) and the cassowary (family Casuariidae). The Common Emu (*Dromaius novaehollandiae*) is the second largest living bird, the cock often standing over 200 centimetres high. It is very like the Common Rhea in that its neck is partly feathered and it has three toes. The plumage of both cock and hen is deep brown, the feathers have two shafts diverging from the base.

Emus are found throughout mainland Australia and their habits are similar to those of other ratites, except that they are monogamous and their courtship is more prolonged. The cock bird makes the nest and hatches the brood. The eggs number fifteen or more and are a fine green colour. Each weighs about 270 grams. Incubation takes two months.

The Common Cassowary (*Casuarius casuarius*) differs from the other ratites: its plumage has the look of fur rather than feathers and it has a helmet or bony crest on its head. The wing quills are reduced to stiff rods which hang over its flanks. Head and neck are partly bare and brightly coloured: yellow, green, blue, violet and red. Some individuals have similarly coloured neck wattles. The rest of the body is all brown or black. Males and females are alike and stand some 140 centimetres high. There are three toes on each foot.

Cassowaries are found in northern Australia, New Guinea and parts of Polynesia. Geographical isolation has led to the evolution of several species distinguished from one another by the presence or absence of wattles, as well as the colouring of the neck. Unlike the Ostrich, rheas and emus, the cassowaries are solitary and usually timid. Their normal habitat is the forests.

Kiwi (Order Apterygiformes)

The kiwis of New Zealand are now rare survivors of this diminished ratite order. There is a single family, Apterygidae, made up of three species: the Common Brown Kiwi (*Apteryx australis*), the Greater Spotted Kiwi (*Apteryx haasti*) and the Little Spotted Kiwi (*Apteryx oweni*). No larger than a Hen, the Common Brown Kiwi has four toes and a long, pointed and curved bill with nostrils near the tip. Its wings are so short that they are hidden beneath its body plumage, which is more like hair than feathers. It has no tail. Both male and female are iron brown.

Kiwis are nocturnal, remaining hidden in the forest during the day and emerging at night to feed on earthworms, insects, larvae, soft fruits and leaves. It is then that they utter the cries of *ki-i-wi*. The scientific name, *Apteryx*, means 'without wings'. They can run and jump with surprising speed and are lively, graceful creatures. The hens lay a single egg in a hollow roughly lined with moss. The egg is white and relatively large for the size of the birds.

Tinamous (Order Tinamiformes)

The neotropical tinamous look remarkably like game birds, and the smallest is the size of a Quail. Size apart, there is a close uniformity of appearance throughout the group. Although they are carinate birds, palate structure has determined classification of the fifty species with the palaeognathous birds. But unlike other palaeognathous orders the tinamous can fly, although not very strongly. The tails of some species retain the down feathers.

Most of the tinamous inhabit the dense rainforests of South America and colouring is cryptic to afford protection. Two of the commonest species are the Variegated Tinamou (*Crypturellus variegatus*) and the Crested Tinamou (*Eudromia elegans*), a species of the open pampas.

The eggs, which are laid on the ground, their shiny surfaces blending into the wet, glistening moss and leaves of the forest floor, are the most strikingly beautiful found among birds. Some have the look of burnished metal, but most have the appearance of glazed porcelain in pale pastel grey, lilac and primrose, or olive and dark reds, purples and even blacks. These are incubated by the male.

Penguins (Order Sphenisciformes)

Confined to the southern hemisphere, penguins form a separate order of flightless birds comprising six genera: *Aptenodytes*, *Pygoscelis*, *Eudyptes*, *Megadyptes*, *Eudyptula* and *Spheniscus*. They are the most completely marine of all birds and are able to swim underwater as fast as seals. Webbed toes and wings reduced to form strong flippers that cannot be folded mark their adaptation to their environment.

Ashore they are, of course, bipedal, with an awkward gait. Their diet is mixed, consisting mainly of fish, crustaceans and small squids. They are a gregarious and monogamous order, nesting in large colonies. The male takes an active part in rearing the young.

The Kiwi (*Apteryx australis*) lives in the dense evergreen forests of New Zealand and as the symbol of the country it has appeared on stamps and coins. The bill is long and flexible and unique in having the nostrils at the tip, indicating that the bird finds its food more by smell than sight.

A King Penguin (*Aptenodytes patagonica*) incubating its single egg. Male and female share the task. They build no nest but carry the egg in turn on their feet, covered with a fold of abdominal skin. The chick hatches in summer when food is plentiful and lays down a good supply of fat to last it over the winter. The following spring brings sufficient food to complete its development.

Aptenodytes is a genus which includes the two largest species of this order: the Emperor Penguin (*Aptenodytes forsteri*) and the King Penguin (*A. patagonica*), 120 and 150 centimetres long respectively.

Pygoscelis, also an Antarctic genus, includes the Adélie Penguin (*Pygoscelis adeliae*) and the Gentoo Penguin (*P. papua*). Both are about sixty centimetres long.

The Rockhopper Penguin (*Eudyptes crestatus*) and the Macaroni Penguin (*E. chrysolophus*) belong to the genus *Eudyptes*, common in New Zealand and subantarctic islands. The Yellow-eyed Penguin (*Megadyptes antipodes*) is the only species of its genus.

Eudyptula, a genus of small species, includes the Fairy Penguin (*Eudyptula minor*) and the White-flippered Penguin (*E. albosignata*).

The sixth genus, *Spheniscus*, includes the African Jackass Penguin (*Spheniscus demersus*) and several South American species of medium size.

Divers and loons (Order Gaviiformes)

These are web-footed birds well adapted to swimming and diving, but with short wings that restrict flight. They spend their lives on or in the water, yet occasionally make long flights. Once in the air, they fly strongly. The position of the legs, well back on the body, is indicative of their aquatic habits. Divers are the only birds with legs completely encased in skin. Only the tarsi are exposed, protruding at the rear of the body like twin propellors. Like grebes, they are fast surface swimmers, and partly because their bones are relatively solid and not fully pneumatic they can, by expelling the air from body and plumage, also submerge themselves with barely a ripple to reveal

A vast rookery of Adélie Penguins (*Pygoscelis adeliae*). Adélies return to the rookery in October when the sea is still frozen. The nests are sited at the foot of icy slopes. Some birds return to the same nest site year after year. The two eggs are incubated in turns by the male and female while the other is away feeding at sea. The young chicks congregate in creches and leave to go to sea in February.

Top left
The Magellanic Penguin (*Spheniscus magellanicus*) with its chick. It has a striking piebald plumage, even its bill sometimes being sprinkled with white. It lives on islands off the South American coast nesting in burrows. Usually two eggs are laid. During the breeding season it feeds on cuttlefish found around the inshore kelp beds.

Top right
A nesting colony of the Rockhopper Penguin (*Eudyptes crestatus*). The rookery is usually sited on rocky islands where there is plenty of tussock grass, sometimes several hundred metres away from the sea. The Rockhopper is distinguished by the black feathers of the crown which are elongated into a crest and by narrow yellow lines from the forehead above the eye which fall in five plumes.

Bottom
The Black-throated Diver or Arctic Loon (*Gavia arctica*) is distributed round the North Pole, being absent only from Greenland and Iceland. It prefers to breed on large inland waters from which it can obtain plenty of food. The two olive-brown eggs with dark spots are laid in a scrape near the water's edge.

The Little Grebe (*Podiceps ruficollis*), also known as the Dabchick, is widespread across Europe and races are found throughout Asia and Africa, Australia and New Zealand. It nests on semi-floating vegetation on ponds and lakes, but is seldom found on open sea. Its food consists of aquatic insects, fishes and frogs.

The Great Crested Grebe (*Podiceps cristatus*). The crest which usually lies flat on the head is raised during a display that incorporates much head shaking. The nest is floating and composed of rotting vegetation. At the slightest alarm the bird covers the eggs with weeds and dives to safety so the pure white eggs soon become well stained and camouflaged.

their presence. Underwater propulsion is by the legs alone. Buoyancy can be increased by trapping pockets of air within the plumage.

Divers seldom leave the water, as they walk with difficulty on land. They prefer freshwater habitats in summer but in winter frequent salt water rather than fresh. They are found only in the northern hemisphere, mainly but not exclusively along the sea coasts of northern Europe and North America, with winter migration southwards. There are four species. The Red-throated Diver or Loon (*Gavia stellata*) is the smallest and the commonest. It nests in northern Asia, America and Europe. The Black-throated Diver or Arctic Loon (*G. arctica*) has an arctic-boreal distribution. The Great Northern Diver or Common Loon (*G. immer*) is a species found in the northern United States, Canada, Greenland and Iceland. The White-billed Diver or Yellow-billed Loon (*G. adamsi*), on the other hand, is found in North America and Eurasia.

Adult plumage is similar in both sexes, with strong, bold contrasts of black and white in summer, and somewhat duller plumage in winter. Except during the breeding season the species are rather similar. Flight feathers are moulted simultaneously and during the ensuing flightless period the birds withdraw into protective solitude. Two eggs are laid by the water's edge. The main food is fish.

Grebes (Order Podicipediformes)

Although formerly placed in the same family and order as divers, grebes are now classified separately. The webbing is reduced to lobed fringeing membranes outlining only the three front toes, as it is in members of the coot family. The tail is reduced to a downy stump and the rectrices are atrophied.

Grebes usually prefer freshwater to salt and are often found on reed-fringed lakes and ponds, nesting in masses of floating vegetation. Distribution is world-wide. *Podiceps* is the largest, most widespread genus, with thirteen species. The other three genera are found only in the New World: the large Western Grebe (*Aechmophorus occidentalis*) of North America, the Pied-billed Grebe (*Podilymbus podiceps*), and the flightless Short-winged Grebe (*Centropelma micropterum*) of South America are representative species.

Plumage in all genera is striking. A short tail with a sheared-off look is also typical of the order. Short wings impose weak flight. Elaborate courtship and a curious habit of eating their own feathers is also common to them all. This last feature is still unexplained. Like the divers the grebes are able to expel the air from body and feathers and sink below the surface to safety.

The large genus *Podiceps* includes the dabchicks and the typical ornamented grebes. The commonest dabchicks are: the Least Grebe (*P. dominicus*) found in the southern United States and South America; the Little Grebe (*P. ruficollis*) about twenty-five centimetres, with bright red neck patches, found in the Arctic regions of the Old World and the eastern hemisphere; and Australia's Black-throated Little Grebe (*P. novaehollandiae*). It is usual to include among the dabchicks the Hoary-headed Grebe (*P. poliocephalus*) of Australia and the New Zealand Dabchick (*P. rufopectus*).

The ornamented forms include the Old World Great Crested Grebe (*P. cristatus*); three South American species, the Lesser Golden Grebe (*P. chilensis*), the Great Grebe (*P. major*) and the Silver Grebe (*P. occipitalis*); and the Horned Grebe (*P. auritus*), the Red-necked Grebe (*P. grisegena*) and Black-necked Grebe (*P. nigricollis*). The last three are common in North America and occur in the Old World too.

The Great Crested Grebe (*P. cristatus*), the largest and an inhabitant of the Old World, is about the size of a gull. It is identifiable by its long white neck and white front, which are in contrast to the brown upper parts. Two stiff tufts of black feathers project backwards from the head. In the breeding season the head of both male and female is framed by a fringe of rufous and black feathers.

As a prelude to nesting and breeding the pair indulge in an elaborate courtship behaviour of head-shaking, displaying, the presentation of nesting materials to each other, loud and excited vocal display, preening and, most characteristic, hard rushes towards each other until they meet and rise neck to neck and breast to breast. The hen lays three or four whitish eggs. The chicks leave the nest shortly after they are hatched and seek protection from time to time beneath the parental wings. It is quite common for the male or the female to carry the young on its back.

The Black-necked Grebe (*P. nigricollis*) differs from the Great Crested Grebe in its plumage. The upper parts are black, except for the red wings and a fan of yellow feathers behind each eye.

Albatrosses, shearwaters and petrels (Order Procellariiformes)

The essentially oceanic birds of this order seldom come to land except during the breeding season. The main characteristics are the hooked bill sheathed in horny plates and the long tubular nostrils. A variety of aquatic creatures make up their diet. They nest in a burrow, a depression in the ground or on a pile of soil and vegetation and lay only one egg. The chicks are altricial and are fed by regurgitation.

Albatrosses (Family Diomedeidae)

These large, long-winged birds have a strong, easy gliding flight that can be maintained over long distances. For the most part they belong to the southern hemisphere. There are two genera: *Diomedea* and *Phoebetria*. A few species occur regularly and breed in the North Pacific, none in the North Atlantic.

One of the most striking of the fourteen species is the Wandering Albatross (*Diomedea exulans*) of the southern oceans. It is the largest of this family, with a wingspan of 330 centimetres or more and a weight of nine kilograms.

In flight the Albatross glides without effort, sailing in wide sweeps over the waves, neck withdrawn, so that the head lies along the axis of the body, which itself is spindle-shaped. The legs are extended tailwards and the webbed feet, often protruding beyond the tips of the tail feathers, move only to act as a rudder. The long wings, their tips slightly inflected, are similarly motionless. An occasional twist of the widespread tail and a turn of the head are the only visible movements as the bird exploits the force of the wind currents. In strong gusts the wing tips curve inwards and come closer together and the bird lets itself be borne along at a dizzy speed, describing a vast circle across the sea before resuming its former position, perhaps in the wake of a ship.

The take-off of an Albatross is aerodynamically similar to that of a seaplane. Stretching out its neck and spreading its wings, it paddles at full speed into the wind with its webbed feet. Soon the bird's breast is out of the water with only the feet beating the surface. The moment it is airborne the Albatross resumes its aerodynamic shape, neck retracted and undercarriage drawn up.

The gliding feats of the Albatross have been the subject of speculation. Although it has not been possible to make precise tests to prove how these feats are performed, it seems that the Albatross normally flies no higher than fourteen metres. It uses the slight increase in wind speed at this height to remain airborne. The bird glides downwind, gathering speed, then turns upwind and climbs with the increased wind speed providing lift to bring it back to the original height. The Albatross also makes use of the slight air currents generated by the movement of waves.

These birds have a protracted and complicated courtship involving display, dancing, squawking and bill fencing. Both mates collaborate in building the nest, usually in colonies. Incubation of the single egg takes about eight weeks, and up to ten months more are needed to rear the fledgling until it is able to take care of itself. As it takes a whole year to rear a single Royal Albatross or Wandering Albatross chick these species breed once every

The Wandering Albatross (*Diomedea exulans*) on its nest on the ground. Like others of the family, it breeds in colonies on remote islands in the southern hemisphere. The single chick is at first covered with white fluffy down, changing after a few weeks to buff-grey. It develops rapidly, its only enemy at this time being the marauding skua.

The White-tailed Tropic Bird (*Phaethon lepturus*) in flight. Tropic birds fly with rapid wing-beats and feed by plunging on their prey of fish and squid from a height of about fifteen metres, catching it just below the surface. Although they breed in colonies, at sea outside the breeding season they are seen only in ones and twos.

other year. The breeding cycle for the smaller albatrosses is shorter.

In the North Pacific the best known and most common are the Black-footed Albatross (*Diomedea nigripes*), and the Laysan Albatross (*D. immutabilis*), the Black Gooney and White Gooney respectively, particularly on or near the Hawaiian Islands where both species breed. At Midway Island, western-most of the Hawaiian chain, they have created safety problems through their persistent attempts to land and nest on or near the aircraft runways. Their courtship performances, performed heedless of the hazards of ships and aircraft led to their being dubbed 'Gooney Birds'.

Shearwaters and fulmars (Family Procellariidae)

This is a migratory and wholly marine family with certain common characteristics: thick plumage, hooked bill, long tubular nostrils and webbed feet. Genera are distributed throughout the oceans of both hemispheres. There are four main groups: the true shearwaters, the fulmars, the typical petrels and the prions.

The shearwaters nest in vast colonies, each pair digging a deep burrow that ends in an incubation chamber where one of the parents sits on the egg while the other brings it food. Once hatched, the chick is left alone and fed at intervals. Later it is abandoned altogether until it takes wing and fends for itself. The Manx Shearwater (*Puffinus puffinus*) is a typical species found in the Mediterranean and eastern North Atlantic areas. Other typical species include the Short-tailed Shearwater or Slender-tailed Shearwater (*P. tenuirostris*) of Australia, the Greater Shearwater (*P. gravis*) found throughout the Atlantic, and the Sooty Shearwater (*P. griseus*) of the southern hemisphere.

The fulmars or foul-gulls are typically represented in the northern hemisphere by the Northern Fulmar (*Fulmar glacialis*) and in the southern hemisphere by the smaller Silver-grey Fulmar (*F. glacialoides*). An ill-smelling oil that is spat out at intruders at the nest has earned the fulmar its alternative common name. Also included in this group are the polymorphic Giant Fulmars (*Macronectes giganteus* and *M. halli*) of southern oceans, the black and and white Cape Pigeon or Cape Petrel (*Daption capensis*), and the pure white Snow Petrel (*Pagodroma nivea*) of the Antarctic ice fields.

The typical petrels include the gadfly petrels, *Bulweria* and *Pterodroma* (which includes the Cahow (*P. hasitata* of Bermuda) species. Little is known about many of them due to their pelagic haunts and rather secretive breeding habits.

And finally there are the prions, a small genus of only four species of *Pachyptila* found in Antarctic waters.

Storm petrels (Family Hydrabatidae)

This is a family of tube-nosed birds about the size of the swallow. They are strong in flight, skimming the waves on long, pointed wings and pattering over the surface on their long legs. The commonest southern species is Wilson's Storm Petrel (*Oceanites oceanicus*) also known as Mother Carey's chickens. The common northern species is simply known as the Storm Petrel (*Hydrobates pelagicus*). Leach's Storm Petrel (*Oceanodroma leucorhoa*) is abundant in the northern oceans; it and Wilson's Storm Petrel are among the most abundant of birds. The storm petrels also breed on islets in dense colonies.

Diving petrels (Family Pelecanoididae)

Black and white on the underparts, with small beaks and feet, the five species of the single genus *Pelecanoides* are found in the waters of the Antarctic and radiate northwards to Peru, New Zealand, Australia and other parts of the South Atlantic and Pacific. Unlike other tube-nosed birds their flight is very direct and they dive into the water where they swim with their wings. A single egg is laid in a burrow in soft soil.

Pelicans and allies (Order Pelecaniformes)

The major characteristic common to this group of large, aquatic birds is that they are totipalmate, that is, all four toes are joined by a web. Such complete webbing of the foot is found only in the Pelecaniformes. The families of the group have an extensible beak pouch. Nesting is usually colonial, and the chicks are altricial, fed by regurgitation. Distribution is world-wide.

Tropic birds (Family Phaethontidae)

A single genus contains the three species and is found only in the tropics. The Red-billed Tropicbird (*Phaëthon aethereus*) is a native of the Atlantic, eastern Pacific and northern Indian oceans. It looks rather like a large tern. Plumage is white or pinkish white on the underparts, and white finely barred with black on the back. Its most charac-

The Old World or Great White Pelican (*Pelecanus onocrotalus*) breeds in large colonies building a simple nest on the ground. Up to 40,000 pairs of birds have been seen in one colony in Africa. The same nesting colonies are used year after year and in the tropics breeding may continue throughout the year.

teristic feature is a much elongated, central pair of tail feathers. Its shrill, piercing call has earned it the name Bosun Bird from sailors. With its grace and agility the Tropic-bird is master of the air, and an expert fisherman. Courtship behaviour is excited and often violent. It breeds on rocky and desolate islands. Each pair produces a single egg, laid on a cliff ledge without a nest of any kind. The globular chick is thickly covered in white down and looks more like a powder-puff than a bird.

The other two species of the single genus are the smaller White-tailed or Yellow-billed Tropic-bird (*P. lepturus*) of the Atlantic, Indian and Pacific oceans and the Caribbean and the Red-tailed Tropic-bird (*P. rubricauda*) of the Indian and western and central pacific oceans.

Pelicans (Family Pelecanidae)

Pelicans, among the largest of birds, have extremely large bills with great distensible pouches suspended below the lower mandibles, which they use as scoops in their fishing operations. They never fly with fishes in the pouch. There are six species, four of them from the Old World, and two from the New. Generally the beak is blue edged with red, and the pouch and the area round the eyes are ochre yellow. The plumage in both sexes is mainly white, though variations occur—white tinged with grey in the Dalmatian Pelican (*Pelecanus crispus*), which has curly feathers on its nape, and white tinged with rose in the Old World White Pelican (*P. onocrotalus*). The Dalmatian Pelican is also found over a wide area in southern Asia, the White Pelican throughout Africa and Asia and occasionally in some parts of south-east Europe.

The American White Pelican (*P. erythrorhynchos*), of North and Central America, has a wingspan of 300 centimetres. The Brown Pelican (*P. occidentalis*) which is one of the few non-white species, ranging from Canada to southern South America, does its fishing in salt water, diving from a great height and with an enormous splash.

Though clumsy looking, pelicans swim and fly extremely well. Only the Brown Pelican dives underwater. The others employ a variety of tactics to catch their fishes. Sometimes they capture them by dropping on to them from a considerable height, at other times they act as 'beaters', forming a semi-circle and driving the fishes together so they can take them at their ease.

Pelicans nest near water, choosing places covered by high vegetation. They lay three or four pure white eggs. The chicks are quite helpless and are fed large quantities of food by the parents. In two months the young are able to fly.

Gannets and boobies (Family Sulidae)

The Sulidae fall into two groups, the gannets of temperate seas, and the more tropical boobies. The gannets are colonial cliff-nesters. Here both birds incubate the single egg, covering it with their overlapped feet before settling down to brood as they lack a brood patch. When the chick develops flight feathers it flutters down to the sea. Hunting tactics are spectacular, often involving straight-as-a-plummet dives from a height of thirty metres.

The fishes are swallowed before the bird resurfaces. The commonest species are the Northern Gannet (*Sula bassana*), the Cape Gannet (*S. capensis*) of South Africa, and the Australian Gannet (*S. serrator*) although these may be but subspecies of the Northern Gannet. Adult plumage is white with a black tip to the wings.

There are six species of booby. Three are well distributed throughout the tropical world: the Masked or Blue-faced Booby (*Sula dactylatra*), the Red-footed Booby (*S. sula*) and the Brown Booby (*S. leucogaster*). The masked species is the largest and the brown the commonest. The other three species are more limited in range. The Peruvian Booby (*S. variegata*) and the Blue-footed Booby (*S. nebouxii*) are restricted to the western coast of the American continent, and Abbott's Booby (*S. abbotti*) is confined in its distribution to only two islands, Assumption Island and Christmas Island, in the Indian Ocean.

The King Shag (*Phalacrocorax albiventer*) of the Falkland Islands, one of the white-breasted cormorants which are found exclusively in the southern hemisphere. Like all cormorants it is highly gregarious both in the water and on the breeding and roosting grounds.

A male Anhinga or Snakebird (*Anhinga anhinga*), also called the Darter, from its habit of darting its long, slender bill forward from its coiled neck, before it dives. As it hunts through the water it spears its prey, surfaces, then throws the fish into the air and swallows it as it falls.

Cormorants and shags (Family Phalacrocoracidae)

These are sombre-looking birds with long bodies, long necks, long beaks with a hooked upper mandible, completely webbed feet, short legs and wedge-shaped tails. Plumage is predominantly black with a greenish or bronze sheen in both sexes. The wings are short and do not permit long flights out to sea. One species is known to be flightless. They are, like the seagulls, birds of the coast. They hunt by diving and picking up their prey underwater. When a cormorant meets resistance from its victim it beats it on the water, submerges it, shakes it, and somehow manages to keep it away from the unwanted interest of its comrades brought to the spot by the commotion. After diving, the cormorant always seeks out an elevated spot, where it perches with wings outspread. It is commonly supposed that this is to dry the feathers, which are not as 'waterproof' as those of other birds, but it is interesting to note that even captive species in zoos, who do not have to dive for food, persist in spreading their wings after feeding.

The mating habits of the Great Cormorant (*Phalacrocorax carbo*) are unusual. Both female and male take an active role in the courtship.

The nests are built of twigs or seaweed and are set close together on the ground in crowded colonial sites, and sometimes in trees. Eggs usually number two to six and are white. The young are covered in black down. Their appetites are apparently insatiable and their beaks remain permanently agape for food regurgitated by the parents. The enormous shaggy chicks jostle continuously to keep their place in a nest much too small for them. Incongruity is heightened when the parent arrives, sits down on the heap, and tramples over its huge children as it distributes the fishes into their ravenous beaks. One of the eager chicks will stimulate the parent to disgorge by putting its head into the adult's throat.

There are thirty cormorant species, eleven of which are white-breasted cormorants (black above and white below) found exclusively in the southern hemisphere. The Common or Great Cormorant (*Phalacrocorax carbo*), the largest and most widely distributed species, breeds on the coasts of northern Europe, Iceland, western Greenland and around the mouth of the St Lawrence River. It is also extensively distributed over Asia, Australia and New Zealand and is the species trained by Japanese fisherman to catch fishes for them. The Green Cormorant (*P. aristotelis*), known as the Shag in the British Isles, is crested for a few months during the spring and breeds along the coasts of northern Europe and the Mediterranean. The commonest cormorant of North America, the Double-crested Cormorant (*P. auritus*), breeds in large colonies from Alaska to Central America. During the breeding season it has an orange and yellow face and tufts of curly black and white feathers on each side of its head.

The Cape Gannet (*Sula capensis*) has the largest population of all gannets. On islands off South Africa, Cape Gannets probably occupy more than half-a-million nests a year, crowding on cliff sites to nest and rear their young. Like the North Atlantic Gannet (*S. bassana*), the Cape Gannet migrates towards the equator outside the breeding season.

The Blue-footed Booby (*Sula nebouxii*) of the Galapagos and Seymour Island is large to medium in size with proportionally long bill and tail. It is a coastal fisher, the male especially being able to plunge dive into very shallow inland water from the air for food. They take mainly fish, but they also take squid.

Most of the species belong to the southern hemisphere and are typically represented by the King Cormorant (*P. albiventer*) of the Falkland Islands, and Pied Cormorant (*P. varius*) of Australia and New Zealand. The Pygmy Cormorant (*P. pygmaeus*) ranges throughout the eastern hemisphere, and the flightless Galapagos Cormorant (*Nannopterum harrisi*) is found only in the Galapagos Islands.

Darters and anhingas (Family Anhingidae)

A close relative of the cormorants, the darters or anhingas—sometimes called the snakebirds—are distinguished by their long and slender necks, which terminate in long, straight, pointed bills. They are a little like herons, with raven-black bodies and webbed feet. Inhabitants of the inland tropical rivers, lakes and swamps, they perch and nest in trees and feed on fishes speared with their beaks. Nesting is colonial. Both parent birds incubate the eggs and care for the young.

The New World Anhinga or Darter (*Anhinga anhinga*) is found from the southern United States to Argentina. The African Darter (*A. rufa*) is widely distributed in Africa, Madagascar and Iraq. There is also an Indian Darter (*A. melanogaster*) and an Australian Darter (*A. novaehollandiae*). The last two may be subspecies of the African Darter.

Frigate-birds (Family Fregatidae)

A peculiarity of these birds is that the tips of both lower and upper mandible are hooked downwards. They also have feathered tarsi, and a web that extends only halfway along the toes. The wings are long, like the tails, which are deeply forked. They are clearly adapted to flying best.

An extraordinary feature is the 210 centimetre wingspan to the 1.5 kilograms body weight. This

The male Magnificent Frigate-bird (*Fregata magnificens*) inflates its red throat pouch to an enormous size and spreads its wings when displaying to the females. These Frigate-birds breed in colonies on tropical and sub-tropical American islands. They are spectacular fliers but very ungainly on land.

The Grey or European Common Heron (*Ardea cinerea*) is common throughout most of Europe and Palearctic Asia, and also parts of Africa. In Britain it is unpopular around trout farms, where it is often seen perched close by watching motionless or stepping slowly through the water, waiting for a fish to come within reach, when it spears it in one swift jab. Even so, it often damages more fish than it eats.

ratio gives unequalled powers of effortless flight that can be transformed into a swift and accurate attack on another bird, causing it to give up its food. This aggressive piece of behaviour has earned it the name Man-o'-war Bird. If the Frigate-bird is a successful pirate, it is also a most efficient fisher in its own right. It has been seen to dive from a great height with deadly accuracy to pluck small fishes from the water without so much as brushing its feathers on the surface. It usually nests near gannet or cormorant colonies and preys on their young.

Frigate-birds are indigenous to the tropical waters of the south Atlantic, the Pacific and the Indian oceans. The Ascension Frigate-bird (*Fregata aquila*), found only on Ascension Island, is believed to be one of the swiftest of large birds. Its body is black with a metallic sheen. The male has a bright red pouch of naked skin under the throat which he inflates during courtship and before mating. The young have a white head and neck.

Other species are the New World's Magnificent Frigate-bird (*F. magnificens*), the Great Frigate-bird (*F. minor*), and the Lesser or Least Frigate-bird (*F. ariel*), the smallest of them all.

Herons, storks and allies (Order Ciconiiformes)

This order, which includes six families, herons, hammerhead, shoebill, storks, ibises and spoonbills, is characterised by long, featherless legs adapted to a wading mode of life. All are capable of strong flight, and each foot has four toes. The shape of the beak varies, but in all it has sharp cutting edges and appears to be hafted to the long neck. The Circoniiformes are not adapted for speedy movement. Herons generally have a slow and formal gait as they stride along on the edges of marshes, ponds and sluggish rivers, marking the exact position of their prey and then seizing it with a swift and precise movement.

Herons, egrets, bitterns (Family Ardeidae)

While individual species differ in size, length of feet, size and shape of head, and beak, and in nesting habits, there are common family characteristics.

The structure of the neck vertebrae allows the neck to bend only in the vertical plane. It cannot move laterally. In repose the neck is curved in the shape of an 'S' and the head is drawn between the shoulders. The neck is extended only to seize prey by a strong and rapid muscular action which carries the beak to its target. Herons and their relatives are the only birds that fly with neck tucked back and head between the shoulders. This makes it impossible to confuse them, even at a distance, with storks and cranes. There is only a rudimentary uropygial gland but under the breast and flank feathers there are thick patches of powder down which reduces to a very fine dust that is used when preening soiled feathers. The down soaks up the slime and is removed when the feathers are combed with the pectinated comb-like inside of the middle claw and also acts somewhat as a water repellant.

The Ardeidae are widely distributed waterbirds, living only in marshy areas and on the seashore. Their food consists mainly of fishes, but includes frogs, reptiles, crustaceans, molluscs and even insects. With the exception of the bitterns, which live alone, they are sociable and live in colonies or heronries, built in trees or among reeds. The family includes the typical or day herons, night herons, egrets, and bitterns and is represented in all but the very cold regions of the world.

TYPICAL HERONS: One of the most widely distributed of the typical herons is the Grey or European Common Heron (*Ardea cinerea*), more than a metre in height with a wingspan of 150 to 180 centimetres. Its plumage is ashy grey above, with white underparts and slaty blue to black quill feathers. It has a black pendent crest, a band of white feathers spotted with black on the front of the neck, a long yellow beak and greyish-brown legs. The iris of the eye is yellow, a characteristic that gives an almost fierce appearance. It is, however, a wary and timid bird. It will readily take to flight, but will defend itself with its beak, as will most members of the family.

The heron goes hunting mainly at dawn and at dusk, stepping slowly and cautiously along the water's edge, and sometimes remaining immobile for long periods, intently watching the water at its feet. When it sees a fish or a frog it takes careful aim, then with a swift forward movement of the head and neck seizes it, and usually swallows it whole if it is small enough. The heron is not, however, a selective feeder and will catch what it can when it can. Although a skilful fisherman, it will, like all the Ardeidae, consume large quantities of other animals, even river mussels, the shells of which it will crack with one stab of its beak. Its daily intake of food is estimated at about 340 grams, little enough for a bird weighing over two kilograms.

Heronries are not always situated near the fishing grounds. They may be some distance away and the birds will then visit them several times a day in heavy, almost leisurely, flight. The nests are generally built in the tops of tall trees, occasionally among reeds, or even on the ground. They may be bulky, more than a metre in diameter and about sixty centimetres deep, with walls made of interlaced twigs and branches. As many as a hundred nests have been seen in a single tree.

From the end of February until May there is great activity in the heronries, which resound with raucous cries, some of fear, threat or anger, and some used only in courtship and mating.

The courtship display consists of bowing with neck extended, or with beak pointed towards the sky and feathers raised. Bill snapping or rattling forms part of the prenuptial display. The male holds out a branch in his beak and the female takes it, possibly as a token of acquiescence. This branch is the first used in building the new nest or in repairing an old one. The male assumes the task of bringing the materials, while the female builds.

The period of sexual display is, in many species, marked by colour changes of the 'soft' parts, such as bill, legs and feet. However, the brighter colours do not last for very long. The iris of the Green Heron (*Butorides virescens*) turns from its usual yellow to orange, and its legs and feet from their normal near-yellow to bright orange, almost coral. The colours may even fade during the egg-laying period, though it has been observed that if either

The Purple Heron (*Ardea purpurea*) is widespread over the Old World, but a rare vagrant to the British Isles. It resembles the Grey Heron in appearance and habits but is smaller. It breeds in reed-covered swamps, the nests usually consisting of dead reeds, built on a platform of reed debris just above the water level. The nests are not usually built close together.

The Little Egret (*Egretta garzetta*) is distributed throughout the Old World. It grows specially adapted feathers on its mantles for use during displays. These plumes are called aigrettes. They are moulted at the end of each breeding season. In the early 1900s immense numbers of egrets were slaughtered for their plumes which were used in millinery.

the first nest or clutch is destroyed the colour change occurs again.

The nest is usually finished towards the middle of March, when four or five eggs are laid in the course of a week. They are bluish green and without spots, usually six centimetres long and about two centimetres across. Both parents share the incubation period of a little less than a month. When hatched, each chick is covered with a shaggy down. The young birds eat voraciously. At first the parent will thrust regurgitated food into the mouth of the young; later it is placed on the edge of the nest. The chicks fight and jostle for the food, and often the latest to hatch are smothered by the others, while the parents, lacking instinctive behaviour to deal with the situation, look on undisturbed. For several weeks the young birds are unable to fly or to fend for themselves. After about two months they leave the nest, in May or June. Four or five months later comes the great migration which precedes the winter.

The Squacco Heron (*Ardeola ralloides*) on its nest with young. It is distributed over southern Europe, Asia and Africa. It breeds in mixed colonies with other egrets and herons. The nests may be built in trees, bushes or among reeds, and are usually no more than loosely-woven reeds. A more elaborate structure is needed in trees, however, when sticks and grass may be added.

The Night Heron (*Nycticorax nycticorax*) is found throughout North and South America, Europe and southern Asia. It lives in a wide variety of habitats, including salt and fresh water. Towards dusk, Night Herons gather and fly to the feeding grounds. They feed on a wide variety of animals including fish, crustaceans, insects and amphibians.

The Grey Heron is most widely distributed over Europe and across central Asia, but its breeding area extends into southern and south-east Asia, with sporadic areas of distribution in Africa. Those breeding in the more northerly parts of the range migrate south for the winter. Some of the herons from other parts also migrate.

The Purple Heron (*Ardea purpurea*) is smaller and, as its name implies, has feathers of a fiery magenta on head, neck and breast. The wings are grey all over, instead of grey and black like those of the Grey Heron. The habits of the two species are very similar, but the Purple Heron does not live in the temperate regions of Europe, Asia and Africa; it is found nearer the Equator. It never nests in tree tops.

Common New World species include the Great Blue Heron (*A. herodias*) and the Little Blue Heron (*Egretta caerulea*).

The egrets are more slender and distinguished looking than the herons. Their plumage is usually a brilliant white. The Common or Great Egret (*Egretta alba*) is almost the same shape as the Grey Heron and has much the same habits. Sometimes it nests in trees and sometimes among reeds. It is rarely found in Europe, except near the Danube and in southern Russia. One sub-species is distributed over Australia, Africa, Asia and the parts of Europe; another subspecies ranges from the central United States as far south as Argentina.

The Little Egret (*Egretta garzetta*), distributed throughout the Old World, is barely sixty centimetres high and has a wingspan of a metre. With its black bill and feet, yellow eyes, and dazzling white plumage, it is, together with the Flamingo, one of the most beautiful birds found in Europe. It breeds in large colonies in river marshes, building its nest in elms, ash trees, poplars, tamarisks, and even among reeds and rushes. Colonies are found all over southern Europe and North Africa, and in suitable areas in the Far East. Every winter these migrate further south.

The Cattle Egret (*Bulbulcus ibis*) is a common heron found in Asia and Africa, where it associates with cattle. Its plumage is white like that of the egret, but its plume is of long, single feathers of a reddish brown colour. It is thickset and has a short, strong bill and short feet. One of the ornithological surprises of recent times has been the arrival of the Cattle Egret in America, probably through Guyana, whence it has spread into South America and northwards into Canada.

Three species of egret in North America were being rapidly destroyed a few years ago to supply milliners with plumes for women's hats. Protective laws put an end to what threatened the species with extinction, and the Snowy Egret (*Egretta thula*) and large Common Egret (*E. alba*) are common again.

The Squacco Heron (*Ardeola ralloides*) is another white heron, distinguished by a crest of long, yellowish feathers streaked with black, and a dozen or so white feathers edged with black falling in a tuft over the back of its head. It is no bigger than a gull, but its silhouette closely resembles that of a heron or egret. It nests in the heronries of other species of herons, ibises and egrets in southern Europe, Asia, Africa and Madagascar. It feeds on fishes, frogs, crustaceans and insects.

BITTERNS: There are twelve species of bittern, four large bitterns of the genus *Botaurus* and eight small bitterns of the genus *Ixobrychus*. Distribution of the first group is throughout America, Eurasia, South Africa, Australia and New Zealand. The small bitterns are found throughout the tropical and temperate regions. Both genera have marked cryptic colouring and similar concealment posture.

The Little Bittern (*Ixobrychus minutus*) is little known because it is nocturnal, spending the day squatting in solitude in places where its brown, black, yellow and white plumage gives perfect camouflage. Sitting quite still, neck upstretched, it is easily taken for a dry reed. Maximum length is thirty-eight centimetres.The very similar Least Bittern (*I. exilis*) of North and South America is, however, not nocturnal.

The genus *Botaurus*, which includes the Australian Bittern (*Botaurus poiciloptilus*), the American Bittern (*B. lentignosus*) and the South American Bittern (*B. pinnatus*), is typically represented by the Eurasian Bittern (*B. stellaris*), another nocturnal species easily identified by three longitudinal black stripes on a chestnut breast and by the curious posture it adopts. When at rest it leans slightly forward and pulls back its long neck so that the head appears to rest on the nape. When alarmed it ruffles its plumage, the feathers on the neck bristling, and opens its beak ready to attack. In its concealment attitude the feathers are compressed, the body rigid, and neck, head and beak pointed obliquely upwards in an unbroken line.

The booming cry of the male bittern, audible from five kilometres, is unforgettable. The sound is made by a protracted and noisy inhalation of a large quantity of air, which is then exhaled in explosive bursts. The booming is most frequent during the mating season, since this is the way in which the bittern lays claim to its territory and attracts the female—or females, for it is reputedly polygamous. It nests solitarily, not in colonies like the other Ardeidae. It is a partial migrant in Britain, now breeding in parts of Norfolk, and is well distributed over Europe, central Asia, and the extreme south of Africa.

NIGHT HERONS: The genera, *Gorsachius* and *Nycticorax* contain nine species of night heron. Typical of the first is the Japanese Night Heron (*Gorsachius goisagi*), a timid forest bird, rather like a bittern in appearance. The most widely distributed of the second genus is the Black-crowned Night Heron (*Nycticorax nycticorax*), breeding in both Americas, Eurasia, Africa and the East Indies. Nesting is colonial, in stick nests set high up in trees. The Yellow-crowned Night Heron (*Nycticorax violaceus*) which is found in North and South America is also a colonial nester.

Boatbilled heron or boatbill (Family Cochleariidae)

Considered by many experts as an aberrant member of the heron family Ardeidae, the Boat-

The African Little Bittern (*Ixobrychus minutus*) lives among reed-beds and is widespread throughout the Old World. At thirty-five centimetres, it is one of the smaller herons. The Little Bittern feeds on all manner of prey, including fish, frogs, eggs of other reed-bed birds and also other heron chicks. It is a fast and agile climber of bushes and trees. Nests are usually built at the water's edge, but nests in trees are not unusual up to a height of three metres.

At eighty centimetres long the European Bittern (*Botaurus stellaris*) is larger and less agile than the Little Bittern. In spring, and chiefly at night, the male utters a characteristic deep 'booming' call that can be heard as far as five kilometres away. The nest, built among the reeds, on mud or floating, is constructed from dead reeds with finer material for lining. Nest-building, incubation and feeding the young are carried out by the female. Although it looks passive, a Bittern readily shows aggression. It does not wait to be attacked but advances menacingly on an intruder.

The European White Stork (*Ciconia ciconia*) of Europe and Africa is traditionally the bearer of good luck and babies. Here a White Stork is making a submissive gesture on landing at the nest already occupied by its mate. Although large birds, they often look quite small against their massive nests.

bill's (*Cochlearius cochlearius*) bill sometimes resembles that of the Shoebill, except that the upper mandible is not hooked. Except for the remarkable bill it is very much like the Black-crowned Night Heron. It inhibits the mangrove swamps of Guyana and Brazil, and is a night-feeder. Both sexes incubate the eggs in a shallow stick nest.

Shoebill (Family Balaenicipitidae)

The Shoebill, or Whale-headed Stork (*Balaeniceps rex*), looks remarkably stork-like, with long, strong legs and unwebbed toes. The tip of its large, broad bill is hooked. Its plumage is dark bluish-brown and the back of the head is ornamented with an occipital crest. Shoebills live mainly in the marshes along the banks of the White Nile and its tributaries and are ground-nesters. It is the only species of the family.

Hammerhead or hammerkop (Family Scopidae)

The single species of this family, *Scopus umbretta*, is peculiar to Arabia, tropical Africa and Madagascar. It takes its common name from the heavy bill and the crest at the back of the head, which, with the neck, resembles the top of a hammer. Its habits are those of the stork and heron. Its nest, placed in the fork of a tree, is a stout dome built of sticks and mud and lined with grass. Each nest is made by a single pair who use it and repair it annually. According to an African legend the nest is built for the Hammerhead by the labour of other birds.

Storks and jabiru (Family Ciconiidae)

There are seventeen species, all with stout bodies, long, slender legs, and short toes only slightly webbed. The claws are blunt and nail-like. In their strong, easy flight the relatively short neck is stretched forward. Unlike the herons, they are almost voiceless. The only sound they make is a clattering of the beak. Their young have two successive coats of down.

Although protected almost everywhere, storks are diminishing in all countries where once they nested in great numbers. This decrease has been variously attributed to the draining of marshy regions, and to the increased dangers from lighthouses, beacons and high-tension cables encountered during migration. On the other hand, the reduction may be merely a normal fluctuation.

The White Stork (*Ciconia ciconia*) is the type bird of the group. It has a strong body, a long, straight, conical bill with cutting edges, white plumage with black wing coverts and flight feathers, and long, pointed feathers directed downwards under the neck. It attains a length of 120 centimetres, has a wingspan of nearly 210 centimetres, and the males may weigh up to four kilograms. Everyone is so familiar with the picture of the stork perched on its chimney-top nest that one is almost surprised to find these storks sedately walking across a marshy meadow in postures similar to the heron. This is its hunting ground and here, mainly in the morning and evening, it will catch and eat great quantities of frogs, snakes, lizards, small rodents and insects.

Since ancient times this bird has enjoyed a kind of veneration, which has served to protect it. It has little fear of man and has become sociable and almost domesticated in regions where feeding conditions allow it to nest, as in Alsace, Germany, Holland and Scandinavia. Elsewhere in Europe it is mainly a summer visitor, passing through on its spring and autumn migration. It winters in Africa, especially in the region of the great lakes. Owing to its wide range and the regularity of its movements, the stork has always been regarded as the typical migratory bird. Like the swallow it is a harbinger of spring to the peoples of the lands it visits.

Ringing has made it possible to identify quite accurately the routes followed by the migrating storks. Those that nest in western Europe cross France, Spain, Morocco, Tibesti, and Lake Chad before reaching the great African lakes where they winter. Those that nest east of the Weser, on the other hand, fly across Hungary, Turkey, Asia Minor, Syria and Egypt by way of the Nile Valley before finally arriving at the same destination. The distance covered by both groups is more than 9,500 kilometres.

In February or March the male stork arrives at his old nest and takes up his station to await the return of his mate, for storks are monogamous. Having once paired, each couple remains paired for life. As soon as they are together again after migration they begin to rebuild their old nest. The male bird brings branches, reeds, straw, rags, paper, lumps of earth and turf. The female assembles them. With the passing of years nests reach enormous dimensions. Some have been known to be over 240 centimetres in diameter, 240 centimetres deep, and over forty-five kilograms in weight. As a foundation, the ridge of a roof, the top of a chimney or a church tower are favourite sites.

During the last fortnight in April or at the beginning of May (a month earlier in the Mediterranean region) the female lays four white, finely grained eggs, each measuring at least eight by five centimetres. Incubation is shared by both parents and generally lasts about a month.

When hatched, the chicks are covered with short, white down, which is replaced eight days later by a second coat of the same colour. Far from being silent like their parents, they can be heard whining, croaking and whistling. They also begin bill clattering, throwing their heads back and then bringing them forward, making their beaks clap. This is the way in which they greet their parents when they return with food. This food is laid on the edge of the nest, but water is given to the young birds by regurgitation.

Not until they are two months old are the young storks able to make their first flight, accompanied by their parents, who still watch over them. Soon after the 'teaching flight' the bond is broken. From August onwards the young birds disperse. A month later all the storks fly to their winter quarters in East Africa.

The Black Stork (*Ciconia nigra*) is slightly smaller than the White Stork and its only white part is on its belly. It is much shyer and builds solitarily in wild forest. It nests in Spain and eastern Europe, in south-west and central Asia, and has recently started to breed in parts of southern Africa. It disappeared from western Europe in the nineteenth century, probably retreating before increasing human settlement, and the remnant in Spain may have been part of a much wider range.

A common American species (the only true stork in the United States) found from Florida swamps to Argentina is the Wood Stork (*Mycteria americana*), once misleadingly known as the Wood Ibis. It is similar in general colouring to the White Stork, but is distinctive in having a black tail and pink legs.

A species found in Africa might be called a giant stork because it reaches a height of 150 centimetres and has a wingspan of 300 centimetres. Its bill is turned slightly upwards and generally covered at the base by a thick skin, or cere, in the shape of a saddle. This has earned the name Saddlebill Stork and the generic name *Ephippiorhynchus* ('beak covered with a horse's saddle'). The Saddlebill Stork (*Ephippiorhynchus senegalensis*) has brilliant black head, neck, wings and tail, while the rest of the plumage is pure white. The iris and cere are golden yellow, the bill red with a black median band, and the feet greyish brown marked with red at the root of the toes.

The Marabou or Adjutant Stork (*Leptoptilos crumeniferus*), is often referred to as 'a stork with the habits of a vulture'. Marabous often congregate in large flocks in marshes or on the fringes of inland waters, feeding mainly on carrion. The pouch hanging down from the front of the neck can be inflated and contains a system of air sacs connected with the left nostril. What use this is to the bird is not yet clear.

The related Maguari Stork (*Euxenura maguari*), of South America, is 100 centimetres long, white with black in the wings and upper tail coverts and red feet. Its tail is slightly forked.

The 140 centimetres long Jabiru (*Jabiru mycteria*), ranging from Mexico to Argentina, is white with naked and blue-black head and upper neck, and orange and scarlet lower neck. It is one of the largest flying birds in America.

The ugliest of all the Ciconiidae are undoubtedly the vulture-like Marabou or Adjutant Stork (*Leptoptilos crumeniferus*) of Africa and the Lesser Adjutant (*L. dubius*) of southern Asia. Its stiff strut has earned it its military name. It has a pouch hanging on the front of its featherless neck. Its head too is bald, except for a few bristles. The back plumage is dark green with metallic tints. The wing quills and rectrices are black, while the back of the neck and the underparts of the body are white.

The carrion-eating marabous are found scavenging in towns, especially near slaughterhouses. The protection given the Marabou is not entirely disinterested, for as well as being a first-class scavenger it has long, white tail feathers

The European or White Spoonbill (*Platalea leucorodia*) is found in the marshy areas of Europe. It nests solitarily, more rarely in colonies of mixed species. Usually four eggs are laid in a nest which is built either in a tree or on the ground and constructed from sticks or reeds. Incubation takes twenty-one days.

Opposite
The Sacred Ibis (*Threskiornis aethiopica*) is common now only in subsaharan Africa. It was held sacred by the Ancient Egyptians but is now extinct in Egypt. It feeds by probing for crustaceans and molluscs in soft mud with its long decurved bill, but also eats locusts, grasshoppers, frogs, small reptiles and fish. It nests in colonies on the tops of thorn trees or in rushes in swamps.

which are highly prized in India as ornaments.

The open-bills or shell-storks (*Anastomus*) have mandibles which, when shut, are in contact only at the ends, leaving an open space in the middle, adapted for the capture of the shell fish which form their food. Two kinds are known, one in Asia and the other in Africa. In the African Open-bill (*Anastomus lamelligerus*) plumage is dark and the feathers of the neck, belly and thigh end in a long, narrow plaque with a horny appearance.

Spoonbills and ibises (Family Threskiornithidae)

A highly specialised bill is also seen in the European or White Spoonbill (*Platalea leucorodia*) and the closely related American Roseate Spoonbill (*P. ajaja*). The beak tip is flat and wide, like that of a duck, but more markedly so. The bird sweeps this spoon-shaped bill back and forth, filtering crustaceans from the water.

This feature apart, the White Spoonbill resembles the Little Egret, but is somewhat larger. It has the same white colour and is found in the marshy regions of Europe as well as on the seashore, lagoons and estuaries. There are nesting colonies in Holland, the south of Spain, and especially in the lands bordering the Danube. Elsewhere they are vagrant. The only New World species, the Roseate Spoonbill (*A. ajaja*), is found in Florida, although it is commoner in South America.

The ibises, with their long down-curving beaks, are familiar among the hieroglyphics on ancient Egyptian monuments. The Sacred or Tantalus Ibis (*Threskiornis aethiopica*) has white plumage except for the wings which are partly black. The head and neck are naked and covered with black skin.

The Scarlet Ibis (*Eudocimus ruber*) inhabits tropical South America. Two more species of medium height are found throughout the tropics: the Glossy Ibis (*Plegadis falcinellus*) and the Hadeda Ibis (*Bostrychia hagedash*) of Africa. The Glossy Ibis inhabits both Old and New Worlds. It sometimes strays into southern Europe and is an autumn visitor to southern Britain and breeds as far north as the southern United States. It was once thought to be a courser on account of its size and shape, but it has the gait and the habits of the herons and storks. Its plumage is red-brown and black with a magnificent metallic gloss of purple and green. The lower Danube valley is the only region in Europe where the Glossy Ibis nests. From there it tends to wander to a number of places before reaching Africa for the winter season.

Flamingo (Family Phoenicopteridae)

The three flamingo genera used to be grouped in a separate order Phoenicopteriformes since the three front toes are completely webbed. They have some habits and a raucous and resounding cry similar to those of the Goose. Yet their very long legs and other aspects of their behaviour are more stork-like, their gait and stance especially resembling those of the Heron, Crane and Stork. Both in water and on land they assume unusual postures and are able to stand for hours on one leg, the other folded under the belly, and the head laid on the back. When swimming they look rather like swans. They breed in large colonies on lakes, sometimes numbering several thousands of individuals.

In the breeding season the lakes look as though surrounded by a dam of red bricks, or as though masses of red leaves are floating on the surface.

A flight of these birds is itself an unforgettable sight. When something disturbs them, one of them gives the alarm and the rest straighten their necks, and march in Indian file, uttering their unpleasant cries as their pace quickens, develops into a trot, and then into a gallop. At the same time the wings start beating and at last they take off with a display of rose and red, broken by the ebony black of the wing-feather tips. In flight the birds' necks are outstretched and their legs fully extended behind.

The flamingo's beak is as highly specialised as that of the Boatbill. The upper part of the mandible is smaller than the lower and forms a kind of lid. The inside edges have transverse lamellae, as in the bills of ducks and geese. Through these the flamingo sieves out small crustaceans, worms and other small animals by pressing its tongue against the lamellae to drive out the water and hold back all the edible matter. Flamingo bills maybe of two kinds; shallow-keeled as in the Greater Flamingo (*Phoenicopterus ruber*) and deep-keeled as in the Lesser Flamingo (*Phoenicomaias minor*). The latter filters the surface water, extracting diatoms and fine blue-green algae. The former feeds in the mud, taking insect larvae, crustaceans and seeds. The two flamingos can therefore feed side by side without competing.

The nest is a low cone-shaped mound of mud. Usually two white eggs are laid, measuring nine by five centimetres. Incubation lasts a month.

The Greater Flamingo sometimes called the Rose-coloured Flamingo, lives in temperate and tropical regions throughout the world. Colonies can be found in southern France, East Africa, the Bahamas, the Greater Antilles, northern South America and India. The great centres of nest building in the Old World, however, appear to be in the Rann of Kutch, in north-west India. In the New World the same species is common on tropical mud-flats, although some are found as far north as Florida.

Ducks, geese and swans (Order Anseriformes)

This is a group of aquatic birds made up of two families, the widely distributed Anatidae, which contains all the familiar ducks, geese and swans, and the tropical Anhimidae or screamers that are inhabitants of the New World.

Screamers (Family Anhimidae)

Although screamers of South America do not look much like ducks or geese, anatomically they are very similar. They have very little webbing between the front toes and a bill like that of a Moorhen. The Horned Screamer (*Anhima cornuta*) lives in the rain-forests of tropical South America. It is about the size of a turkey, almost uniform greyish black above and white below, with white rings around the eyes and neck. It is remarkable for the eight-centimetre 'horn' or caruncle on its forehead and for the two sharp spurs on its wing. A related but hornless species, the Crested Screamer (*Chauna torquata*), lives in the lagoons, swamps and pampas in Paraguay, southern Brazil, Uraguay and northeastern Argentina. Its nest, lightly built

The Scarlet Ibis (*Eudocimus ruber*) with its magnificent scarlet plumage lives in the coastal areas of tropical South America. It roosts and nests in large colonies in mangrove swamps and feeds on the beaches and mudflats, picking up small marine creatures. Birds kept in captivity often lose their brilliant scarlet colour possibly due to deficient diet.

The Crested Screamer (*Chauna torquata*) is one of three species of screamers confined to tropical and subtropical South America. Screamers are large, ungainly birds rather like turkeys but related to ducks and geese. They are wading and swimming birds and their long toes, which are only slightly webbed, enable the birds to walk over vegetation mats floating on the lakes.

A pair of Mute Swans (*Cygnus olor*) which, like most swans, mate for life. In the wild the Mute Swan breeds across northern Europe and Asia, migrating southwards in winter from the colder parts of its range. In most parts of Europe it has been introduced to lakes and rivers and lives a resident, semi-domestic life.

of rushes, stands in the water. About six buffish-white eggs are usually laid, and from these hatch out yellowish-brown, down-covered chicks. There is one other species, the Black-necked Screamer (*C. chavaria*) of northern Columbia and Venezuela.

Swans, Geese and Ducks (Family Anatidae)

There are forty-three genera in this family, grouped in three subfamilies and ten tribes: the subfamily Anseranatinae contains only the tribe Anseranatini; the Anserinae contains the tribes Anserini, Dendrocygnini; the Anatinae contains the Tadornini, Anatini, Aythyini, Cairinini, Somateriini, Mergini and Oxyurini. All are known as ducks except for the Magpie Goose of the Anseranatini and the geese and swans of the Anserini.

Certain characteristics are common to all ten. Bills are long and flat, and soft except for a hard 'nail' at the tip. Necks are long. Eggs are pale

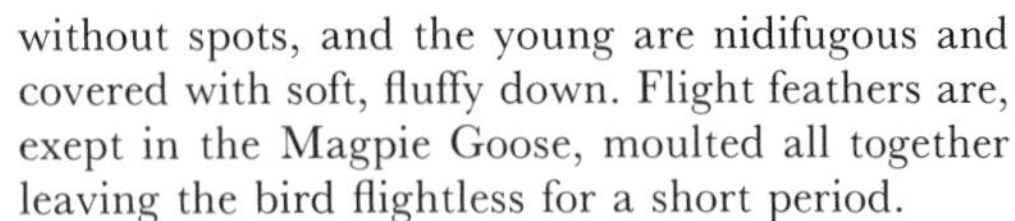

without spots, and the young are nidifugous and covered with soft, fluffy down. Flight feathers are, exept in the Magpie Goose, moulted all together leaving the bird flightless for a short period.

The edges of the bill bear rows of fine serrations or lamellae. In geese, these are used for cutting grass and in the mergansers they are sharp teeth for holding fish. The dabbling ducks have many fine lamellae which serve as filters. The tongue is particularly fleshy and muscular and it acts like a piston, sucking water into the mouth and expelling it again. The transverse plates allow only certain particles into the mouth and these are retained and swallowed. Presumably there is also some selection of edible from inedible particles, since the tongue and bill are lined with taste buds.

Most ducks are poor walkers because their feet are set far back on the body. The feet, webbed across the three front toes, are not suitable for locomotion on land. Ducks, swans and geese are essentially aquatic, excellent swimmers and many are good divers. Many, like the Mallard, are able to remain upended in order to rummage in the mud at the bottom, with only the tail showing, while the feet paddle to maintain equilibrium. The divers use their feet to swim underwater. Ducks are as expert in flight as in swimming. They have no difficulty in taking off from the water.

The swans and geese usually mate for life. They have no sexual dimorphism in their plumage; their courtship is simple and the male helps to care for the brood. In most ducks there is a marked dimorphism, with elaborate courtship displays and the pair bond is temporary. In common with other aquatic birds, ducks make their plumage waterproof with the oily secretion of the uropygial gland situated at the base of the tail.

MAGPIE GOOSE: This is the only species of the tribe Anseranatini. The Magpie Goose (*Anseranas semipalmata*) is an Australian bird. Unlike the other Anatidae it moults its flight feathers gradually.

WHISTLING DUCKS OR TREE DUCKS: These, the

Dendrocygnini, are found mostly in the tropics. Unlike the typical ducks they show no sexual dimorphism. The commonest of the eight species is the Fulvous Tree Duck (*Dendrocygna bicolor*) of the New World and Africa.

SWANS: The Anserini can be reviewed in two convenient groups, the swans and the geese. Swans, the largest of the Anseriformes, have long flexible necks,and are able to swim and paddle but unable to dive. The species are grouped into two genera, *Coscoroba* and *Cygnus*.

The Coscoroba Swan (*Coscoroba coscoroba*) is a small species found in South America. The others include three all-white European swans—the Whooper or Wild Swan (*Cygnus cygnus*), Bewick's Swan (*C. bewickii*) and the Mute Swan (*C. olor*)—two all-white North American species, the Whistling Swan (*C. columbianus*) and the rare Trumpeter Swan (*C. buccinator*); and to conclude the list, two southern hemisphere species, the Australian Black Swan (*C. atratus*) and the Black-necked Swan (*C. melanocoryphus*) of South America.

The Whooper Swan and Bewick's Swan breed in the Arctic tundra of Europe and Asia and migrate southwards in winter. Bewick's Swan can be found as far north as northern Siberia, where it blends with its snow-covered surroundings. From October to April it migratres to more southerly countries. The Mute Swan is particularly well known in Britain, where it now lives as a partially domesticated species. During the breeding season its behaviour is aggressive, driving off all other ducks and even drowning their young. It is recognisable by a knob at the base of the beak.

The Whistling Swan is nearctic, breeding from Alaska to Hudson Bay and migrating south. The Trumpeter Swan, the largest swan of all, does not appear to migrate far from its breeding grounds.

Swans are strictly monogamous, the male remaining attached to its mate for life. During part of the courtship display he caresses her head and neck uttering soft and gentle cries. Both birds collaborate in building the nest, although the female does the actual building. During incubation the male watches over his companion and sits on the eggs while she is away feeding. When the cygnets are hatched he helps to feed and protect them. The family remains thus united until the following year when the cygnets separate from their parents. If alarmed while swimming, young cygnets take refuge between the uplifted wings on the back of the father (cob) or mother (pen).

TRUE GEESE: The true geese are less markedly aquatic than the swans. Two genera, the grey *Anser* and the 'black' *Branta*, both of the northern hemisphere, make up most of the group. Both are strongly migratory. Wild geese breed mainly on the vast swamps and cold lake-dotted tundra regions. In winter they fly south to temperate parts of Europe and Asia, or—in the New World—to the southern states of North America.

The type bird of the genus *Anser* is the Wild or Greylag Goose (*Anser anser*). From this species the Domestic Goose was derived. Yet there is strong contrast between the mobility of the one and the ponderousness of the other. The Wild Goose is the largest and strongest of the geese. Extremely long flights during migration are quite common.

Other species are the White-fronted Goose (*A. albifrons*), the Bean Goose (*A. fabilis*), the Pink-footed Goose (*A. brachyrhynchus*), the Snow Goose (*A. caerulescens*) and the Emperor Goose (*A. canagicus*). Both the Bean Goose and the White-fronted Goose are regular formation flyers. Family parties stay together during migration and they gather on traditional wintering grounds where they become a pest because of the way they damage crops and pasture.

The common species of the genus *Branta* are the Canada Goose (*Branta canadensis*), the Barnacle Goose (*B. leucopsis*), the Brant or Brent Goose (*B. bernicla*) and the Nene or Hawaiian Goose (*B. sandvicensis*).

The Black-billed or Cuban Tree Duck (*Dendrocygna arborea*), the largest of the tree ducks, is confined to the West Indies. It lives in swamps and pools of tropical forests feeding on tree fruits and other vegetation. For most of the year these tree ducks live in flocks and are active mainly at night.

The Lesser White-fronted Goose (*Anser erythropus*) is distinguished from the larger White-fronted Goose (*A. albifrons*) by its larger white facial patch which extends onto the forehead and by the wing tips which extend beyond the tail.

The Ruddy Shelduck (*Tadorna ferruginea*) used to have a much larger breeding range in Europe but marsh drainage and shooting has taken its toll and breeding is now restricted to northeast Greece, Turkey and the Black Sea coast. It is still common in Asia ranging as far as southwest China. It is a large handsome duck with orange-brown plumage and in the breeding season the males have a black collar.

Barnacle geese are sturdier, have shorter bills and are more pronouncedly black and white than the so-called grey geese. Except that they frequent the sea coasts and rarely penetrate far inland, their habits are much the same. Their food consists of marine plants, molluscs, crustaceans and insects. Like other wild geese, the Barnacle is an Arctic bird, moving south only in winter.

The Brant or Brent Goose is black and brown with a white breast. The Canada Goose has white throat and cheek patches, a black head and neck.

SHELDUCKS AND SHELDGEESE: The Tadornini is the most primitive tribe of the subfamily Anatinae and includes the typical shelducks or sheldgeese of the Old World: the Common Shelduck (*Tadorna tadorna*), the Ruddy Shelduck (*Casarca ferruginea*), the Egyptian Goose (*Alopochen aegyptiacus*), the New Zealand Shelduck (*Tadorna variegata*), and the Cape Barren Goose (*Cereopsis novaehollandiae*).

DABBLING DUCKS: Perhaps the most attractive and certainly the largest tribe is the Anatini, the dabbling or dipping ducks. In the very large genus *Anas* are grouped the colourful European Common Teal (*Anas crecca*), Mallard (*A. platyrhynchos*), Pintail (*A. acuta*), Shoveler (*A. clypeata*), Gadwall (*A. strepera*), European Wigeon (*A. penelope*) and the Black Duck (*A. rubripes*).

The dabblers are so called because they feed by dipping their heads, necks, and bills underwater for food on the bottom, not by diving. Usually classified with them are the three steamer ducks, two of which are completely flightless, of the genus *Tachyeres* of South America, which propel themselves along the surface by paddling with both their feet and wings.

Generally the breeding plumage of the male is bright and conspicuous, whereas that of the female is dull. Greens, russets, blues and yellows occur in patterns characteristic of each species. Only in summer do the two sexes look alike, when the male goes into eclipse plumage. This coincides with the renewal of his body feathers and with a period when he moults all his wing quills and becomes temporarily incapable of flight. Many species have a patch of bright coloured feathers (the speculum) on the wing, which plays a big part in species-recognition and in courtship display.

The favourite haunts of wild ducks are ponds, marshes and flooded meadows, the borders of lakes and watercourses. But the nest is built on land, lined with down plucked from the breast of the female, who builds the nest and sits on the eggs. The ducklings are covered with a thick coat of down when hatched. They are essentially precocial and, led by their mother, enter the water immediately after hatching.

Dabbling ducks of all species—mallards, gadwalls, shovelers, pintails, teals—are the favourite game birds and so many are taken annually that in recent years several countries have had to take legal measures for their preservation.

The commonest is that known as the Wild Duck, the Mallard (*A. platyrhynchos*), from which the Domestic Duck originates and with which it still interbreeds occasionally. In mating plumage the drake's head and neck are a beautiful glossy green, separated by a white band from the brown nape and breast. The wings are brown with a superb violet-blue speculum, framed with black and white. The rest of the body is a greyish white. The beak is yellow, the feet orange-red. The four middle tail coverts are longer than the others and are turned upwards. By contrast the male in eclipse resembles the female, both being brown marked with black, but retaining the speculum that is characteristic of the species.

The annual cycle of the Mallard Duck may be taken as typical of all northern species of duck. It begins in September or October, when the drakes have regained their brilliant plumage and have already paired off, though the mating season is still a long way off. On expanses of fresh water, and even in estuaries and salt-water lagoons, ducks gather by the hundreds, dabbling in search of food. They are forever foraging and will eat almost any living thing in the water, from leaves and seeds of water plants to molluscs, worms, larvae, insects, frogs and small fishes. According to statistics compiled in the United States their stomach contents consist of ninety per cent vegetable matter and ten per cent animal matter. As the mating season approaches, their feeding activity becomes even greater and their appetites insatiable.

After the end of the winter, to the ordinary call are added the many variations of voice that accompany the courtship. Mating usually takes place on the water. The male and female then choose a site for the nest, usually a tussock of grass on the shore or on an islet.

There are a dozen eggs in a clutch, looking very like those of the Domestic Duck. The female broods alone for twenty-four to twenty-eight days, at the end of which time the ducklings hatch, and the protective duck can be seen at the head of her bustling family. It is two full months before the ducklings, then half-grown, can fly and look after themselves. The drake meanwhile often goes after other females, promiscuity being common.

June comes and suddenly neither duck nor drake is anywhere to be seen. This is the period of the eclipse, when the drakes lose their flight quills and are unable to fly. They hide, silent, in the reed beds, males and females together. Here they remain until the end of August, when the males have regrown their full plumage and are able to fly again.

Whereas Mallards that nest in western or southern Europe also winter there, those breeding farther north, in Scandinavia or Canada, for instance, migrate southwards at the approach of the cold season.

Many species, such as the Gadwall and the Wigeon (sometimes Widgeon), are winter visitors to Britain and other parts of Europe. The males of these two species can be distinguished from each other by their plumage; the first has a grey head and body with a white speculum, the second a chestnut head and green speculum. Their cries are quite different. The quacking Gadwall is answered by the whistling cry of the Wigeon. The Gadwalls like dabbling, while the Wigeons prefer probing in mud and grass for their food. The Wigeon and Pintail are often seen in small groups in North America. The second of the two is a most elegant duck, with a sombre plumage in which black and white dominate. It has a swan-like neck and pointed tail.

The teals are the smallest of the European and American ducks. No bigger than pigeons, they are livelier, more alert, and stronger in flight than other ducks. In Europe there are the Garganey Teal (*A. querquedula*) and the Common or European Teal (*A. crecca*), while in America and Canada there are the Green-winged Teal (*A. carolinensis*) and the Blue-winged Teal (*A. discors*). The Garganey's speculum is green with a white margin, and the Common Teal's black with a white margin. The males can be distinguished even more easily in nuptial plumage, when the male Garganey has a brown head and enormous white 'eyebrows', and the Common Teal a head plumage that is of glowing red with a broad green band extending from the eye to the nape.

POCHARDS: These are the Aythyini, the diving or 'bay' ducks. Primarily birds of the northern hemisphere, their distribution is world-wide. The specific gravity of the group is higher than that of the dabblers, making diving easier. Under water they propel themselves with their feet. They are poor walkers and fly with a quick wing beat.

The best-known pochard is the Canvasback (*Aythya vallisneria*), of North America. Its back is finely barred with black and white, and its head and neck are reddish brown.

The Red-crested Pochard (*Netta rufina*) is a very handsome European duck, about the same size as the Mallard. The drake can be recognised by its big reddish head and vivid red beak, its black

The Mallard or Wild Duck (*Anas platyrhynchos*). The female duck is less colourful than the drake, although in summer he goes into an eclipse plumage that is little different from his mate's. The Mallard ranges across the whole of North America, Europe and Asia, from the Arctic Circle southwards. It is one of the most adaptable species in the world.

The male Red-crested Pochard (*Netta rufina*) can be recognised by its striking bright ginger head and scarlet bill. The female lacks these distinctive markings. Being a diving duck it prefers fairly deep water, although its best-known breeding area in Europe, the Camargue, consists of fairly shallow saline lagoons.

breast and belly, grey-brown back, and grey wings. Today it is found only on large, open expanses of water. It approaches the banks only at nesting time, in search of reeds amongst which to build its nest.

Other species are the Ferruginous Duck or White-eyed Pochard (*Aythya ferina*) and the Tufted Duck (*A. fuligula*), both resident in and winter visitors to Britain and Europe. In nuptial plumage the first has a shining chestnut-red head and a very light grey body, bordered with black on breast and tail. The Tufted Duck's head, back and chest are dominated by a brilliant black with iridescent lights, contrasting with the pure white of its flanks. It has a crest which drops gracefully on to its nape.

PERCHING DUCKS AND GEESE: The tribe Cairinini are the brightest coloured ducks of all. Two interesting species are the Barbary Duck and the Mandarin Duck. The perching ducks are forest birds that nest in trees. In addition to the webbed feet of the more aquatic tribes they have claws, and a sturdy hind toe well adapted to clinging to tree branches.

The Barbary Duck (*Cairina moschata*), also called the Muscovy Duck, originally came from South America. Freed slaves introduced it to Africa whence it ultimately spread to Europe finding popularity where there was no pond on which to keep ordinary ducks. Its habitual colouring is a metallic dark green with white spots, which may be more or less extensive (mixed variety), or dominant (white variety). Fleshy excrescences appear at the base of the beak. This is a polygamous species.

The Mandarin Duck (*Aix galericulata*) of China, is a popular ornamental bird. Its vivid and varied colours almost defy description. Reds, greens, blues, yellows and browns contrast with the pure white of its front. The mutual affection shown by each pair explains why the Chinese make this bird the symbol of conjugal fidelity.

EIDER DUCKS: The marine tribe Somateriini has four species: the Common Eider (*Somateria mollissima*), the King Eider (*S. spectabilis*), the Spectacled Eider (*S. fischeri*) and Steller's Eider (*Polysticta stelleri*). The first, the Common Eider, is highly prized for its excellent and abundant down, commercially exploited as eiderdown. The female plucks the down from her breast to line the nest.

MERGANSERS OR SEA DUCKS: The Mergini is a northern hemisphere tribe with marked diving ability. Most are sea birds. The mergansers or sawbills, the goldeneyes and the black, velvet and surf scoters make up the tribe. Two mergansers are common in Europe, the Goosander (*Mergus merganser*) and the Red-breasted Merganser (*M. serrator*). Both are common in North America too. Both have the same long silhouette on the water and in flight, the same thin, hooked beak, the same green head, black back, and white breast when in breeding plumage. The distinguishing marks are a crest and reddish hood in the red-breasted species and white neck and body of the Goosander. Both breed in northern latitudes and come south only during extreme cold. In America the Red-breasted Merganser rarely flies farther south than the northern United States. The Hooded Merganser (*Lophodytes cucullatus*) is found only in North America. Mergansers feed mainly on fish caught

The King Vulture (*Sarcorhampus papa*) is a scavenger of the tropical forests of Central and South America. With its keen sense of smell it seeks out carrion but it has been known to kill newly-born calves and small reptiles. Unlike most other vultures it will not scavenge human refuse.

in the saw-toothed bill. They roost in holes in trees, except for the Red-breasted Merganser.

STIFF-TAILED DUCKS: With the Oxyurini the catalogue of the Anatidae tribes is complete. These are small, chubby ducks distributed through all five continents. Their name is earned by the rigid rectrices of most species. The type bird is the Ruddy Duck (*Oxyura jamaicensis*) of North America.

Birds of prey (Order Falconiformes)

Eagles, buzzards, sparrowhawks, falcons and vultures are sometimes called diurnal birds of prey to distinguish them from the unrelated nocturnal birds of prey, as owls used to be known. All are admirably built for a predatory life. Many are strong, fierce, and most of them are large. Sight and rarely sense of smell are well developed. The wings may be broad or narrow but they are always long, to give powerful sustained flight. Legs are short and strong, with four digits, three forward and one in opposition except in the Osprey which can reverse one toe so that it has two pointed in each direction. The digits end in curved, pointed claws or talons. Prominent identifying features are the powerful hooked beak, and the cere, a fleshy protuberance, on the upper mandible. The head is fairly large and carried on a short, robust neck. The overall impression is one of great physical power. The lower mandible is shorter than the upper and partly enclosed within it when the beak is shut. The upper mandible sometimes has a pointed, tooth-like projection on each side, the sharp edges forming a double pair of cutters. The cere is pierced by the nostrils and is usually coloured yellow, red or green. The same colours are often repeated on digits and tarsus.

Prey is normally warm-blooded vertebrates, though some hunt fishes, reptiles, amphibians, or insects, and some are carrion-feeders. Victims are held in the talons while the bird plucks out tufts of feathers or fur and then dismembers them. Powers of digestion are considerable, and the few indigestible parts are regurgitated as pellets. Analysis of these seems to indicate that birds of prey eat many small animals harmful to man and his crops.

The raptors are strong flyers and the stiff feathers covering wing and body produce a

Opposite top
The Goosander or Common Merganser (*Mergus merganser*) is sometimes called a 'saw-bill' because its long, narrow bill has backward-pointing serrations in both mandibles which prevents slippery fish escaping. Goosanders have been persecuted for preying on salmon and trout but they are beneficial in so far as they also take predatory fish such as pike and eels.

Opposite bottom
The male King Eider Duck (*Somateria spectabilis*) as shown here is an impressively coloured bird; the female is a more sober brown colour and easily camouflaged when on her nest. The species is found throughout the Arctic and north temperate marine waters. The King Eider is believed to feed at greater depths than the Common Eider (*S. mollissima*), taking animals such as sea urchins and crabs.

The Andean Condor (*Vultur gryphus*) is the largest bird of prey in the world. Although now fairly rare it has suffered less persecution than the Californian Condor (*V. californianus*) of North America. Although feeding mainly on carrion it will also take eggs from the large colonies of seabirds on the Peruvian coast.

Opposite
Flamingos are a family of large, beautifully-coloured aquatic birds living on alkaline or saline lakes in America, Asia, Europe and Africa. They have specialised bills for filtering out small animals or microscopic plants from the mud or water. They are gregarious birds and colonies of the Lesser Flamingo (*Phoeniconaias minor*) sometimes number over a million pairs.

characteristic noise during flight. Feathers cover all or part of each tarus, giving the bird a trousered look, an effect seen in most species. Only the digits are always bare. The beak is clearly outlined in profile along the whole of its length. The eyes are laterally placed in the head.

The birds of prey live singly or in pairs, except when migrating. All are monogamous. Mating occurs in the spring, preceded by fighting and display, which the female appears to watch with a measure of interest. The eggs are few in number (in some species there is only one) and these are brooded by the female alone, the male feeding her as she sits.

The nests or eyries are built in high, inaccessible situations, a necessary precaution for a bird whose young remain helpless longer than most.

New World vultures (Family Cathartidae)

The American vultures are distinguished from the Old World species by several anatomical features. The nostrils are not completely separated internally and are elongated, not round, in section. The hind toe is set slightly higher than the three front ones, which are slightly webbed at the base. They are voiceless birds.

The best-known member of this group is the Andean Condor (*Vultur gryphus*), more than ninety centimetres in length and with a wingspan of about three metres. It is easily recognised by its shining black plumage, embellished with a white band on each wing and a white collaret at the base of the neck. The red colour of the fleshy comb and wattles contrasts with the grey head, neck and crop region. It is an impressive bird. In the Andean Cordilleras it is said to soar to a height of 4,800 to 6,000 metres.

The Andean Condor is found northwards from the Magellan Straits to the Equator on the west coast of South America, but only to the Rio Negro (Argentina) on the east. In Chile and Peru it is the most widespread bird of prey. Its habits are much like those of other vultures and it forms flocks that disperse only in the breeding season. A crude nest is built on a rocky ledge and during. November to December (the southern summer) two eggs are laid, whitish yellow with small brown spots. The young birds remain with their parents for a long

time before flying away to fend for themselves.

The California Condor (*Vultur californianus*), the largest North American bird, was numerous until the westward trek in the middle of last century, when it fell victim to poison put down for wolves and coyotes, and doubtless many were shot also. Estimates put its present number at about sixty individuals. It incubates a single egg.

The King Vulture (*Sarcorhamphus papa*) has a wingspan of two metres. It is a richly coloured bird, with black wings and tail, white underparts, flesh-coloured head and front and red-tipped black beak. Unlike the condor, the King Vulture is a forest bird, found in South America.

The Black Vulture (*Coragyps atratus*), also known as the Urubu or Gallinazo, is smaller than the King Vulture and is entirely black. It inhabits the central United States and South America, where it acts as a scavenger and in certain towns has become quite domesticated.

The Turkey Vulture (*Cathartes aura*) is the most widespread and common member of the family. It is found from southern Canada to the Straits of Magellan. Particularly in the southeastern United States, it is known as the Turkey Buzzard as its almost naked red head and neck does remind one of a turkey and its soaring flight is similar to that of the birds known in England as buzzards. Its value as a scavenger has afforded it the protection of law in some of the United States.

Old World vultures, hawks, harriers (Family Accipitridae)

Nine subfamilies of large raptorial birds make up the Accipitridae: the Old World vultures (Aegypiinae), the kites (Elaninae, Milvinae and Perninae), the lammergeier (Gypaetinae), the true hawks and eagles (Accipitrinae), the harriers (Circinae), and bat-hawk (Machaerhamphinae), and the serpent eagles (Circaetinae). All have powerful beaks and the female is in every case larger than the male, as in raptorial birds generally.

In some classifications, particularly in America, the Gypaetinae are placed under the Aegypiinae; the Machaerhamphinae are considered members of the Elaninae; the eagles and soaring hawks are placed in a separate subfamily the Buteoninae;

A group of vultures feeding off a carcase in Africa. Vultures soar all day in their search for food. The large powerful vultures, such as the African Lappet-faced Vulture (*Torgos tracheliotus*), are able to tear the hide of a large animal with their strong beaks. Smaller vultures have to wait their turn and pick over the remains.

Opposite
The Secretary Bird (*Sagittarius serpentarius*), the sole living species of the family, is found only on the plains and grasslands of subsaharan Africa and is completely absent from the equatorial rainforests. It usually walks or runs and only takes to the wing when seriously disturbed. It covers long distances on foot looking for food; mainly insects, small mammals, snakes and occasionally birds.

The Black Kite (*Milvus migrans*), with its wide distribution in the Old World, is one of the most numerous birds of prey. A pair may mate for life and in the spring indulge in spectacular courtship flights. They are more sociable breeders than most birds of prey, sometimes two or three pairs nesting in one tree. In Africa and Asia nests are sometimes found on buildings.

The Lammergeier (*Gypaetus barbatus*) in flight. With a wing-span of up to three metres, when circling high above its rocky habitat, its flight is most distinctive. Its long pointed wings are swept back in a gentle curve and with the long wedge-shaped tail give an impression of power and grace.

and in the ospreys become a subfamily, Pandioninae.

Old World vultures (Subfamily Aegypiinae)

These birds have nostrils separated by a median partition. They feed almost exclusively on carrion and faecal matter and, because of this, certain species are tolerated scavengers in hot climates, for without them hygiene would be a more difficult problem. Their appearance and odour are as repellent as their food. They are adapted neither for hunting at high speed nor for fighting. Their feet are strong, the toes armed with sharp curved claws. The hooked beak is strong and built for shearing and dismembering dead animals. Most have unfeathered but vividly coloured head or neck. The long neck enables them to get the whole head into the corpse that is being dismembered. They have an enormous, protruding crop, which becomes gorged with food. The digestive juices of the stomach are powerful enough to break down even bones, and only remnants of these are regurgitated in the small pellet.

Like the New World vultures they have remarkable powers of gliding and soaring. On immense wings they plane effortlessly for hours, using rising convection currents. High up out of sight, at a height of several thousand metres, they scan the land below with keen eyes, and on sighting food plummet to the ground and run towards the corpse with outstretched neck, tail erect, and wings half open.

One of the largest species is the Hooded Vulture (*Neophron monachus*), 100 to 106 centimetres long, with a wingspan of nearly 200 centimetres. The plumage is a uniform dark brown, and the bare parts of the head a bluish coloration. There is a collaret of feathers at the base of the neck. This vulture ranges across central Asia, the countries bordering the Mediterranean and North Africa. It nests in mountainous and wooded regions.

The Griffon Vulture (*Gyps fulvus*) is only slightly smaller than the Black Vulture, has a lighter coloration and has no collaret at the base of the neck. It has much the same range and habitat, however, and is also found in South Africa. It used to nest extensively along the Mediterranean coast, but has now disappeared from much of it, driven out by the march of civilisation, which has deprived it of the carrion and excreta that form its food. It may occasionally find its way into the northern parts of Europe.

The Griffon Vulture lays a single white egg, just over nine centimetres long by seven centimetres wide, which may be spotted with brown. Both sexes share the long incubation, which lasts for about fifty days, and the long fledgling period. The chick is ravenous from the moment it is hatched. One observer relates that a young bird taken from the nest soon devoured two thrushes and a cuckoo. The next day it ate a kite, a carp, and the entrails of several birds. Three weeks afterwards it could scarcely be satisfied. In one day it swallowed the viscera of two calves and devoured all else it could find, even pieces of wood and soil in an attempt to satisfy its large appetite.

The Egyptian White Vulture, or Pharaoh's Chicken (*Neophron percnopterus*), is smaller. It was among the sacred birds of ancient Egypt and figures in stylised form in Egyptian sculpture and reliefs. Its wings span no more than 165 centimetres. The plumage is white, tinged with brown to a varying degree on the underparts, particularly on the edges of the wings. Its range covers south-west Asia, including peninsular India, the Mediterranean countries and North Africa. It is found in large numbers in Africa and India, where it is accepted for its scavenging activities. Flocks of these birds swoop down on town squares and streets and quickly remove refuse. Others follow desert caravans, seeking some beast that has had to be abandoned. It also has the habit of opening Ostrich eggs by hurling stones at them.

KITES: There are three subfamilies: the white-tailed Elaninae, the swallow-tailed Perninae and the true kites or Milvinae. All are characterised by slim form, long narrow wings, and an elongated tail. They are fast in flight but not fast enough to catch other birds on the wing. Often they take dead prey or steal the prey from falcons and ospreys by harrassing them continually.

The European species, the Red Kite (*Milvus milvus*) and the Black Kite (*M. migrans*), of Eurasia, Africa and Australia, are both migratory, those nesting in Europe appearing in March and leaving for Africa in September. They live in plains, meadows and marshes, and less commonly in hilly or mountainous country. The first species was once abundant in the British Isles, but is now found only in Wales, where it is resident. Kites have been known to enter farmyards and seize chicks, but generally they are scavengers and even line their nests with rags and papers collected in the vicinity of human habitations. Urban cleanliness is the main reason for their rarity in Europe today. The Brahminy Kite (*Haliastur indus*) is a common species in Australasia.

Some North American species are less inclined to scavenge, and usually hunt their food. One, a true kite of the subfamily Milvinae is the Mississippi Kite (*Ictinia mississippiensis*) and another the Swallow-tailed Kite (*Elanoides forficatus*) a member of the subfamily Perninae, the fork-tailed kites. Both are great destroyers of insects. The second species is rather like a swallow or swift in form; with wings that cross over each other when at rest, and a forked tail. It is sixty centimetres long, with two deeply sunk eyes, a hooked beak, and claws shaped into talons. The plumage on head, neck, breast and underparts is snow white, while the rest of the body is black, with a metallic sheen. This species is social in habit, and flights of forty to fifty soaring and gliding individuals are not uncommon. Another American species is the Everglade Kite (*Rostrhamus sociabilis*), a true kite (Milvinae), which feeds on freshwater snails.

The Honey-buzzard (*Pernis apivorus*) which, despite the English name, is a kite of the subfamily Perninae, is insectivorous and feeds mainly on wasps, bumblebees and wild-honey bees. It is the only bird of prey in which the area between the eyes and the beak is covered with small, scale-like feathers instead of stiff, bristle-like feathers. It is identifiable by three transverse, unevenly spaced brown bands on the tail. In other details the plumage coloration varies greatly, but the dominant colour is a coppery brown. The wingspan may reach almost 150 centimetres.

This species lives in Europe, Asia and Africa, being fairly common throughout north-west Europe, although it stays only to breed, arriving in May and leaving for equatorial Africa in September. During this five-month period pairing, nesting, egg-laying, incubation and the rearing of the young take place. The birds are therefore fully occupied, and while at work they seem to take delight in aerial displays, uttering their incessant cries as they wheel through the air. The two egges are usually rounded, and white with brown spots. As in the buzzard, incubation takes a month.

The American White-tailed Kite (*Elanus leucurus*) is a representative of the subfamily Elaninae which is resident from southern Europe, central Asia and the south-western United States to Australia and southern South America. It is a white and grey kite found flying over marshes, river valleys, and well-watered foothills where it preys on rodents, lizards and large insects.

LAMMERGEIER: The Lammergeier or Bearded Vulture (*Gypaëtus barbatus*), the single species of the subfamily Gypaetinae, is unlike other vultures in having feathers on head and neck, and in its eagle-like bearing. The name *Gypaëtus* means both vulture (*gyps*) and eagle (*aëtos*), which emphasises that it is an eagle that has taken to eating carrion.

The Lammergeier is found mainly in high mountainous regions, but is gradually disappearing from Europe through persecution by man. It lives alone or in pairs, builds its nest in remote rocky regions and produces its eggs early (February to March) despite the high altitude. The young have a thick covering of down, which protects them against the cold.

Eagles and sea-eagles (Subfamily Accipitrinae)

Some authors call this subfamily the Buteoninae. Of all the birds of prey the eagle holds pride of place. It has figured in mythology, literature and art, and has been widely used as a symbol of greatness. Length of beak and of wing make the numerous genera easy to recognise. The beak is straight and ungrooved over the greater part of its length, with the tip of the upper mandible curved and brought to a point. The wings, when spread, are roughly quadrangular in shape and have a scalloped appearance at the tips. The feet are feathered down to the toes. The principal genera are *Aquila*, *Hieraëtus*, *Spizaetus*, *Haliaeetus*. All are aggressive predators and some are carrion feeders.

The most majestic species is the Golden Eagle (*Aquila chrysaëtos*), found as a rare species in mountain and forest areas of Europe, Asia and North America. The female, as in most birds of prey, is a little larger than the male, about a metre long, with a wingspan of over two metres. The plumage is dark brown, although it looks almost black when the bird is seen in flight.

The Golden Eagle has great muscular strength and can carry in its talons prey as large as the young of a chamois, a goat or a sheepdog. Exaggerations are only too common, and there is no truth in the stories of these eagles carrying off human beings. It is very unlikely that even the largest could fly off with any weight exceeding nine kilograms.

It invariably nests in a tall tree or on a steep rock ledge. The main structure consists of dried

The Tawny Eagle (*Aquila rapax*), distributed widely in open country in Asia and Africa, is the most common of the world's large eagles. There are many sub-species, all with brown plumage, which makes identification difficult. It feeds on small mammals and carrion and will chase other birds to steal their prey.

branches, some as thick as a man's arm, lined with twigs, bark and dried grass. To start with it is only about twenty-five centimetres deep, but over the years, with the constant addition of new materials, it may become as much as 120 centimetres deep.

The female lays a single egg or two eggs in March or April, each measuring about 7.5 centimetres long by six centimetres wide, and having an average weight of just over 150 grams. The shell is white with red spots and rough to the touch. Incubation lasts a month-and-a-half, the male taking no part except to bring food.

The two or three eaglets hatch at intervals of two or three days. The first to hatch usually survives the others, either by killing them or by taking their share of the food. The mother provides food of a suitable size for her brood and prepares it with care. The eaglet's plumage is first white. This gradually turns grey and then brown, and by the end of four or five years has assumed its typical coloration and appearance.

A closely related species is the Imperial Eagle (*A. heliaca*), a little smaller and distinguished by its square-cut tail, the cleft in its beak extending behind the eyes, and by the white or partially white feathers on its shoulders. It breeds from south-eastern Europe to central Asia, and also in Spain and north-west Africa, but winters in parts of Africa and southern and eastern Asia. Unlike the Golden Eagle, it prefers the plain and the steppe to mountainous country, building its nest in trees or even on the ground. It has a cry rather like the cackling of fowl, and it destroys many rodents.

The smaller Spotted Eagle (*A. clanga*), almost black in colour, is found particularly in marshy regions or near rivers over the same area as the Imperial Eagle, but it is not so magnificent, and its prey is seldom larger than small rodents, lizards, snakes, frogs and insects.

The Booted Eagle (*Hieraëtus pennatus*), no bigger than a Buzzard or Red-tailed Hawk, is more or less pure white on the front of the body and dark brown on the back and ear regions. It has a tuft of white feathers projecting from the point where the wings join the body. It was once a summer migrant common in the wooded areas of western Europe, but today it is found mainly in central Europe, Asia Minor and Africa. It can fly at heights as great as the other members of its family, but it will also take cover in trees and perch on a branch to watch for its prey, small mammals, birds, reptiles and insects. Spotted and Booted Eagles are easily reared in captivity—another indication of the great difference between them and the Golden and Imperial Eagles.

The Harpy Eagle (*Harpia harpyja*) of South America is the largest and most powerful eagle.

At certain times of the year migrating bands of sea-eagles or fish-eagles appear off the coasts of Europe, northern Asia and North America. Their aquatic habits set them apart from other eagles. Their food consists almost entirely of fishes, aquatic birds, and a diversity of carrion. The European Sea-eagle or White-tailed Eagle (*Haliaëtus albicilla*) is brown with a white tail. The Bald Eagle (*H. leucocephalus*), a species resident in America, has a white head and neck. This is the species that is the national emblem of the United States. It lays two eggs in a tree-top nest and enjoys a diet almost wholly consisting of fish. Another species (*H. vocifer*), named for the loud cries it utters, lives on the banks of the great African rivers and lakes.

SERPENT EAGLES: These birds are so slow and indolent in movement that they fall easy prey to human hunters. They are not prolific, the female laying only a single, relatively large egg in a tree-top nest where the parents take turns sitting on the egg. Both help to feed the chick, which is said to have such an enormous appetite that it requires two or three snakes a day.

Visitors to southern France, particularly the Camargue, will be familiar with the Short-toed Eagle (*Circaëtus gallicus*). The underparts of the body are white with brown spots, while the back and upper sides of the wings are brownish grey. There are three dark bands across the rear part of the tail.

The migrations of these fine-looking birds extend over southern Europe, North Africa and parts of Asia. They arrive in France in May and

The Red-tailed Hawk (*Buteo jamaicensis*), of North America, with two young in its nest. It is not a true hawk, but a large buzzard with a wing-span of up to 130 centimetres. It is widespread from the deserts of the south up to the Yukon and Alaska in the north, feeding mainly on small rodents and birds.

leave in September, and are most commonly found in the Vosges, the Alps and the Pyrenees, and sometimes in lowland regions. Forest clearings and ponds are particularly favoured sites. They stalk all kinds of rodents, reptiles, amphibians and insects. As they destroy vipers, they are protected in most countries.

One curious species the Bateleur (*Terathopius ecaudatus*) is fairly often seen in zoological gardens. Its specific name refers to its short tail, the feathers of which barely extend beyond the rump. The bird is somewhat variable in colour, with a black breast and underparts, a brownish-red back, and wings ranging from cream to black or dark blue, but the underparts are almost entirely of a silvery sheen. When at rest it has a curious appearance, for it fluffs out its feathers, particularly those on the head and neck. It preys mainly on snakes, and has also been reported to attack young gazelles, lambs and young ostriches. It is found through much of Africa.

BUZZARDS: (The word buzzard is used in America to refer to New World vultures. In this text it refers to members of the subfamily Buteoninae, which is considered by some a part of the Accipitrinae). These birds resemble the typical eagles in their massive form and long, quadrangular wings with rounded, 'fingered' tips. But here the resemblance stops, for the beak is curved to the base, and the lower legs are without feathers. They are slow-moving, somewhat wary birds, preferring to stalk terrestrial prey rather than to attack other birds. They sometimes eat carrion or vegetable matter.

While an adult Short-toed Eagle has a wingspan of nearly 200 centimetres, the Common Buzzard's (*Buteo buteo*) is no more than 150 centimetres. Both have a short beak, curved over its whole length, and bare, rather slender tarsi. But the Common Buzzard's short wings make it less able in the air. Plumage and coloration vary so much from locality to locality that a number of district geographic races or even species have been recognised.

The Common Buzzard is one of the commonest European birds of prey, widely distributed over Europe, Asia and Africa, resident in some areas and migratory in others. Individuals nesting in the summer in Scandinavia and Germany pass over or spend the winter in western Europe. In the British Isles the bird breeds in Scotland, Wales and western England. It tends to inhabit hedged and tree-lined fields. Here it sits unseen and watches for its prey. For long periods it will remain motionless, perched on one foot with the other hidden beneath its feathers. As soon as it spots a mouse or some other small rodent it glides quickly towards it, seizes it and devours it on the spot. Its diet also includes moles, shrews, reptiles, amphibians and insects. The buzzard is thus a useful animal and deserves protection.

Great care goes into building the nest, placed high in the fork of a tree. It is lined with fine twigs, which are covered with moss, fur and other small pieces of material. The bird will often refurnish an earlier nest or even take over an old rook's nest and adapt it to its needs. The same nest, repaired year after year, may be used by buzzards, goshawks, kites and crows in turn, the former owner rarely seeking to evict the current occupant.

Pairing takes place during March to April and is accompanied by flight displays, during which the birds make mewing sounds. Two to four near-spherical eggs are laid at intervals of several days. They are white with brown spots and take about a month to hatch, the male and female taking turns to brood them, one sitting while the other catches the food needed by both. The young are reared over a period of several months. When they are big enough, they fly away to fend for themselves in some other area.

HARRIERS OR MARSH HAWKS: These are small-sized birds of prey with a wingspan of no more than 140 centimetres. They are slender in form with long, slim legs and an elongated tail, while the ruff of feathers around the front part of the head gives them an owl-like look. They prefer flat terrain, particularly near water, and take a wide range of food. Their habit of harrying or flying to and fro over an area in search of prey gives them their common name. The nest is built on the ground

A female Hen Harrier (*Circus cyaneus*). This slender, long-legged bird of prey has an unusually large ear-opening hidden by a ruff of feathers, giving it an owlish appearance. This adaptation presumably enables it to locate mice and other small animals rustling in the leaf litter, for it hunts always by flying low over the ground.

and shelters the four or five white, rounded eggs.

All harriers are at least partially migratory, spending the summer in the temperate parts of Europe, Asia and North America and moving somewhat southwards in winter. The Hen Harrier (*Circus cyaneus*) is found over much of Europe, North Africa, Asia and North America, where it is known as the Marsh Hawk. It breeds in the northern parts of its range. The habits of the related Montagu's Harrier (*C. pygargus*) gives a good general idea of the life of birds of prey.

Montagu's Harrier arrives from Africa or Asia towards the end of March and during the early days of April. At the end of its long journey it heads for its old nesting area. In many regions suitable nesting sites are rare and it must therefore take possession of favourable territory as soon as possible. The male appears alone and as he flies over the site his flight is on leisurely wing-beats broken by gliding movements. In round wide circles, he describes interlacing curves, as if surveying the land where the nest will be built.

The female, which arrives about ten days after the male, is the mate of previous years, for many birds of prey are not only monogamous, but mate for life. Almost immediately the two birds begin their courtship, swirling together in a spiralling flight interrupted by downward glides and turns, which demonstrate their remarkable agility in the air. Then comes the mating flight, when the male displays to his watching mate. His usual circling movements cease and he begins to glide slowly towards the female and hovers before her with outspread wings. With ever-increasing speed he flies straight at her until he makes a short and sudden dive, his wings swinging over her. During this lordly, almost aggressive display he seems about to collide with her, but soars upwards, expending the impetus gained in the dive. He passes so close to the female that she gives an uncertain flap of her wings as though momentarily thrown off balance, and is forced to fly out of his way. There is a magnificent rhythm in the flight during which the male displays his light-coloured breast and then the silvery underparts of his wings to his mate. The rush of air through his feathers produces a whistling sound, and his plumage glistens in the light. This display is repeated several times, almost without pause. The male may even fly high into the air, to repeat his aerobatics with elaborate rolls and spins.

These manoeuvres become more and more frequent and before long are reinforced with a new and most curious form of display, which can be watched only through binoculars as it takes place high in the sky. As the male utters shrill cries like those he usually makes when returning with prey, the female turns to meet him and then flies below her mate, keeping to his rhythm. When she is a suitable distance, the male lets fall his prey. With a sudden beat of her wings the female brakes in the air and begins to fall. Then she stretches out her feet and in one of them seizes the food. By now the male has resumed his circling and gliding flight, in which the female takes part after she has eaten his offering. Soon she will leave all the foraging to the male and for ten weeks remain at the nesting site.

As the female is relieved from regular hunting for food, she devotes herself to building the nest. This is laid in the heather and is made of interwoven roots and twigs. The first egg is laid towards the end of May and is soon followed by several others. Incubation is undertaken by the female alone, while the male continues to provide the food. Prey is handed over in full flight, away from the nest.

A ground nest is particularly vulnerable, and the female will use any diversionary behaviour when leaving or returning to her nest to distract the unwanted attention of potential predators.

As with the Common Buzzard, incubation lasts for about a month. The chicks hatch at intervals of two days, following the order in which the eggs were laid. To begin with the chicks are mere balls of down, but they soon become more active. They have enormous appetites, and at two hourly intervals the male can be heard calling as he returns from hunting. The female takes the prey from him, kills it, dismembers it at the nest and distributes the pieces to her hungry chicks.

At this stage more than ever, attention must be diverted from the nest with its three or four white balls of feathers, an easy prey for high-flying marauders, and the parents show fight to any buzzard or crow which might make off with the chicks. And at the slightest alarm the chicks hide.

One month after hatching, the young harrier has its first lesson in flight, when it is rewarded with a piece of food. Little by little it is forced to fly higher and higher in pursuit of the parent birds and the prey that they drop for it in full flight. Their most difficult task is to make the young bird leave the nest altogether, and then they must urge it to hunt. But this is not entirely a matter of training. At the appropriate time instinct begins to take over.

True hawks (Subfamily Accipitrinae)

These are perhaps best described as forest hawks, broad-winged and long-tailed. The commonest genus is *Accipiter*, to which both the Goshawk and the European Common Sparrowhawk belong. (The Sparrowhawk described here is the European hawk and should not be confused with the American Sparrowhawk, which is an unrelated falcon (*Falco sparverius*)

The Goshawk and the European Sparrowhawk are so similar in appearance that they are often confused with each other. However, the Goshawk is larger than the Sparrowhawk and has shorter and stouter toes. Both have a long tail and broad, rounded wings, and are good flyers. The plumage, which varies slightly according to age and sex, is slate blue above and white barred with reddish brown below. There are characteristic reddish crescent-shaped markings on the underparts.

The Goshawk (*Accipiter gentilis*) reaches a length of sixty centimetres from head to tail and has a wingspan of nearly 120 centimetres. It can be recognised in flight from the breadth of the wings, which is more than half the bird's length, and by the three black bands across the tail. The flight is rapid and the wings are nearly always in motion. Although the Goshawk usually takes its prey on the wing, it will also seize an animal that is resting on the ground, running or swimming. In a forest it can rapidly pursue its victim through trees and bushes by closing its wings and steering itself with its outspread tail, even following the victim into a burrow or a hole in a tree.

In short the Goshawk is a first-class hunter that takes all manner of prey. And for this reason it has been hunted and destroyed without compunction, with the result that in many places, including North America, it has become very rare.

The Goshawk builds its nest high in a forked beech, oak, pine or fir. One nest may be used for several years, being repaired with new twigs before each brood is reared. The eggs, which number three or four, are bluish, sometimes spotted with brown. Incubation requires about three weeks. The female feeds the young with food caught by the male and left in a place set well away from the nest for her to collect.

The Dark Chanting Goshawk (*Melierax metabates*) together with its near relative the Pale Chanting Goshawk (*M. canorus*) are large grey hawks common and widespread in open country in Africa, with little to distinguish between them. They are called Chanting Goshawks from their habit of perching on trees in the breeding season and whistling for long periods in a monotonous way reminiscent of monks chanting. They feed mainly on lizards.

The European Sparrowhawk (*A. nisus*), which is smaller than the Goshawk and has longer and more slender digits, ranges throughout Europe, North Africa and much of Asia. It is one of the smaller birds of prey, being little bigger than a pigeon. Its habits are rather like those of the Goshawk except that it attacks smaller prey. Small birds seem to be aware of its threatening presence and will unite in flocks to harry it and put it to flight. Wagtails and swallows will hotly mob and pursue a stray individual within their territory.

The breeding habits of the European Sparrowhawk and the Goshawk are very similar. The nest is built at a medium height and contains whitish yellow eggs with reddish spots, which often form a circle round the broader end of the egg. During the incubation period and the first week after the young are hatched, the Sparrowhawk follows the same precautionary measures as the Goshawk. The male bird never brings food direct to the nest.

Newly hatched Sparrowhawks are completely white, except for the beak and feet. The crescent-shaped markings on the underparts first appear at the end of about three weeks.

The Goshawk and Sparrowhawk were formerly used in the chase, but as they are 'birds of low flight' as opposed to the falcons, 'birds of high flight', they were used to hunt only hares, rabbits and partridges. This practice still exists in certain parts of Asia and India.

Osprey (Family Pandionidae)

The single species *Pandion haliaëtus* is a handsome, medium-sized bird of prey, easily recognised by its whitish underparts and the absence of 'trousered'

A female Osprey (*Pandion haliaetus*) seen on the nest with her two chicks. The Osprey breeds on all continents except South America where it occurs as a winter visitor only. It has recently returned to Scotland where it breeds only by freshwater lochs. In other parts of the world it is also found along sea coasts.

feathering on the legs. The head is also white, and there is a brown band running downwards from each eye to the nape. The rest of the body plumage is dark brown.

Pandion haliaëtus is a 'fishing eagle' and always lives near water. Flying at a height of ten to thirty metres, alternately flapping and gliding, it watches for fishes in the water below. As soon as it sees one within reach, it plummets down to seize it, sometimes submerging for a second or two. Then it emerges and flies off, holding its prey horizontally with its feet. The prey is eaten in the nest, which is generally at the top of a tree or on some inaccessible rock. The Osprey's eggs are elliptical in outline, and white with slate-grey and brownish-red spots.

The Osprey is found throughout northern Europe, Asia and North America on freshwater lakes and coasts. Because its diet consists exclusively of fish it is threatened by pollution.

Falcons (Family Falconidae)

The true falcons, perhaps not so regal in their bearing as the Golden Eagle, are still imposing birds, and are perhaps the most specialised of all birds of prey. The long, narrow pointed wings, slender tail, and rapid flight are reminiscent of swallows or martins. The beak is short, powerful and curved down to the base, and differs from an eagle's beak in having a pair of teeth on the upper mandible corresponding to a pair of notches on the lower mandible.

Falcons are merciless and unerring hunters, destroying great numbers of animal pests. At the same time they are highly discriminating, never killing for killing's sake and eating only what they themselves have taken while in flight. Such restraint has led to their being trained for use in hunting.

Their usual habitat is the forest, where they build their large nests, but several species range the prairies and other practically treeless regions. Although they are usually migratory, if a region suits them well they stay on permanently. There are numerous species, including the well-known Peregrine Falcon.

The Peregrine Falcon (*Falco peregrinus*) is the species commonly found over most of Europe, Asia and also in America, where it is also known as the Duck-hawk.

The Gyrfalcon (*F. rusticolus*) is the largest, strongest and handsomest of the falcons. There are three major phases; one completely white apart from a black spot on each feather; another very dark grey; and one in between the other two. It is found in Arctic America, Greenland, Iceland and Scandinavia, and in days when falconry was popular the Danish government used to send a special ship each year to search for specimens. It is a bird that has always been held in the highest esteem and is easily handled and trained.

The Saker (*F. cherrug*) is an eastern species, whose commonest wintering places are in the Balkans, Asia Minor and Egypt. In habits and coloration it resembles the Peregrine Falcon, and has, as one description puts it, 'a crow's breast, a kite's head, a beak between that of an eagle and a crow, and a hand between that of a crow and a falcon'. It is, however, paler than the Peregrine Falcon and is considerably larger.

The hobbies are small, fast-flying insectivorous falcons. The European species (*F. subbuteo*) is often said to be the most graceful and agile of European falcons. The upper parts are slate grey and the underparts white with crescent-shaped markings. The European birds migrate to equatorial Africa each winter and return north in the summer, and are sometimes even seen in towns. It is a curious fact, however, that this fearless hunter does not defend itself against attacks from other birds, and kites, for example, will lie in wait for it and take away its food.

Its normal prey is the lark, caught in flight, but at times it will also take dragonflies, butterflies, grasshoppers and other insects.

The Merlin (*F. columbarius*), called the Pigeonhawk in America, is a small falcon with a wingspan of no more than sixty centimetres. Its flight is like that of a Swallow: fast, zigzagging, skimming across the ground, soaring into the air, and going wherever the chase may lead. It breeds in northern Europe, Asia and North America, and in winter migrates to southern Europe, North Africa, India and South America.

The Kestrel (*F. tinnunculus*)—closely related to the confusingly named Sparrowhawk (*F. sparverius*) of America—is one of the commonest European falcons. Its colouring resembles that of the Red-legged Partridge, the upper parts being reddish brown with small blackspots, and the underparts rather lighter in colour. The most characteristic feature of this hawk is its manner of hovering, as though held on the end of a string, while exploring its hunting grounds. This habit has earned it the name of Wind-hover. It does this repeatedly throughout the day. Together with its high-pitched cry, this makes it easily recognised. The Kestrel seldom takes birds in flight, and it

A Kestrel (*Falco tinnunculus*) with prey: it occupies a wide variety of habitats from mountains and wooded valleys to open moorland and farmlands, even breeding successfully in suburbs and city centres. A common and widespread falcon of the Old World, its numbers fluctuate in relation to that of its main prey, the Short-tailed Vole. In England it was highly susceptible to certain agricultural chemicals until these were banned.

feeds mainly on rodents and insects, a characteristic which makes it unsuitable for falconry but an asset to farmers. The American Kestrel (*F. sparverius*) is very similar in size, appearance, and habits, to the Kestrel, as mentioned already.

The Red-footed Falcon (*F. vespertinus*) is handsomely marked, the plumage being slate grey, variegated with white in the female, while the beak, feet and leg feathers are reddish orange. It is rarely seen in western Europe, except in southern France, but it is very common in eastern Europe and Asia, where flocks of a hundred or so are not unusual. It has the habit of flying to and fro, rather like a bat, over what seems to be a carefully marked out area, taking in insects as it goes. Its cry is like the Kestrel's but uttered more slowly and less often. This little falcon is also useful to man.

FALCONRY: The art of training hawks, especially peregrine falcons, or duck-hawks as they are known in America, for hunting was practised in India several centuries before the Christian era. The sport spread to Europe and North Africa. At the French court falconry was particularly favoured under the Valois and in England it was a favourite sport of kings and noblemen, from the Norman conquest to the seventeenth century.

Falcon training was something of an art, with its own rules and rituals. The falcon was held in captivity, starved, and kept in a disturbed condition to weaken it and make it more tractable. The bird's head was covered by a leather 'hood' during training so that it should not be disturbed or frightened by the sight of men, dogs and horses. After much care it eventually became accustomed to its master and would perch quietly on his arm. Falconry is still practised in many parts of the world and virtually all species of hawks, eagles and falcons have been trained at some time.

A male American Kestrel (*Falco sparverius*), known as the Sparrowhawk in America, although it is, in fact, a falcon and nearly identical to the European Kestrel (*F. tinnunculus*). In North America many other species, such as buzzards and harriers, are also called hawks making identification confusing.

Opposite
The Bald Eagle (*Haliaeetus leucocephalus*), so-called because of its snow-white head feathers, is the national emblem of the United States. Because of its depredations on the Blue Fox and on salmon it was persecuted for many years and is now almost extinct except in Alaska and Florida. Now that the eagle is protected throughout North America its population may improve.

Caracaras (Subfamily Polyborinae)

These include nine species of Falconidae in South America, one of which (*Caracara cheriway*) finds its way north to Mexico and the extreme south of the United States and has been adopted as the national bird of Mexico. Caracaras have strong legs and are primarily ground birds, scavenging anything from carcases on which vultures are feeding to insects and snails and birds.

Secretary-bird (Family Sagittariidae)

The scientific name for the lone member of the family is *Sagittarius serpentarius*, the common name referring to the head crest which looks like the quill pens clerks used to stick in their wigs.

Unlike the other raptors, the Secretary-bird has long legs, and long wings and tail. The plumage is ash grey, except on the upper legs and the rear part of the back, which are black. It lives in Africa, south of the Sahara to the Cape.

Groups of secretary-birds may be seen moving rapidly over the ground on their long legs or flying like swans, neck outstretched and legs extended. During the breeding season there is considerable aggression between the males. Both sexes work together to build the nest, which is generally placed low in the fork of a tree.

Like many birds of prey the Secretary-bird has a special partiality for snakes. Using one of its wings as a shield against counter-attack, it batters the reptile with its feet, at the same time retreating and jumping out of reach of the venomous bite with incredible speed. Finally, it seizes its prey and hurls it into the air several times in order to stun it.

The species can be kept in captivity, in South Africa they are kept to destroy snakes and rats.

The Brush Turkey or Brush Megapode (*Alectura lathami*) mainly inhabits the dense rain-forests of eastern Australia. It feeds on the ground during the day, raking over the vegetation with its strong feet to find insects and grubs. It also takes fruits. If disturbed it prefers to run away from danger although it can fly quite well.

Gallinaceous birds (Order Galliformes)

The cosmopolitan order Galliformes includes the domestic fowls, turkeys, guinea-fowls, pheasants, partidges, grouse and quail, and less well-known species such as brush-turkeys and curassows. All have thick-set bodies and small heads. The smallest species is about thirteen centimetres long and the longest, the Peafowl, may reach 230 centimetres counting its tremendous tail. The legs are moderately long and strongly built, and the strong feet are adapted for scratching the soil in search of food. They run well, but short, rounded wings are not adapted to long flight, and most species are essentially terrestrial and non-migratory in habit.

A stout arched bill and strong claws stamp the galliform birds as graminivorous, finding seeds either on or under the soil. On each foot there are three toes pointing forwards and one backwards, the latter generally being set higher than the others. The males often have spurs for fighting.

Most of the galliform birds are sexually dimorphic, with differences in size, plumage, spurs and various integumentary organs such as the comb and wattles. The males are usually polygamous and take no part in the building of the nest or in the rearing of the young. They are fierce and aggressive. The females lay numerous eggs in a crudely made nest. The young are precocial.

The Galliformes are divided into seven families. In Tetraonidae (ptarmigan, grouse, capercaillies), which live in cold and temperate parts of the northern hemisphere, the tarsi and toes are more or less feathered and the males have no spurs. The Phasianidae (pheasants, jungle and domestic fowls, partridges, quail, bobwhites, francolins, peacocks and argus pheasants) live in warm and temperate regions and are particularly numerous in Asia. They have naked tarsi, while the males have one or two spurs on each leg. The nostrils are not covered with feathers. The other families are: Numididae (guinea-fowls), Meleagrididae (turkeys), Megapodidae (brush turkeys), Cracidae (curassows, guans, chachalacas), and Opisthocomidae (hoatzin).

Megapodes (Family Megapodiidae)

Also known as brush-turkeys, incubator birds or moundbuilders, these have the stout, arched beak typical of the galliform birds. They have short, rounded wings, large tails and stout legs with strong claws, and are not unlike the turkeys of the New World. Native to Australia and New Guinea, they were carried to South Pacific islands.

Unlike the other galliform species, the megapodes do not brood their eggs but lay them in enormous mounds of sand and earth mixed with sticks and leaves, scraped together by pairs or groups of birds. Some of these mounds are the work of generations of birds and may reach a height of five metres and a diameter of sixteen metres. Each egg is laid in a separate hole, which is then carefully filled up. Heat from the decomposing vegetable matter hatches the eggs by a form of artificial incubation. When hatched the chicks are strong enough to fend for themselves and can usually fly within twenty-four hours of hatching. Some species lay the eggs in fissures in rocks allowing the heat of the sun, retained by the rock at night, to incubate the eggs.

One of the genera is *Leipoa*, meaning a 'deserter of eggs'. This expresses an earlier belief that, having built the mound and laid their eggs, the megapodes took no further interest in them. Far from deserting their eggs, they provide them with optimum conditions of temperature and humidity and have merely relieved themselves of the personal contacts of incubation. The territory of each male contains a mound. In many species the cocks are polygamous and the hens of each harem lay their eggs in the mound made or defended by their mate. It is now known that the cock not only stays in the vicinity of the mound, calling and displaying thoughout the breeding season, but regulates the temperature of the mound, thus justifying yet another name given to the megapodes: thermometer birds. He appears to know, with the accuracy of a thermometer, when the mound is getting too warm, and he scrapes away some of the mound material to increase ventilation. If the temperature drops below the optimum he adds rotting material to raise it.

Curassows (Family Cracidae)

Curassows, guans and chachalacas are all confined to the Americas, between Texas in the north and the Argentine in the south. They are arboreal roosters but ground-feeders, scratching among dead leaves for food in much the same way as domestic fowls, with which they readily associate. Curassows have a fine crest of recurved feathers and the beak is stout at the base, which is provided in many species with a fleshy cere or a frontal protuberance. The males are usually black with white underparts, and the females brown. The male of the Great Curassow (*Crax rubra*) is a metre long, and black with a yellow knob on top of the beak. The female is reddish brown, and her head and neck are black spotted with white; she has no beak knob. Ornamentation of the beak is a feature of other male curassows: the Black Curassow (*C. alector*) has a pendent wattle on the beak, and the Great Razor-billed Curassow (*C. mitu*) has a blade-like casque.

In the guans, which are smaller than curassows about sixty centimetres long, the sexes are alike and both are brown to olive with a metallic sheen. The Horned Guan (*Oreophasis derbianus*) has a long, red spike growing up between the eyes. Guans of the genus *Penelope* seem to be irresistibly attracted to fire, and a method of luring them is to light fires in the branches of a tree.

Chachalacas are smaller than guans. They are slender, with long tails, brownish green to olive. They are named after their cackling calls.

Ptarmigan or grouse (Family Tetraonidae)

The ptarmigan's generic name, *Lagopus*, refers to the hair-like feathers that cover its feet in winter, enabling it to walk in its snow-covered environment. There are three species: the Rock Ptarmigan, the White-tailed Ptarmigan of North America and the Willow Ptarmigan with its British subspecies, the Red Grouse. The wings are short and rounded in outline. The end of the tail is also rounded. Nostrils are feathered. The males are larger than the females.

The Rock Ptarmigan (*L. mutus*) and Willow Ptarmigan (*L. lagopus*) are circumpolar in distribution. The northerly part of their range covers Scotland, Sweden, Norway, Lapland, Siberia and Canada. In summer distribution is just below the snow-line, and they nest close to fern-covered and glacial regions. During the winter they may descend to the valleys, where they are confined to rocky areas close to forest.

The winter plumage of most species is white, only the beak and tail being black (the males also have a black band running from the beak to just behind the eyes). It is thus well camouflaged against the snow. The Red Grouse alone does not assume this winter plumage.

About February, red and black-barred feathers of the breeding plumage appear on the wings and the upper parts of the body. With this comes a change in the bird's behaviour. The flocks split up into pairs, which then look for nesting sites. The male engages in a vigorous leaping display and utters raucous calls which are answered by the softer cries of the female.

The shallow scrape in the ground that serves as a nest may be placed in the shelter of a rock, under a bush, or in a clump of heather, and is lined with leaves and plants. There are from six to ten eggs, which vary in colour from reddish yellow to whitish yellow with brown specks. They are incubated for three weeks. As soon as they are hatched, the chicks leave the nest and follow the mother. If disturbed with her family by a predator, she seeks to escape, while the young scatter and hide among

The cock Willow Ptarmigan (*Lagopus lagopus*) showing his white winter plumage against a background of snow. In spring, after the thaw, the cock dons his breeding plumage and starts his spectacular courtship displays. Favourite hillocks or boulders are used as look-out posts, from which he defends his territory against other males. The hens move from one territory to another to choose their mates.

Opposite
The African Jacana (*Actophilornis africana*), sometimes called the Lilytrotter, has exceedingly long toes and long straight claws, which enable it to walk over floating vegetation on tropical and subtropical pools and lakes. It is a good swimmer and will often dive under water to escape a predator. It feeds on small aquatic animals, seeds and sometimes fish.

the stones and plants. When the alarm is over she returns and re-musters her brood with a particular call, which plays much the same part as the clucking of the Domestic Hen.

During the summer the family stays together, feeding on bilberries, wild strawberries, buds and shoots of shrubs, together with insects, worms and snails. The plumage has now taken on brown, grey, yellow and black mottlings, which render the birds practically invisible as they crouch against the ground. When they take wing they display the white undersurface of their wings and their black tails, leaving no doubt as to their identity. When on the ground, ptarmigan run and walk partridge-like. Less highly prized as game birds than related species, they are hunted in some northern areas.

The summer plumage of the Willow Ptarmigan or Grouse (*L. lagopus*) is redder and browner than that of the Rock Ptarmigan, and during winter there is no black band in the eye region. Their habits are very similar, except that the Willow Grouse is found in the birch forests, peat bogs, and frozen plains of northern Europe and America, but not in the more southerly mountainous regions. Its flesh is regarded as a great delicacy, and the bird is hunted by British and Scandinavian sportsmen.

The subspecies, Red Grouse, is peculiar to the British Isles, where it lives on moorlands in Scotland, northern England, Wales and Ireland. The plumage is mainly reddish brown without any trace of white, although the hen is paler than the cock. The plumage maintains this coloration throughout the year. The Red Grouse feeds mainly on heather shoots and other moorland plants, but the young take insects also. The hen lays from five to fifteen eggs, which take twenty-four days to hatch. It is only within recent years that the Red Grouse has become recognised as a separate form of the Willow Ptarmigan.

Capercaillie and Black Grouse differ from those of the genus *Lagopus*. They have a wider tail, in which the rectrices and contour feathers may be erected and spread like those of a peacock. The tarsal part of each leg is feathered, and the toes are bare. The eyes of both sexes are surrounded by a ring of bare bright red skin. They are polygamous, too, a habit related to the more marked dimorphism between the sexes. The cocks are more agressive and take no part in rearing the young.

The Wood-grouse or Capercaillie (*Tetrao urogallus*), the largest grouse, is one of the larger European birds, with a wingspan up to 150 centimetres and a weight of six to eight kilograms. Although not brilliantly coloured, the cock is a handsome bird with bluish-black upper parts and greyis, zigzag stripes. The breast feathers have a metallic sheen. The tail is dark blue and can be erected and fanned to display its white crescent-shaped markings. The hen, smaller and with duller plumage, is mainly reddish with brown stripes on the upper parts.

This bird was once widespread in central Europe, but it has been so heavily hunted and so ravaged by epizootic diseases (e.g. coccidiosis, to which most galliform birds are prone) that it now occurs only over a much more restricted area. In the British Isles it became extinct about 1770, but was reintroduced into Perthshire in 1838, and is now locally quite common. In France it is almost entirely confined to the Vosges, Jura and Pyrenees, where it occurs between heights of about 1,000 and 1,500 metres. It is still fairly or locally common in Scandinavia, Russia, and central and northwestern Siberia. It is a vegetarian feeder.

The Capercaillie is a shy bird and leads a solitary existence. Outside the breeding season the cock lives apart from his harem. Even at the height of winter, with thick snow on the ground, it may spend weeks on the same conifer, stripping it of its needles and shoots. When seeking food on the ground, it is a fair runner, but its flight is both clumsy and noisy.

The breeding season begins in April, when the cocks assemble on display grounds, and fierce combats may ensue to establish breeding territories. Young males have to fight for a place, and the combats often end in the death of one of the protagonists. This is a season of great activity. Just before sunrise the cock leaves the top of his favoured fir-tree where he has spent the night, crows a little during a noisy flight from tree to tree, and then descends to the ground where, rain, snow or frost, he begins to call. With head erect, throat feathers bristling, tail fan outspread, and wings half-open and dropping, he struts along, lifting his feet high at each step. His first calls consist of a series of isolated notes, which rapidly fall in pitch and lead finally to a full-throated song like the noise of a bottle being opened suddenly, followed by grating and low whispering sounds. The song lasts for no more than a few seconds. During this brief time the cock is quite unaware of anything going on around him and may be easily caught off guard by hunters. (The bird is also rather unwary during his courtship display, but does not close his eyes as is often supposed.) From time to time he leaps high into the air, noisily beating his wings. His calls are feeble and are barely audible a hundred metres away, the range being particularly short when the ground is uneven. But the noise of his wings as he jumps and the 'bottle-opening' sound are louder. During the entire display the cock maintains the same posture, sometimes trailing his wings as he runs across the forest floor or the short grass in clearings.

This ceremony continues until nine or ten in the morning and may be resumed briefly in the evening. As the cock calls, struts and displays his fan-like tail, the hens watch intently and respond with raucous cries. After mating the cock leaves the hens to their nest building, egg-laying, and chick-rearing. As early as the end of May he withdraws from his harem and returns to his solitary life until the following year.

The hen makes a simple bowl-shaped hollow in the ground under a clump of heather or a bush, and lines it with dried grass. The five to eight eggs are about the size of those of a Domestic Hen and are reddish yellow with innumerable brown spots. The incubation period is rather less than a month. The young can run as soon as they are hatched, but are accompanied by their mother, who may still continue to live with them during the winter. Their food consists of ant pupae, small insects, soft berries, young shoots and so on. As the stomach gradually becomes stronger, the young birds are able to ingest conifer needles and buds, which form the bulk of their food in winter.

The Black Grouse (*Lyrurus tetrix*) is placed in another genus, mainly because of its lyre-shaped tail. It should not, however, be confused with the Lyrebird, which belongs to the order of perching birds. The male is about the size of a fowl cock, his plumage a bluish black with a metallic sheen. There is a broad white bar set obliquely on the wings, and the under-surface of the tail also is pure white. The lyre-shaped tail is due to the outer rectrices being longer than those in the middle and turned outwards. This arrangement is particularly noticeable when the bird spreads its tail and at the same time moves the feathers downwards and backwards. Another characteristic of the Black Grouse is that the upper part of the bare red ring round the eyes is swollen and has something of the appearance of an eyebrow ridge. The hen, which is smaller than the cock, has a brownish-red plumage with brown stripes and a white band across the wings.

The Black Grouse is found in the wooded regions and mountain areas of northern Asia and Europe, where it may occur up to a height of over 1,800 metres. A few small trees are sufficient as perching places. Most of the time the bird spends running quickly over the ground in search of berries, shoots and insects, or flying off in its cumbersome and noisy fashion at the least sign of alarm. It is quieter in its habits than the Capercaillie, less wild and more sociable. Although sedentary, it moves about in search of sun and food.

Courtship takes place from April to May, when from twenty to thirty males gather in a particular place to call, display and fight, with the females as spectators. The first mating call, usually heard half an hour before sunrise, is so loud and clear that it can sometimes be heard over half a kilometre away. It begins with mewing sounds, followed by rising and falling hissing noises. Then come sonorous, rolling sounds, a little like the gobbling of a turkey. These calls are accompanied by a dance recalling that of the Capercaillie. The bird circles around, prancing with outstretched neck, wings drooping and tail erect. The movements are quick and jerky.

Each cock has a harem of three or four hens, which remain with him during the breeding season. Afterwards the sexes separate and the hens rear the young. Like that of the Wood-grouse, the nest is a simple depression in the ground lined with dry leaves. The six to ten eggs of the clutch, about the same size as those of the Domestic Hen, are yellowish red with brown spots. Incubation lasts four weeks. The chicks are like those of the Wood-grouse and are reared in the same way.

Hybrids between Black Grouse and Capercaillie and the Red Grouse and Capercaillie have been known to occur occasionally.

The Hazel Hen (*Tetrastes bonasia*) has only the upper two-thirds of the tarsi covered with feathers. The beak is partly hidden by the adjacent feathers and the cocks have an erectile crest on the head. But sexual dimorphism is less marked than in the Wood-grouse and Black Grouse. Both are brownish red in colour with grey and white markings, while the male also has a black throat. The tail is short and non-erectile.

This species lives in mountainous regions of central Europe and northern Asia. It is found most often in mixed deciduous and coniferous woods and has a particular liking for oak, birch, walnut and hazel trees. During the summer months it finds much of its food on the ground and, being a fast and powerful flyer, is able to change its feeding grounds. In winter, when the ground is covered with snow, it becomes almost entirely arboreal. Except during the breeding season when the birds break up into pairs, for they are monogamous, the Hazel Hen lives in coveys.

Unlike most of the galliform birds, both sexes work together building the nest, which is as roughly constructed as that of other grouse. The cock calls loudly as they work, while the hen at his side responds with softer notes. The eggs are reddish in colour with brown spots. They measure four by three centimetres and there are eight to ten in a clutch. Incubation lasts three weeks. The plumage of newly hatched chicks provides good camouflage against the soil. Accompanied by the parent birds, they spend the summer months looking for insects, worms and ant pupae. Later on they take more and more vegetable food, and eventually on the approach of winter become entirely herbivorous.

Three North American grouse are the Greater Prairie Chicken (*Tympanuchus cupido*), the Lesser Prairie Chicken (*T. pallidicinctus*) and the Sage Grouse (*Centrocercus urophasianus*). All lead the same kind of life as the Partridge. All inhabit the grasslands. The prairie chickens can be recognised by the two tufts of feathers on the neck. These are

The Sage Grouse (*Centrocercus urophasianus*) is the largest and most colourful of the American gamebirds and best known for its spectacular mating dance. The cock is here seen in display which is accompanied by a loud booming mating call. The Sage Grouse is found only in the western half of the United States where sage-brush grows. Its plumage blends perfectly with this vegetation.

The Chukar Partridge was once thought to belong to the same species as the Rock Partridge (*Alectoris graeca*), but is now regarded as a separate species (*A. chukar*). The Chukar is found on barren hillsides in Asia, Asia Minor and the Middle East. It has been successfully introduced into New Zealand and the United States.

inserted above air sacs in the skin and stand erect when the cock inflates the air sac during his dancing display in the breeding season. Accompanying the display is the unmistakable booming mating call.

Prairie chickens are polygamous like the Capercaillie and Black Grouse. The cocks are very aggressive. They perform a vigorous dance displaying to one another at a special place, called a booming ground, from the calls they make there. This popular game bird is being rapidly decimated in the United States and will ultimately become extinct if not given protection. The subspecies known as the Heath Hen, which formerly occupied much of the northeastern United States, became extinct only in 1932.

A resident forest species of most of Canada and the United States is the Ruffed Grouse (*Bonasa umbellus*). It is fairly common in mixed and deciduous woodlands where it is a popular game bird known to hunters as the partridge. Its 'drumming', heard particularly during spring, is part of its courtship-territorial procedure. It perches firmly on a log or stump and beats its wings in a vertical position making a noise much like that made by shaking a heavy piece of cardboard or paperboard. The beats start slowly and rapidly increase before abruptly terminating.

Pheasants and allies (Family Phasianidae)

The game birds of the pheasant family include the partridges, quails, true pheasants and peafowls. The tarsi are bare, and there are no feathers round the nostrils or inflatable air sacs in the neck. Some species are heavily spurred. They are ground feeders and tree roosters. Plumage is copious. Sexual dimorphism is exhibited by some members of the family, and for the most part these are the species that are polygamous. The rest are monogamous. The family is more widely represented in the Old World; the American quails are the sole representatives in the New World.

European partridges belong to two genera, the typical representatives of which are the Red-legged Partridge and the Common Partridge.

The Red-legged Partridge lives in southern Europe and North Africa. In about 1770 it was introduced into England, where it is now quite common in the southern and eastern parts.

The birds live together in groups and are most commonly found in open and hilly country. They run quickly but are poor flyers, taking off only when disturbed. Opinion is divided as to whether they perch or not. Their calls are by no means harmonious, the female responding to the male with loud cacklings.

Red is the dominant plumage colour of the Red-legged Partridge (*Alectoris rufa*), while bill, legs and toes are also red. A black band borders the throat, and the feathers along the sides have red and brown markings.

This species is about the size of a large pigeon. The hen is a little smaller than the cock and has no spurs, but otherwise looks quite similar.

The Red-legged Partridge appears to be monogamous. Pairing occurs in spring, and in April and May the female lays ten to sixteen eggs in a simple depression in the ground. On leaving the nest (after a month's incubation) the young move around with one or both parents. The family does not break up until the height of summer, when both the adults and the young birds join groups of their own age.

In southern Europe the Red-legged Partridge is often confused with the Rock Partridge (*A. graeca*), a species which also occurs in the French Alps above about 1,500 metres. It is also found further south in the most arid areas of the Carpathian, Balkan and Apennine regions in the Near East, and central Asia. But the two species can be readily distinguished. In the Rock Partridge the black throat band has no pendant feathers such as are found on the breast of the Red-legged Partridge. And there are two black bands along the sides of *graeca* and only one in *rufa*. They are also dissimilar in habitat, since the Rock Partridge favours high altitudes in arid and rocky areas, coming down to the valleys only in winter.

The breeding habits of both species are similar. For most of the year the birds live in groups, which break up into pairs in spring and summer and then reform in autumn when the young have been reared. The nest is hollowed out in the ground and, as in the Red-legged Partridge, the female lays about fifteen eggs, which take a little over three weeks to hatch.

The Common Partridge (*Perdix perdix*) differs from the preceding species in a number of characteristics. The beak is shorter; cocks have no spurs; colour is mostly greyish; there is no black band round the neck; the plumage below the throat and around the eyes is reddish and wings and sides bear reddish bands; the legs and feet are grey. There is also a chestnut, horseshoe-shaped marking on the breast, which is not always very distinct.

The Common Partridge is found over most of Europe and in North Africa and western Asia. As the species has a wide area of distribution and is of sedentary habits, it is not surprising that it is divided into numerous subspecies or geographical races distinguished in slight details of plumage.

Frequenting open country, the Common Partridge always lives in groups, except during the breeding season. They are thus able to exploit fully the food resources of their territory.

Like the Red-legged Partridge, the common species has behaviour characteristics that are well known to sportsmen. When undisturbed, it walks with neck withdrawn into the shoulder region and back curved, pecking from one side to the other. When hurrying, it runs quickly on its small feet, with neck outstretched. If it is disturbed, it immediately crouches against the ground, preferably in a furrow, where its colour helps to conceal it. The flight is cumbersome and relatively short in extent, and they take off at the last moment with a whirring of wings and soon plane down to earth again. They rarely perch.

Pairing takes place in early spring and is accompanied by considerable restlessness. Each pair selects a definite territory suitable for feeding the brood. The nest is a makeshift hollow in the ground, lined with dead leaves. The hen lays up to twenty pear-shaped eggs, of a uniform yellowish green. As in the Red-legged Partridge, the eggs are brooded for rather more than three weeks. During this time the cock stays close to the nest, and after the eggs have hatched he accompanies the brood.

In caring for the young, the cock runs hither and thither, looking in all directions for possible danger. A low warning call from the hen is a sign for the young to gather around her, and she then leads them to some hiding place among the crops, trees, bushes, furrows or ruts. As soon as the chicks are safe the hen and her mate indulge in a distraction display, facing the enemy and striving to draw him away from their young. If they succeed, the hen is the first to fly away, rejoining the young in their hiding place and leading them further away.

Partridges rest during the middle of the day, and feed mostly during the morning and in the early evening. They eat a good many insects, worms and molluscs, as well as seeds, berries, shoots and weeds. They are consequently more of a help than a pest to agriculture.

The Common Partridge is one of the most abundant European game birds. In parts of the Continent, however, it has become rare locally and requires frequent restocking. This is usually without much success, however, since birds raised in captivity are not adapted to a free-living existence and are easily taken by foxes and birds of prey. Even worse, they may be carrying parasites common among captive birds, particularly of the coccidial variety, which cause much damage.

QUAIL: Old World quail differ from partridges in structure and habits. They have a shorter beak—always less than half the length of the head. The tarsi are slender and without spurs or horny tubercles. The primary wing feathers are longer than the secondaries, and the eye areas are feathered, not bare.

They are also less social in habit than partridges, forming flocks only when they migrate. They are among the few gallinaceous birds that fly south in winter and they may range as far as Africa. Although monogamous, the males pay little attention to the young. Quail are more insectivorous than granivorous. They have a tendency to plumpness, which makes them choice game birds.

The Common Quail (*Coturnix coturnix*) is the only species of this group inhabiting Europe. It is also the smallest of the European galliform birds, being something like a miniature partridge, and about the size of the European Blackbird or an American Robin. The head is striped, the body greyish brown variegated with black, white and yellow spots on the back and sides which merge with the more uniformly coloured underparts. The black speckling on the breast of the female is the main feature distinguishing her from the male.

The species has wide distribution in Europe, Asia and Africa, and has been introduced into New Zealand and the United States. Throughout its range it lives in lowland plains offering good grass cover. A few birds visit the British Isles.

Quail appear to be poor flyers, yet they manage to travel thousands of kilometres between their nesting and winter quarters. In a single night they may fly from Rome to Tunis, covering 600 kilometres at a speed of about sixty kilometres per hour. After this long trip they are exhausted and on landing fall easy prey to hunters. Only the remarkable rate of reproduction has kept this species from extinction.

The Common Quail breeds during its short stay in the northern countries, when each male takes charge of a territory and fiercely defends it against rival birds. If there are enough females the males are polygamous, but if not, they are monogamous. In any event they play no part in nest building, brooding or rearing the young. The female broods seven to fifteen pear-shaped eggs, which are yellowish with brown spots. Incubation takes three weeks and the young quail are precocial, lively and alert as soon as they are hatched. They grow rapidly and at the end of five or six weeks are already strong enough to join the parent birds in their annual migration.

It often happens that quail miss the northward migration in early spring, having already nested in Africa. In this event they arrive in western Europe in July and August when they may produce a second clutch. These late broods are easily attributed to spring-nesting birds.

The characteristic call notes of the Common Quail are heard mainly during the breeding season. The three short-syllabled notes of the male sound something like the words 'wet my lips'.

The Chinese Quail (*Coturnix chinensis*) is related to the Common Quail. The Chinese are said to have used these birds to warm their hands, and there are several old tapestries that show them doing this.

The type bird of the New World quails is the Bobwhite (*Colinus virginianus*), although in the southern United States it is often called a partridge. In Virgina and California it is among the commonest of the game birds. Like the Common Quail, some groups in northern regions migrate south at the beginning of winter, although ordinarily the Bobwhite is not a migrant. It is monogamous, the males staying with the females to take part in brooding the eggs.

Attempts to introduce the Bobwhite into Europe to increase the supply of game birds have never been successful.

Other New World quails are the Scaled Quail (*Callipepla squamata*) of Mexico and the south-

Opposite
The Golden Pheasant (*Chrysolophus pictus*), one of the most brightly-coloured of all pheasants. In the wild in China it inhabits areas of low scrub and bamboo thickets on the higher rocky slopes of mountains. Although little is known of its habits in the wild it breeds readily in captivity and is popular in zoos and ornamental collections.

western United States, the California Quail (*Lophortyx californicus*) and its close relative Gambell's Quail (*L. gambelii*) of western America, the Mountain Quail (*Oreortyx pictus*), and the Harlequin Quail (*Cyrtonyx montezumae*). Many species have picturesque plumes arising from the crown of the heads. Other species range through Mexico, Central and South America.

The francolins (*Francolinus*) are partridge-like birds found in Africa and Asia. As in pheasants, the cocks have two pairs of spurs on the upper parts of the strong tarsi. One species (*Francolinus francolinus*) was formerly found farther north to the Mediterranean basin, particularly in Sicily, the Aegean area and Turkey.

TRUE PHEASANTS: These form an extremely striking group of birds, in which the males have a brilliant plumage and the females look plain and modest in contrast. Pheasants have little defence against their numerous enemies, and the males, belligerent among themselves, fall an easy prey to foxes and other predators. They can be kept in semi-captivity only when they are guarded with care.

All pheasants have a long tapering tail, which in certain species reaches a length of over two metres. The head is often ornamented with a crest or ruff, and the cocks have spurs. They are sedentary, passing the time in fields, heaths, thickets or even in forests in search of seeds, grain, fruit, leaves, roots, insects, earthworms and slugs. They have a quick way of walking and running, and they may occasionally perch, particularly at night. The flight is noisy and of short duration.

The males have a harsh cry, something between that of a Peafowl and a Guinea-fowl, and it is heard particularly during the breeding season, when their calls may attract the females or perhaps provoke other males. Being essentially polygamous, they assist in neither nest building nor brooding, and they exhibit no evidence of parental care towards the chicks. The nest, built by the female alone, is a depression hollowed out in the ground in the shelter of a hedge or a bush. There are usually about ten green or olive-brown eggs in a clutch. The young hatch after twenty-five days and are almost ready to fly about twelve days later. The hen stays with them until autumn.

The principal game bird is the Common Ring-necked Pheasant (*Phasianus colchicus*). Its plumage is predominantly brown, enhanced with a beautiful pattern of spots and metallic glints. The feathers of the head and neck are a brilliant greenish gold merging with blue and violet. The cheeks and the margins of the eyes are vivid red, while the long tail feathers are coppery red with purple highlights. The specific name indicates its origin in Colchis, the ancient name of a province in what is now the Soviet Republic of Georgia.

The Ring-neck has been introduced into the plains region of the United States, where it had never lived before. It has successfully established itself in this new environment and has increased to an amazing number and is a popular game bird.

Reeve's Pheasant (*Syrmaticus reevesii*) is named after the English traveller who brought it from China during the first half of the nineteenth century. This species has a white head and a golden throat and neck, while the feathers over the rest of the body have yellow, white, black and chestnut mottlings.

Other cock pheasants are no less striking. The Golden Pheasant (*Chrysolophus pictus*), a native of China and Tibet, has a crest of golden hair-like feathers and an orange ruff with black markings.

The Silver Pheasant (*Lophura nycthemera*) has a shining black crest and silver back marked with zigzag black lines. The underparts are black with metallic glints. The beak is white and the feet pink.

Lady Amherst's Pheasant (*Chrysolophus amherstiae*), a particularly handsome bird was introduced into England by Lady Amherst. The crest of the cock is red and the collaret is silvery. The back is green and the underparts white, while the wings and tail are black and white.

The short-tailed pheasants, or monals, have wings like partridges and a glittering plumage. The Impeyan Pheasant (*Lophophorus impejanus*) is typical. This has an iridescent plumage of blues, greens and bronze, like burnished metal. The Blood-pheasant (*Ithaginis cruentus*) of the Himalayas is grey and green with splashes of red on head, throat and tail. In the Crimson or Satyr Tragopan (*Tragopan satyra*) the cocks have erectile feathers on each side of the head, like horns. Tragopans are the only Phasianidae to build large nests of twigs and leaves in trees. In the Brown-eared Pheasant (*Crossoptilon mantchuricum*) both sexes have cheek feathers which project like ears.

Fowls of the genus *Gallus* form a well-defined group within the family Phasianidae. Whether wild or domesticated, all have the following distinguishing features: a fleshy crest or comb on the head, sometimes associated with a tuft of feathers; fleshy ear-lobes below the eyes and wattles hanging below the beak; long drooping feathers on the neck and breast that form the hackles of the cock; wing coverts developed as pendent, lancet-shaped feathers; a tail usually projecting upwards and bearing a number of curved sickle feathers; pointed spurs on the cock's legs. Sexual dimorphism is well marked and polygamy is the rule. The eggs are uniformly white or brown, according to the bird's food.

The wild fowls include Sonnerat's Fowl (India), Stanley's Fowl (Ceylon), the Javan Fowl and the Red Jungle Fowl, which is found in India, Malaya, Indo-China and the Philippine Islands.

The most important of these is the Red Jungle Fowl (*Gallus gallus*) which, apart from its wide distribution, is rightly considered to be the source of all domestic breeds. The head and neck are a brilliant yellow. The feathers of the back are purple-brown, being bright red in the middle and brownish-yellow round the edges. The long, drooping upper covert feathers of the tail are the same colour as those of the neck. The medium-sized wing coverts are a vivid chestnut brown, while the larger feathers have greenish-black tints. The breast feathers are black and greenish-golden glints. The primary feathers of the wing are a dark greyish black with lighter edgings, while the secondaries are red outside and black in the middle. The tail feathers are black. The eye is orange-red, the comb red, the bill brownish, and the feet a dark slate colour. The hen is smaller in size and duller in colour, and the comb and wattles are little developed.

The Red Jungle Fowl prefers high mountainous regions and rarely comes below a height of 1,000 metres. It is usually found in thickly wooded country, where it lives in flocks, feeding on seeds, fruit, buds and insects, particularly termites. The ringing calls of the cock and his aggressive instincts are like those of game cocks. He is polygamous and takes no part in rearing the brood.

It was Darwin who showed that the present-day varieties of domestic fowls were bred from the Red Jungle Fowl by long-term selection of chance variations. In the first place, of all wild species the Red Jungle Fowl is the closest to certain domestic races. And it is the only wild species to give fertile hybrids with domestic breeds. Lastly, domestic fowls, even though very specialised, are always liable to revert to the ancestral type, when the characters of the plumage resemble closely those of the Red Jungle Fowl.

According to Darwin, the wild species was first introduced into Europe in the sixth century B.C. At the beginning of that century the Romans already had six or seven distinct breeds. There were barely as many in England and France in the fifteenth century, but since then the numbers have increased. Present-day breeders now recognise nearly seventy kinds, difficult to classify, but with differences in the number of toes on each foot (usually four but sometimes five), the shape of the comb, the presence or absence of a ruff of curly feathers on the sides of the head or below the beak, the presence or absence of feathers on the feet, the colour of the ear-lobes and tarsi, fecundity (measured by the number and weight of the eggs laid each year), brooding capacity, hardiness of the chicks, capacity for putting on fat, and the delicacy of the flesh.

In practive five large groups of domestic breeds may be distinguished: four-toed with a single dentated comb, four-toed with a flattened type of comb (e.g. Pea or Rose Fowl), four-toed with a crest of curly feathers, four-toed with feathered legs and five-toed.

The Game Cock, the closest to the ancestral species, is large with an upright and stately carriage, a strong hooked beak, and fearsome spurs. The comb is single and dentate, while the tarsi are bare and end in four digits. Its plumage is quite like that of the Red Jungle Fowl.

What may be called the common breed of fowl is reared on many small farms. It is like the Red Jungle Fowl with a single dentate comb, white or red ear lobes, well-developed wattles, grey unfeathered legs, plumage with metallic glints, and a tail with gracefully curving sickle feathers.

The Red Jungle Fowl (*Gallus gallus*), regarded as the ancestor of all domestic poultry. In the wild, it is extremely wary and still survives in fair numbers in spite of centuries of persecution by man. During the breeding season jungle fowl are found in family parties of one cock and several hens. In winter they congregate in larger flocks.

The Peacock is the male of the Common or Blue Peafowl (*Pavo cristatus*). Here it is displaying the magnificent plumes of its tail-coverts, decorated with colourful eyespots. Although a native of India and Sri Lanka, the peacock has been kept in captivity in Europe and many other parts of the world for over 2,000 years.

The Leghorn Fowl is rather similar to the common breed, but is distinguished by a comb that is erect in the cock and drooping in the hen.

The giant of the pheasant group, and also one of the most remarkable, is the Argus Pheasant (*Argusianus argus*), a forest bird of Malaya, Sumatra and Borneo. The secondary feathers of the wing and those in the middle of the tail are extremely long and are decorated with eye-spots with brilliantly coloured centres. When these feathers are spread the bird is transformed and well deserves the name Argus, a reference to the mythical Argus with a hundred eyes. The bird is more than 180 centimetres long, over 120 centimetres of which is tail.

At the beginning of the breeding season each male Argus Pheasant prepares a large display ground in the heart of the forest, stripping it of its vegetation and afterwards keeping it completely cleared. When females come into breeding condition a number of them are likely to respond to his calls and visit the display ground.

The cock displaying to a hen is a magnificent sight. First he dances around her in ever smaller circles, smartly striking the ground at each step. Having come close to his partner, he stops suddenly and spreads one of his wings sideways. If the female appears to accept this display and makes no show of flight, the male then positions himself in front of her and suddenly displays the full splendour of his wings, an immense screen starred with delicately coloured eye-spots. The primary wing feathers touch the ground on each side, while the extremely long secondary feathers rise almost vertically above the back. The long tail feathers are also raised, undulating with the swaying of the body. The trembling of all these quill feathers makes a noise like that of a Peafowl spreading. Meanwhile the bird bends his neck back to bring the head behind one of the wings. From there he keeps watch, peering through a fold of the wing. This display usually causes the hen to take up a submissive attitude, whereupon mating follows immediately.

The Argus Pheasant and the Peacock, or more properly the Peafowl species, could be confused, as both have feathers with eyespots, but those of the Peafowl are the tail coverts (the feathers that lie over the true tail quills) not the wing feathers. These, too, can be erected in a fan, by the strong muscles under the skin of the rump.

The long train makes it easy to identify the Peafowl. Other characteristics are a long neck, a stout hooked bill, a crest on the head, fairly long legs and small spurs. Peafowl live in the forests and jungles of northern Asia, remaining on the ground by day and perching at night. In common with most galliform birds they are omnivorous. They live in groups which split up when pairing takes place during the breeding season. It is then that the Peacock fully displays his fan. His harsh scream is quite unearthly, and heard at daybreak it can be most startling. There are two shrill notes. The first seems to pierce the last traces of the dawn twilight. The second is a fifth lower in pitch and ends so abruptly it can be heard only at close quarters. Then follows a harsher cry, and this may be repeated as many as seven times at intervals of three or four seconds. After pairing the cock leaves the Peahen to build the nest, normally under a bush. The clutch consists of about ten eggs that are closely brooded by the female, which also takes great care of the young, though they are not difficult to rear in the Peafowl's native land.

The genus *Pavo* includes two species with much the same habits: the Common Peafowl (*P. cristatus*) of India and Ceylon, and the Green Peafowl (*P. muticus*), found in Indo-China and Java. The head, neck and breast are blue in the first and green in the second. The crest feathers of the Common Peacock have barbs at the tips, while those of the Javan species are barbed over most of their length.

The so-called Black Peacock, with dark blue wings, and the White Peacock appear to be varieties of *P. cristatus*. The precise date at which the Peafowl was introduced into Europe is not known, and in the fifteenth century it was still a rarity. The Congo Peafowl (*Afropavo congensis*), a fairly close relative of *Pavo*, was first described in 1936. It is very rare, which explains why such a large bird was unknown for so long.

Guinea-fowl (Family Numididae)

The various guinea-fowl species of Africa, Arabia, Madagascar and the Mascarene Islands have few or no feathers on neck or head. The head bears a crest of feathers or, in some species, a bony casque. There are also fleshy appendages, such as ear-lobes and wattles, and horny tubercles. The naked skin is variously coloured, but usually is blue. The plumage is dark with a white mottling. The cocks of some species have spurs.

These birds dwell in large groups in forest clearings, steppes and savannas, uttering their harsh cries. They scatter at the slightest alarm, coming together again later when called by one of the old cocks. They feed on insects or plants according to season. During breeding they break up into pairs, which later return to the group. The hen builds the nest on the ground and lays about ten eggs.

The Vulturine Guinea-fowl (*Acryllium vulturinum*) of East Africa, so named because its head and neck are almost bare, has a feathered fringe extending at ear-level round the back of the head. It can also be recognised by the long white band running down each hackle. The Crested Guinea-fowl (*Guttera cristata*), also of East Africa, has spurs and a crest of feathers on the head.

Lastly, there are two species with blue or red wattles hanging below the bill. Both were domesticated in Greek and Roman times, when they were known as African fowls, but were later allowed to revert to the wild state. Today only the species with red wattles, the Common or Domestic Guinea-fowl (*Numida meleagris*), is found in captivity. It comes originally from West Africa and the Cape Verde Islands and is recognisable by its pearly-green plumage. The same species exists in a wild state in Central America, where it became established from domesticated stock originally brought from Europe.

Guinea-fowls are easy to rear, and the hen produces a yearly average of eighty eggs, small, yellowish or brown with various mottlings, each weighing about fifty grams. The eggs make good eating, and the flesh has the same taste as pheasant meat.

Turkeys (Family Meleagrididae)

Two species of wild turkey are found in North and Central America. The neck and head are bare. A fleshy, pendent wattle, which can be distended and erected, springs from the base of the bill and hangs down on one side. The cocks also have a tuft of stiff, hair-like feathers on the breast and, like the Peafowl, are able to raise and spread the tail. The tarsi are spurred and the plumage has a metallic sheen.

The Vulturine Guinea-fowl (*Acryllium vulturinum*) is one of the most beautiful of African gamebirds. It is particularly numerous in northern Kenya where it inhabits regions of semi-desert and acacia scrub and also wild mountainous areas. When the flock is feeding two birds usually act as sentinels to keep watch for predators. The African Hawk-eagle, the Martial Eagle, the Caracal and Serval all prey on it.

The Common Turkey (*Meleagris gallopavo*) still occurs in the wild in North America. After years of persecution it has become exceedingly wary. It is a very strong flier over short distances. The hen nests on the ground laying between eight and fifteen eggs. Sometimes more than one female will lay in the same nest.

In the wild state turkeys live in small groups in open forests, feeding on insects, seeds and fallen fruit. The males make gobbling noises like those of the Domestic Turkey. During the breeding season fights occur between the cocks, which may wound or even kill each other. Then come the courtship displays during which the cocks, which are polygamous, make grating sounds, revolving and spreading their tails. The nest, built by the hen, is a simple depression lined with dry leaves, in which about twelve cream-coloured eggs with reddish spots are laid.

The Common Turkey (*Meleagris gallopavo*) extends from southern Canada by way of the eastern and southern United States to Mexico. The Domestic Turkey has been bred from this. The most valued of the breeds is a bronze-coloured variety in which the cock may weigh over eighteen kilograms and the hen seven to ten kilograms.

This turkey was introduced into Europe after the Spanish conquest of Mexico and by 1541 was known in England. As a domestic bird it was taken back to North America by the first settlers. When they first settled in the eastern states the wild turkey was abundant there. Its numbers were decimated by encroaching settlement. Conservation measures in recent years have resulted in the original wild bird becoming more numerous and it is now beginning to spread into areas from which it has been absent for generations. The Domestic Turkey is descended from the Mexican species introduced from Europe. The one other species is the Ocellated Turkey (*Agriocharis ocellata*) of Mexico and northern Central America.

Hoatzin (Family Opisthocomidae)

The single species (*Opisthocomus hoazin*), of north-eastern South America, has so many curious features that it is placed in a separate family. The adults are crow-sized, and brown with pale streaks on the breast. They have a long tail of ten loosely arranged feathers and an untidy crest on a very small head. The nest, built by both male and female, is an untidy collection of sticks in a tree-fork by a river bank.

Young Hoatzins have claws on the first and second digits of the wings. With the bill and feet these are used to climb about the nest or among the branches of the tree. As the Hoatzin grows and is able to fly the digits and claws grow smaller. These 'quadrupedal' birds recall the fossil *Archaeopteryx*.

It is interesting that the Hoatzin has a musky odour like a crocodile and that its call sounds more like a reptile than a bird. For reasons that are obvious it is sometimes known as the Reptile-bird.

Cranes and rails (Order Gruiformes)

This primarily aquatic order is divided into several families whose similarities are mainly anatomical and skeletal. Most species of cranes and their allies have a raised hind toe and only the extremity rests on the ground. Feet are not webbed, but are sometimes lobed. The young are nidifugous, and nests are built on the ground. Diet is vegetarian rather than insectivorous.

Mesites (Family Mesitornithidae)

There are three species of these rail-like birds found only in Madagascar, alternatively called mesites, roatelos, or monias. All are near flightless (they even climb to their nests). They measure just under thirty centimetres in length and have more powder-down patches than any other bird. At least one species, Bensch's Monia or Rail (*Monias benschi*) is polyandrous, and the males build the nest, a loose platform of sticks several feet from the ground, and incubate the eggs.

Hemipodes and button-quails (Family Turnicidae)

This is another odd family of quail-like birds whose behaviour is more like that of the bustards. They are small birds found from southern Spain eastwards to the Philippines and the Solomon Islands and southwards to South Africa and Australia, in flat grasslands. They seldom take wing but are speedy swimmers. They lack a fourth, backwardly directed toe (whence hemipode or half-foot). Hemipodes are polyandrous and the female does the courting. The males build the nests and incubate the eggs. The incubation period is very short (a mere thirteen days in some species) and the chicks precocial.

The Striped Button-quail (*Turnix sylvatica*) is a rather widespread species of Africa, which just reaches southern Spain. Like all fourteen other species of button-quail, it is mainly sedentary with little or no true migration. Its behaviour and feeding habits are more like those of the quail, which it resembles in appearance, than those of the cranes, to which it is more closely related. The Quail-plover (*Ortyxelos meiffrenii*) of Africa is the only species of its genus; all other members of the family are in the genus *Turnix* except for the Collared Hemipode.

Plains-wanderer (Family Pedionomidae)

The Collard Hemipode (*Pedionomus torquatus*), or Plains-wanderer, closely resembles the button-quail but has a well-developed hind toe, paired carotid arteries and pear-shaped rather than oval eggs. It is thought to be nearer the ancestral button-quails. The Collared Hemipode looks like a quail with orange-yellow legs. It rarely flies but tends to run or crouch in the grass if disturbed. The female, about twelve centimetres long, is greyish brown with a vivid chestnut patch on the chest and a black and white collar. The male is smaller, more uniformly coloured, and he makes the grass-lined scrape in which the female lays three or four grey blotched eggs. He incubates the eggs and feeds the precocial young.

Cranes (Family Gruidae)

Shy and wary when alone, the cranes are watchful and always on the alert; but for the most part they are gregarious creatures, and in flocks a few birds detach themselves from the main group as sentinels to give warning of danger. Driven from a particular place, the flocks never return *en masse* but straggle back one at a time until they have been reformed. A powerful call keeps individuals in constant touch. When nesting, cranes are particularly shy. They are seen usually only when they emerge in search of grain and occasionally insects, worms, molluscs, frogs and small rodents.

They are gregarious except during the breeding season which, in northern countries, is in the spring and early summer. The males are monogamous and help in hatching and rearing the chicks, which leave the nest shortly after hatching.

The most widely distributed species in Europe is the Common Crane (*Grus grus*), 120 centimetres high, with a wingspan of over 240 centimetres, and

A young Hoatzin (*Opisthocomus hoazin*) using its wing claws to move along a branch. It can also swim well and when coming out of the water clambers back into the trees using feet, wing claws and bill. Although the wing claws disappear as the young develop, adults often use their wings to help in climbing over branches.

One of the most striking of all cranes, the Crowned Crane (*Balearica pavonina*) is found over much of Africa from the Sudan and Ethiopia southwards. In the breeding season it indulges in spectacular courtship dancing, when the crown is displayed to full effect. Some of the dances of local tribes in West Africa are based on these courtship displays.

A group of Sandhill Cranes (*Grus canadensis*) feeding. Their breeding range extends from the Canadian, United States and Russian arctic southwards. Several sub-species occur in the American population, some resident and some migratory. The Sandhill Crane is similar in size and colour to the Common Crane (*G. grus*) except that the forehead is red instead of the crown.

weighing over four kilograms. Its plumage is ashen grey, except for the forehead, nape, throat, remiges and rectrices, which are black. On the top of the head is a bald red patch. The bill is straight and longer than the head. A particular feature of the adult is a tuft of long feathers, curved and separated to form a plume over the tail.

Migration begins in August or September and reaches its peak in Europe in October or November, when squadrons flying in V-formation at an estimated thirty kilometres an hour attract attention with their resounding cries. The return takes place in February or March. The flocks winter in India and in Africa, from Morocco and Tunisia to Ethiopia and the Sudan, and from Israel to the delta of the Congo.

The beautiful Crowned Crane (*Balearica pavonina*) of tropical Africa was once known as the Balearic Crane, for it could then be found as far north as the Mediterranean islands of that name. It is a striking bird with head doubly decorated with a black velvet cap and an occipital tuft of bristle-shaped feathers.

One American species is particularly well known, the Whooping Crane (*Grus americana*), a large white bird with red face and black primary wing feathers. Every individual is known, for the species is on the verge of extinction, and on the only wintering grounds at Aransas Refuge in Texas, the entire population (thirty-eight in 1965) may be counted. In 1952 numbers had dropped to only twenty-three birds. By 1956 they had increased to thirty, by 1960 the census showed thirty-six in the wild and six in captivity. In the breeding season the birds gather in one area of the prairies of northwestern Canada. The 1977 census gave a total of seventy. All migrate south in the non-breeding season, spending the winter in the Texas area. The species is rigorously protected and every encouragement is given to increase its numbers.

The Demoiselle Crane (*Anthropoides virgo*), of central Asia, North Africa, and south-east Europe, is distinguished by dazzling white tufts of feathers on each side of its head. It is smaller than the other cranes (about a metre tall), but even more graceful.

The non-European cranes have much the same habits as their European relatives.

Limpkin (Family Aramidae)

The Limpkin or Courlan (*Aramus guarauna*), the sole member of the family, a sedentary wader of tropical America, has the build of a crane. Its eggs are similar to those of the rail and its chicks dark brown. Its melancholy call has earned it a variety of names: Clucking Hen, Courlan, Lamenting Bird and Crazy Widow. It frequents marshes and waterways, hunting large snails. It swims well although its feet are not webbed. It is found as far north as the states of Georgia and Florida.

Trumpeters (Family Psophiidae)

This is a small family of three South American species. The Common Trumpeter (*Psophia crepitans*) looks rather like a long-legged guinea-fowl and is about the size of a pheasant. It has a magnificent, gaudy plumage: black, purple shot with blue and green, ice-blue shot with bronze, silver grey, and other tints. With the other two species, it makes its home in the humid forests of South America, where it feeds on seeds and fruit. The strange cries (from which it takes its common name) are strongly ventriloquial, deep reverberating sounds from within the bodies, uttered with a closed beak.

Rails, moorhens and coots (Family Rallidae)

Four very long toes, sometimes with membranous lobes, and eminently suited to walking on the wet mud of ponds and lakes or swimming, mark the largest family of the group. Nearly all can swim and dive. But wings are so short as to make prolonged flight impossible. Many species found on remote islands are flightless. The chicks are quite strong at birth, covered with down, and able to leave the nest after a very short time. On each wing the chick has a horny spur enabling it to creep about among the grass. In some species this spur is retained in the adult. The food of most species is mixed animal and vegetable.

The type bird of the Rallidae is the Water-rail (*Rallus aquaticus*), common in all the marshy regions of northern Europe and Asia. Its favourite haunts are among the tangle of water-plants, where it moves easily, because it has flat sides. Since it is solitary and very cautious, a great deal of patience is needed to observe it in its natural surroundings. It is easier to hear than to see. Its cry is repeated several times and on a lower note at each repetition, the whole ending in a grunt.

The Water-rail is little bigger than a Turtle-dove, with a long, slightly down-curved red bill which alone is sufficient to distinguish it from other species of the genus. Plumage is russet-coloured with black streaks on the upper parts, grey on the rest of the body, with transverse black stripes on its flanks.

The nest is bowl-shaped, well hidden among reeds. The female lays six to ten eggs, creamy white with some greyish-mauve spots. The male shares the three-week incubation. When hatched the chicks have a black down with metallic tints, which they moult between July and November. This is also the time when the adult birds lose their summer plumage, including the flight feathers, before acquiring their winter plumage. For some weeks they are highly sensitive to cold and are flightless. This phenomenon is known as the eclipse plumage and also occurs in many of the ducks. Although a poor flyer the European Water-rail migrates south for the winter.

Other typical rails include the Clapper Rail (*R. longirostris*), the Virginia Rail (*R. limicola*), and the King Rail (*R. elegans*) of America, the Slate-breasted Water Rail (*R. pectoralis*) of Australia and South Africa's Cape Rail (*R. caerulescens*).

There are eight species of Wood Rail in Central and South America of which the Grey-necked Wood Rail (*Aramides cajanea*) is figured here. All are large rails with stout bills, generally olive-brown upper parts, a grey breast and black hind parts. When flushed they take wing but with obvious reluctance. Otherwise they rely on their legs.

Rails with shorter bills are known as crakes in Europe. The Corncrake (*Crex crex*) resembles the European Water-rail in size and colouring, but its wings are redder and its belly yellower or dun-coloured. Its bill is much shorter and brownish. Also known as the Land Rail, the Corncrake is essentially a land bird. In company with quails it frequents meadows, fields and moorland. It is timid and not particularly sociable. Its cry, like the sound of a stick being drawn across a comb, is heard chiefly in the evening. When approached it will run swiftly away and is soon lost in the vegetation. It rarely takes refuge in flight.

The Corncrake seldom begins its nest before May or June, when the grass is highest. It builds in a dry place, making a depression in the ground lined with twigs and leaves. Its laying and breeding habits are like those of the Water-rail.

The Corncrake is migratory, leaving Europe each September or October for Africa and returning in April or May. And each year its numbers diminish, partly because it is favoured as game in some countries, and partly because machine-mowing takes a heavy toll of the young.

The Spotted Crake (*Porzana porzana*) has a speckled plumage streaked and dotted with white. Its bill is short and yellow. Its green feet match the grass on which it walks. In habits it differs little from the Water-rail. Its cry is more distinct, however, and is repeated with clockwork regularity. It lays from eight to fifteen eggs, considerably more than the Water-rail. It breeds throughout most of Europe and into central Asia and winters in Africa and southern Asia.

There is a smaller version of the Spotted Crake, the Little Crake (*P. parva*), an active species hardly bigger than a Blackbird.

The most widely distributed, and probably the most common short-billed rail of North America is the Sora (*P. carolina*), sometimes known as the Carolina Rail. It is similar in size and habits to the Spotted Crake but is brownish above with a black cap, mask, and bib; bluish grey face, neck, and breast; and grey-and-white barred flanks.

Forbes Rail (*Rallicula forbesi*), one of four species found in New Guinea, is remarkable for the special nest it builds for sleeping, whereas most birds use a nest only for the reception of the eggs and the rearing of the young.

The smallest rail is the American Black Rail (*Laterallus jamaicensis*) of temperate North America, twelve centimetres long, black with reddish nape and white bars on the back. It is so secretive that it is rarely seen, although its calls can be heard.

One of the largest rails is the Ypecaha Wood-rail (*Aramides ypecaha*), of Brazil to Argentina, forty-five centimetres long, brown with a grey head and throat, blackish tail and chestnut breast. The Flightless Wood-rail or Weka (*Gallirallus australis*), of New Zealand, is as large as a domestic hen. It not only manages to survive near human habitations but will even enter houses and steal bright objects. It is nocturnal and will eat almost anything. It is able to run down rats and mice as well as birds the size of a duck.

The moorhens or gallinules fall, anatomically, between the rails and the coots.

The Moorhen (*Gallinula chloropus*), known in America as the Common Gallinule, has a conical bill, red with a yellow tip and a red frontal shield (that part of the upper bill which flares out into a broad shield-like structure on the forehead). Its plumage is olive green; the rest of the body is slate grey, with white under tail-coverts divided by a black line. Its feet are green.

Resident in the southern parts of its range, migratory in the north, it can be found near pools, ponds and marshes, and any stretch of river where reeds and rushes abound. It prefers small areas of open water, but also needs cover for its nest. It is less timid than the rail and commonly settles near villages and sometimes among waterfowl in public parks. It can often be seen climbing a sloping tree-trunk. When swimming, its head and tail jerk in a characteristic rocking movement. It can dive below the surface, and in shallow water will squat on the bottom, with only its beak breaking the surface. It seldom flies, except when migrating, and seemingly with reluctance. It breeds on all continents but Australia and is the most widespread of the rails.

In the spring, after pairing, the cock and hen jointly build the nest, sometimes on a mud shelf, among water-plants, suspended between the reeds, or even afloat. Some pairs build in trees overhanging the water, and some occupy the old nests of tree-building birds. Five or six eggs are laid in April or May, varying from grey to red with red-brown spots and blotches. Incubation takes three weeks and brooding is by both male and female. At first the chicks are black. They leave the nest on the second day and begin to swim under the supervision of their parents. The families break up at the end of the summer.

The European Purple Gallinule (*Porphyrio porphyrio*) breeds in southern Spain, Sardinia, Sicily, and occasionally in the south of France as well as in Africa, southern and southeastern Asia, Australia, Indonesia, the Philippines, Madagascar, and New Zealand. Twice as big as the Moorhen, it is also distinguished from it by its colouring, which ranges from purple to sky blue, by its more extensive frontal shield and its longer front toes. Its habits are much the same as those of the Moorhen. It is easily kept in captivity.

The American Purple Gallinule (*Porphyrula martinica*) ranges from the southern United States and the West Indies to southern central South America. It resembles the Moorhen or Common Gallinule in size and habits, but its plumage is predominantly a rich purple.

Gallinules are found all over the world, typically on large areas of semi-stagnant water, among clumps of water-plants, their bright plumage harmonising with the colours of the bright green vegetation and its flowers. They feed on vegetation as well as insects, frogs and lizards. One of the most remarkable is the Takahe or Notornis (*Notornis mantelli*), known from only three specimens since 1855 and believed to be extinct, until in 1948 a small group was found living in South Island, New Zealand, in a valley 600 metres above sea-level and a week's journey from the nearest human habitation. The Takahe, now numbering about a hundred, is rigidly protected by law. It is the size of a large domestic hen and has an almost parrot-like beak. Its plumage is purple-blue with a green sheen, and the frontal shield a brilliant red.

The genus *Fulica* contains species of coot, which have toes edged with scalloped membranes, or lobed-webbing very much like a web. The Common Coot of Europe (*Fulica atra*) can be found wherever there is a sizeable expanse of water and is resident and numerous in many districts of the British Isles. Its range extends across Europe, except for the far north, central and southern Asia, northwestern Africa, and Australia. Its dark plumage is broken by its white bill and frontal shield. Unlike rails and moorhens, coots are sociable, and are gregarious outside the breeding period. They remain underwater just long enough to snatch up the plants which form their food.

Floating, or fixed among the weeds, the nest contains six to nine light grey eggs finely speckled and spotted. These are brooded by each parent in turn for a period of three weeks. Often there are two broods, one in May and another in August. The female will brood the second clutch on her own, while the male continues to bring up the young hatched three months earlier. Sometimes the chicks hatched in the first brood will help feed those hatched in the second.

Although the coots of Britain and France are mainly sedentary, those living in northern Europe migrate south as soon as the weather turns cold. They always travel by night and at great speed. Daily distances of 300 to 400 kilometres are not unusual. A ringed coot has been known to cover the 720 kilometres from Hamburg to Cayeux-sur-Mer (Normandy) in thirty-six hours.

The very similar American Coot (*F. americana*) is found from northern North America to north-western South America and in Hawaii.

Finfoot or sun-grebe (Family Heliornithidae)

There are three species in this family: one in tropical Africa, one in Central and South America, and one in Bengal, Malaya and Sumatra. This scattered distribution suggests that sun-grebes were once more widely distributed and had many more species. Now the birds are not common in any area. In addition, they are shy and live singly or in pairs by densely wooded streams, so that their habits are not well-known.

Sun-grebes are similar to grebes in appearance but are probably more closely related to coots, and, like both of these, their feet have scalloped, lobate webs. Bodies, necks, tails and bills are elongate. Bills are grebe-like and bear perforate nostrils. Sun-grebes swim partly submerged or hunt from low perches, feeding on fishes, shrimps, beetles, snails as well as vegetable matter.

The African Finfoot (*Podica senegalensis*) is the best-known species. The male is forty centimetres long, dark brown spotted black and white above, flanks barred and underparts white. A white line runs from the eye along the side of the neck. The throat is sooty grey. The female is smaller and has a white throat. The call is a low booming, heard especially during courtship as the seasonal flood-waters rise. Three to five eggs, white with red and buff streaks, are laid in platform-like nests built of grass and reeds in the forest, away from water.

The American Sun-grebe (*Heliornis fulica*) is the smallest of the family, about thirty centimetres long, olive-brown above and whitish below, with a white stripe behind the eye. The bill is scarlet and the feet are banded with yellow and black.

The Asian Sun-grebe (*Heliopais personata*), fifty centimetres long, is brown above, with black head and throat, yellow bill and green legs. It has the same white stripe behind the eye.

Kagu (Family Rhynochetidae)

The Kagu (*Rhynochetos jubatus*) of New Caledonia, was once common enough but is now close to extinction. It is long-legged, greyish and heron-like, with bright orange-red bill and legs, and a large head with a pronounced crest. The single species of the genus, it is much reduced in number. By day the Kagu sleeps among rocks or under tree roots, emerging only at night in search of insects and snails. Its piercing, rattling scream is audible a distance away.

The breeding habits of the Kagu have been studied in captivity. The courship dance of the male is a remarkable performance, half-running, half-skipping, with the participant tumbling about. A single pale-brown egg, dotted and streaked with reddish brown, is laid in a ground nest of leaves and twigs. Both parents share the incubation.

Sunbittern (Family Eurypygidae)

This family consists of one species, the Sunbittern (*Eurypyga helias*) of Central and South America. It is superficially like a bittern, but seems to be more closely related to the Kagu, and is forty-five to fifty-four centimetres long. It flies very little but walks slowly and deliberately on its orange-coloured heron-like legs, its long, snake-like neck held parallel to the ground. It lives alone or with its mate in dense tropical forests and swamps, usually near water, where it hunts insects or small fishes speared with a quick stroke of the sharp bill. Two eggs are laid in a nest of sticks, grass and mud, in low trees or on the ground. The parents share nest building, incubating and feeding the precocial young.

Cariamas or seriemas (Family Cariamidae)

These large birds have long neck and legs, short broad bill, erectile crest and long tail. They live in pairs or small groups and if pursued run with lowered head, flying only if hard pressed. They feed mainly on insects, especially ants, but also eat fruit and berries, and sometimes snakes and lizards. They breed and tame easily in captivity, and the young are often taken from the nest and raised with domestic fowls, which they protect. The first egg of many birds often differs from the rest of the clutch. This is especially so in cariamas, for one of the two eggs laid is glossier, more heavily pigmented and more pear-shaped than the other.

There are two species, the Crested Seriema (*Cariama cristata*) ranging from central Brazil to Paraguay and northern Argentina, and Burmeister's Seriema (*Chunga burmeisteri*), restricted to

The Crested or Red-knobbed Coot (*Fulica cristata*) of south and central Africa, Morocco and south Spain. It gets its name from the two brownish-red knobs on top of the white plate on the front of its head. Otherwise it is very similar in appearance and habits to the Common Coot (*F. atra*).

The Kori Bustard (*Ardeotis kori*), the largest of the bustards, may weigh over thirteen kilograms which is close to the size limit above which flight is impossible. It flies reluctantly and only for short distances but is a swift runner. Mainly dark brown in colour it lives in dry, open country in South and East Africa. The male is here displaying.

northern Argentina and parts of Paraquay. The first lives on open grasslands and pampas, the second in sparse bushy forest. Both are omnivorous.

Bustards (Family Otididae)

The family comprises several genera of running birds—about thirty species distributed through the dry regions of the Old World. Like the related trumpeters (Psophiidae), bustards look ostrich-like. They have heavy bodies and fly clumsily, but are able to run with great speed; they lack a hind toe. They associate in companies and inhabit grassy plains and arid steppes. The males are polygamous and fight fiercely in the breeding season. They feed off leaves, buds and seeds, with some insects (beetles especially) and voles. The females nest on the ground and alone brood and rear the chicks.

The Great Bustard (*Otis tarda*) looks somewhat like a tan, black-spotted turkey, but has longer legs and a more pointed beak. In breeding plumage the male has a chestnut back with black margins, white underparts, white wings with dark grey tips, and tail feathers that can be erected in a fan. A tuft of long white bristly feathers hangs below the bill. The female, smaller and without the 'beard', is more drab than the male. It still breeds in discrete areas in Europe and central Asia.

During the breeding season the males develop a throat pouch, which disappears at the end of the season. For a long time there was controversy whether such an organ existed or not, but this was finally settled by dissection of an adult male which died in captivity.

The Little Bustard (*O. tetrax*) is more common but less widespread. It is half the size of the Great Bustard and never has a beard, but on the throat of the male is a curious white V-shaped mark on a black ground, below this a white collar, and below that a black one. The Bustard is extremely shy. At mating time the male bird erects his black throat feathers into a sort of ruff and dances, alone or with other males. When a female draws near he leaps into the air in odd, contorted postures.

The Australian Bustard (*Ardeotis australis*), up to fourteen kilograms in weight and with a wingspan of 210 centimetres, is probably the heaviest extant flying bird. Its plumage is of varying shades of brown, white below and with a dark band on the chest. In courtship display the male, which is much bigger than the female, inflates his throat pouch until, when fully distended, it brushes the ground. The single egg is laid on bare ground in the cover of a bush. The chick is cryptically coloured and freezes motionless if alarmed.

In Africa, the stronghold of the bustards, one widely distributed species is the Black-bellied Bustard (*Eupodolis melanogaster*), which lives in high grass and seems to prefer burnt areas. It feeds mainly on insects and flower buds.

Waders and gulls (Order Charadriiformes)

This order includes a diverse collection of plovers, snipe, curlew, redshanks, woodcock, sandpipers, oystercatchers, jacanas, gulls, avocets and auks. Most of the family are small to medium size waders, or shore birds, found on or near water. Their habitats are as varied as the structure of their feet: some webbed, some unwebbed, some with four toes, some with three, some with short toes, others long.

Jacanas or lily-trotters (Family Jacanidae)

The jacanas resemble the Moorhen in size and habits and are found in both Old and New World on tropical marshy shores of lakes and streams. The most outstanding feature of the six genera is the extraordinary length of the legs, toes, and flat, straight claws, which enable them to walk on water-lilies and the floating leaves of other aquatic plants in lakes and rivers. Some have a long, flowing tail and in some species the plumage of the upperparts is iridescent. Male and female are similar, but the hen is usually larger than the male. The male does most of the incubating and looks after the chicks.

The American Jacana (*Jacana spinosa*) ranges from Texas southwards to Argentina. In courtship it displays its wings to reveal bright yellow patches of feathers, but its general colour is maroon and black. The Pheasant-tailed Jacana (*Hydrophasianus chirurgus*) of the Himalayas to Ceylon and eastwards to Java and the Philippines lays its eggs on floating vegetation, sometimes half-submerged. It is believed that the female of this species does the incubation. The thirty centimetres African Jacana (*Actophilornis africanus*), brown with a blue forehead, is found in mountain regions, walking on moss-covered rocks, or in swamps. In Australia and Indonesia the family is represented by the Bronze-coloured Lotus-bird (*Irediparra gallinacea*), a species with an erect comb.

Painted snipe (Family Rostratulidae)

These are so named for their snipe-like build and their bright colours. There are only two species: the Old World Painted Snipe (*Rostratula benghalensis*), of the tropical and subtropical regions of Africa, southern Asia and Australia, and the smaller, American Painted Snipe (*Nycticryphes semicollaris*) of South America. The female is larger and more brilliantly coloured than the male and at mating time it is the females who fight for possession of the males. Both species leave nest building and breeding to the males. Pairing is not permanent.

Oystercatchers (Family Haematopodidae)

The single genus is made up of six species very similar physically and in habits. The European Oystercatcher, or Sea-pie (*Haematopus ostralegus*), is forty to forty-five centimetres long, black and white with an orange-red bill two-and-a-half times the length of the head, and pink legs and feet. Its striking colours and loud, shrill cry are unmistakable. It is a coastal bird, feeding on shellfish such as mussels, limpets and, more rarely, oysters. In some parts of England it is known as the Musselpecker. The American Oystercatcher (*H. palliatus*), of the temperate and tropical coasts of North and South America, is almost identical and is treated by some authorities as the same species. The Black Oystercatcher (*H. bachmani*) of North America and the Sooty Oystercatcher (*H. fuliginosus*) of Australia, are both sooty black with flesh-coloured legs.

During the oystercatchers' nuptial ceremonies the male dances before the female. There may be two males present, in which event one mimics the actions of the other, as if trying to out-dance him. The contest ends with one of the contestants admitting defeat and departing.

Plovers and lapwings (Family Charadriidae)

Plovers are gregarious, disruptively coloured birds fifteen to forty centimetres long, with large eyes in a round head, and a usually straight beak, sometimes slightly enlarged at its extremity. The wings are fairly large, straight and pointed, giving rapid and prolonged flight. On the ground they are always on the move in search of food: worms, insects, molluscs and other small animals. Some frequent the fields, and others river-banks and beaches.

TRUE PLOVERS: There are two principal genera, *Charadrius* and *Pluvialis*, respectively known as the sand or winged plovers, and the golden plovers.

There are four species of *Pluvialis*: the Eurasian Golden Plover (*P. apricaria*) which breeds in northern Europe and north-west Asia; the American Golden Plover (*P. dominica*) found in the northern parts of North America and Russia; the Grey or Black-bellied Plover (*P. squatarola*) with circumpolar distribution; and, last, the New Zealand Dotterel (*P. obscurus*).

Each autumn the Eurasian Golden Plover and the Grey Plover fly south from their breeding grounds. The golden species is the more striking of the two. In its breeding plumage the male's crown, neck and upper parts are brilliant black, spotted with golden yellow. A white line starting above the eyes borders the face and throat and extends right along the flanks. Throat, breast, belly, bill and feet are black.

The breeding plumage of the Grey Plover is a duller, greyish black, with white or silver spots instead of golden ones. It breeds in high latitudes throughout the northern hemisphere. It is, however, one of the most strongly migratory of all birds and in winter is found on virtually every coast in the world.

Charadrius, a large genus of smaller and less colourful species than *Pluvialis*, includes the plovers, so called because they have a black collar on a pure white neck and front. They are also called

The American or Lesser Golden Plover (*Pluvialis dominica*) with its outline broken up by its bold black and white and gold plumage which blends into the background. It breeds in arctic North America and much of arctic Russia. In the Yenisei River area it overlaps slightly with the range of the Eurasian Golden Plover and apparently sometimes interbreeds with it.

The Banded Plover (*Vanellus tricolor*) near its nest. It is confined to Australia, particularly the south and west, and Tasmania. It frequents cultivated areas, swamps, edges of rivers and flood plains, feeding generally in small parties although sometimes large flocks of over 200 birds may build up before breeding.

sand larks or stone-runners, probably because of their preference for sandy or pebbly beaches. The Little Ringed Plover (*Charadrius dubius*) and the Kentish or Snowy Plover (*C. alexandrinus*) are no bigger than a lark. The Ringed Plover (*C. hiaticula*) is the size of a blackbird. Its breeding range covers northern Europe, including the British Isles, and the northernmost parts of Asia. That of the Little Ringed Plover lies further south and is overlapped by the range of the Kentish Plover which breeds on every continent and in America is known as the Snowy Plover. These plovers are active little birds, ceaselessly running about, uttering the little cries by which they probably maintain contact among themselves.

The North American Killdeer (*C. vociferus*) is similar to these in appearance and habits, but is somewhat larger and is graced with bright tawny orange patterns of the tail. Outside the breeding season it ranges south to Peru.

LAPWINGS: Crests, wattles and spurs distinguish the various lapwings (genus *Vanellus*) from the true plovers. Plumage of all species shares some common characteristics: white-tipped tail with black distal bar, and black primaries. They are rather aggressive, found regularly everywhere except North America where they have been known to stray on occasion.

Generically the word lapwing includes numerous species. In a more restricted use it refers to *the* Lapwing, sometimes called the Green Plover or Peewit (*Vanellus vanellus*), found throughout most of Europe and central Asia. This species lives in marshy plains, flat meadows and cultivated land, on the shores of ponds and lakes, and on the sea coast. Its migrations are local and scattered, some birds being sedentary, others migratory, irrespective of age. Breeding plumage consists of a mantle of coppery green with glossy tints of purple; cheeks, tail coverts and underparts are white, skullcap, throat and 'whiskers' a metallic black. It is a timid bird and the slightest disturbance puts it to flight.

At the onset of the breeding season the male Lapwing indulges in an aerial courtship display during which flight is punctuated with rapid ascents, turns and wheeling. It is a whirling, tossing, tumbling flight, with a loud intermittent drumming from the wings, a sound that can be heard some distance away. The nest is a depression in the ground made by the Peewit pivoting on its breast. Usually four pear-shaped eggs are laid, with their more sharply pointed ends directed to the centre of the nest. They are stone-coloured with dark blotches, harmonising with the ground on which they lie. Although afforded some protection by this natural camouflage, they are not difficult to find and the eggs are taken by other birds, notably by jackdaws, and by man in countries where plovers' eggs are considered a delicacy. The female may lay as many as five fresh clutches to replace lost eggs.

In Africa the lapwings are typically represented by the African Blacksmith Plover (*V. armatus*), and in Australia by the Banded Plover (*V. tricolor*).

The Egyptian Plover (*Pluvianus aegyptius*) has a disputed place in the family. Some authorities prefer to place it among the coursers. Equally controversial was its alleged habit of entering the open mouths of crocodiles. The bird may remove leeches from the crocodile's teeth and gums on occasion, but it has never been seen walking inside the mouth and only very rarely has been seen leaning near or within the jaw area. It makes a somewhat reciprocal gesture by uttering a ready cry at the approach of intruders, thereby alerting the crocodile.

OTHER GENERA: These include the Wrybill or Crooked-billed Plover of New Zealand, the turnstones and the Surfbird. The Wrybill (*Anarhynchus fontalis*) is a shore bird with a unique feature: a right-hand lateral twist to its beak. This is supposed to be an adaptation to its habit of seeking out insects and other invertebrates from under stones. A similar habit—though not the bill adaptation—is found in the two species of turnstone. The Black Turnstone (*Arenaria melanocephala*) breeds only in Alaska, and the Ruddy Turnstone (*A. interpres*), the commoner of the two, is a ground-nester in the Arctic tundra. Both species migrate south, the first as far as Cape Horn, the second even further, to Australia and New Zealand. The Surfbird (*Aphriza virgata*) also breeds in Alaska. Mottled grey and white, it has a black tail with a white band at the base. It feeds on small marine creatures along the coasts from Alaska to Chile where it has earned its common name by appearing to be quite at ease in the wild surf region.

Woodcocks, sandpipers, curlews (Family Scolopacidae)

The numerous species of these ground-dwelling waders form a heterogeneous group difficult to classify precisely. Although all have multi-coloured plumage (predominantly of chestnut and brown), the size and shape of their bills and their feet vary widely. Plumage is cryptic, so that individuals on the ground are difficult to see, whether on the seashore, in grass or among dead leaves. This is a family largely native to the northern hemisphere.

The European Woodcock (*Scolopax rusticola*), one of the best known of the Scolopacidae, can be recognised by its autumn-leaf tints and its long, straight, pointed beak. It has a preference for moist woodland, where all day long it searches for food among the leaf mould, only leaving in the evening to fly to marshy meadow or moor. The innumerable holes which it digs in dung to extract insect larvae suggest that it is particularly attracted to grazing land. It digs in mud too, slowly and circumspectly trampling the ground, seemingly to bring the grubs to the surface.

The nest is built in a rough hollow in the ground, deep in the woods. The clutch generally consists of four light brown eggs with reddish spots, incubated by the female alone, her mate being essentially polygamous and without paternal instinct. A wood where woodcocks nest can be identified during the breeding season by the males' regular evening courtship flight song, called 'roding'. In this they follow certain well-marked 'airlanes', until the females call with a soft whistle from the ground.

The species has wide distribution in the Arctic region of the Old World and in the higher regions of Indonesia. Some are resident in northern Europe, others are migratory in habit, leaving in November to return in March. In the United States there is a smaller, monotypic species, the American Woodcock (*Philohela minor*), which lives in alder slashes and other low vegetation. It makes a good game bird because it responds to any disturbance, sitting motionless and quiet until a hunter is upon it, then rising almost vertically with a noisy whistling flurry of its wings before levelling off in swift flight. The hunter must be quick to aim and fire, because the bird will quickly drop back into cover. It also performs a courtship flight similar to that of the European Woodcock.

Snipe are distinguished from woodcock by their more slender build, more delicate beaks, featherless legs, longitudinally striped plumage, and preference for more open terrain. There are several species, the most abundant being the Common Snipe (*Gallinago gallinago*), a form of which (formerly called Wilson's Snipe) is found in America. It is resident in North America, the British Isles and France. Its habits are similar to those of the woodcock.

Another Old World snipe, the European Jacksnipe (*Lymnocryptes minima*), is much smaller. This bird will usually sit until intruders are almost on top of it, as if it were deaf to the approaching steps.

The Short-billed Dowitcher (*Limnodromus griseus*) of North America is the only snipe of that country to be found on open shores. It can be readily identified by the white lower back, rump and tail, and by the straight snipe-like bill. In spring the underparts, especially on the breast, lose their light grey colour and become more rufous. The method of feeding is characteristic: the bird jabs its long bill vertically into the mud with rapid movements rather like the action of a sewing-machine needle.

SANDPIPERS: The true sandpipers, unlike the woodcock and snipe, are predominantly coastal rather than inland birds. The smaller species are known in Britain as stints. All breed in the high latitudes and all undertake long migrations. The most widely distributed species is the Dunlin (*Calidris alpina*), which can be recognised, in its summer plumage, by a black patch on the lower breast. It arrives in April and goes north again in November. The Little Stint (*C. minuta*) is a smaller version of the Dunlin, no bigger than a European Robin or American Bluebird. Temminck's Stint (*C. temminckii*) is even smaller, and the smallest of all is the Least Sandpiper or American Stint (*C. minutilla*) which American ornithologists used to place in the genus *Erolia*. The Knot (*C. canutus*), the largest of the sandpipers, is about the size of a European Song Thrush or American Robin.

The European Woodcock (*Scolopax rusticola*) showing how its plumage camouflages it against the woodland undergrowth. Both sexes have the same coloration. The Woodcock's bill is sensitive at the tip and slightly mobile, enabling it to find earthworms and insect larvae by touch, when probing for them in soft soil.

The closely related Old World species, the Ruff (*Philomachus pugnax*), owes its specific name to the male's beautiful breeding plumage which is set off by a 'ruff' or frill of long, erectile feathers. The colour of the plumage varies considerably from individual to individual, and may be any pattern of chestnut, white and black on a blue ground. Such an attire is unique among birds. The female, or reeve, lacks the long neck feathers or ruff. At the beginning of the breeding season the males assemble at a stamping ground, or lek, where they indulge in a great deal of display and mock fighting. The females select their mates from among the assembled males.

Also closely related are the sandpipers of the genus *Tringa*. They are most familiarly represented in Europe by the Redshank (*Tringa totanus*), a graceful, long red-legged species, markedly sociable. Slightly less common is the Spotted Redshank (*T. erythropus*), larger than the common Redshank and, in its summer plumage, spotted white on black, unlike any other wader. The Greenshank (*T. nebularia*), larger and greyer than the Redshank, has green legs and a long recurved bill. The Lesser Yellowlegs or Yellowshank (*T. flavipes*) of North America, smaller than the Redshank, has—as its common name suggests—bright yellow legs. It is distinguishable from the Greater Yellowlegs (*T. melanoleuca*) only by its smaller size and its call. Its summer plumage is black-brown mottled and spotted with white like that of the Wood Sandpiper (*T. glareola*), which breeds in northern Europe. The Green Sandpiper (*T. ochropus*), also of northern Europe, has green legs but in flight looks black with strongly contrasting white underside, rump and tail. The

The Green Sandpiper (*Tringa ochropus*) and Marsh Sandpiper (*T. stagnatilis*) wading in shallow water. The Marsh Sandpiper is the larger of the two and breeds in marshy areas across northern Europe and as far east as Mongolia and Manchuria. The Green Sandpiper is unique among Palearctic wading birds in nesting in wooded areas.

Common Sandpiper (*T. hypoleucos*) is smaller and frequents the banks of rivers and streams. It swims well, dives with ease and has a characteristic tail-bobbing action. The Common Sandpiper breeds in Eurasia while a similar species, the Spotted Sandpiper (*T. macularia*), breeds throughout North America. Both winter in the Southern Hemisphere. The male is strictly monogamous and participates in rearing of the chicks. There are two monotypic American genera, the Upland Sandpiper (*Bartramia longicauda*) and the Willet (*Catoptrophorus semipalmatus*). The four species of godwit (genus *Limosa*) and the Tattler (*Tringa incana*) are also closely related to the sandpipers.

CURLEWS: This survey of the Scolopacidae ends with the curlews, which are fairly large birds, averaging about the size of a Jackdaw, with long down-curved bills. They are birds of seashores and river banks, where their cry—an exact onomatopoeic rendering of their name—cannot pass unnoticed. Their plumage varies little, either at mating time or between young birds and adults.

Curlews of the genus *Numenius* are the largest representatives of the family. The Long-billed Curlew of North America (*N. americanus*) is the biggest with a length of sixty centimetres. Its Old World counterpart is the Curlew (*N. arquata*). A third species, the holarctic Whimbrel or Hudsonian Curlew (*N. phaeopus*) shares with the rest of the genus the pattern of high latitude breeding and long migrations. The extent of some of the migrations is best illustrated by that of the Bristle-thighed Curlew (*N. tahitiensis*), which breeds in the mountains of Alaska and winters in the islands of Polynesia. The nearly extinct Eskimo Curlew (*N. borealis*) of North America was brought to its present low ebb by hunting pressure during its migration through the United States and Canada.

Stilts and avocets (Family Recurvirostridae)

Although two groups are included in this single family, only the avocets have a recurved or uptilted bill. There are four genera in this cosmopolitan family of long-legged waders. Black and white plumage patterns are common to all four and there is little sexual dimorphism.

The Common or Black-winged Stilt (*Himantopus himantopus*) is resident in southern Europe, Africa and Asia. It occasionally wanders farther north, even reaching into the British Isles. This monotypic species is easily recognised by its black and white colouring, long pink legs, very long, pointed bill and pointed wings longer than the body (like those of a Swallow). The stilt is equally at home in sea water or freshwater. In flight it looks like a miniature stork. Races and similar species are found in Asia, Africa, America, Australia and New Zealand.

The Banded Stilt (*Cladorhynchus leucocephalus*) is an Australian monotypic species. The Ibis-bill (*Ibidorhyncha struthersii*) is a central Asian species with an uncharacteristic down-curved beak.

The Eurasian Avocet (*Recurvirostra avosetta*) is black and white too, but its legs are shorter than those of the stilt and its beak is typically recurved. It sweeps shallow waters with side-to-side movements of its beak to sweep up many different kinds of small invertebrates.

The American Avocet (*R. americana*), the Chilean Avocet (*R. andina*) and the Australian Avocet

(*R. novaehollandiae*) have brown touches in both their head and neck plumage.

Phalaropes (Family Phalaropidae)

The three phalaropes are similar: all are swimmers rather than waders, usually preferring freshwater to salt only during the breeding seasons. All have lobe-webbed feet, like the coot. They rarely venture on land except to nest and feed. The male is smaller than the female, and has less resplendent plumage. Sexual roles are reversed, with the female doing the courting and the male incubating the eggs and caring for the young. Distribution is holarctic.

The Grey Phalarope (*Phalaropus fulicarius*)—called the Red Phalarope in North America—is a circumpolar breeder. The Red-necked or Northern Phalarope (*P. lobatus*) nests in subarctic tundra regions. Wilson's Phalarope (*P. tricolor*) belongs to the prairies of Canada and the United States. Even outside the breeding season it prefers a freshwater habitat; the other two species feed off plankton at sea. All three species habitually undertake long migrations to winter in the seas, principally of the southern hemisphere.

Crab-plover (Family Dromadidae)

The noisy Crab-plover (*Dromas ardeola*), which lives on the coasts of East Africa and the northern and western shores of the Indian Ocean, is the sole member of the family. It is large, with mainly white plumage (primaries and back are black), long greenish-blue legs and a bill like that of a tern. It feeds mainly on crabs, swallowed whole if small enough. Its haunts are coral reefs exposed at low tide, but it nests colonially in the sandy banks on the shore, tunnelling in 120 to 150 centimetres to a nesting chamber. The clutch consists of a single pure white egg, and the chick is mottled grey and white. The Crab-plover is a flock-feeder, and they will try to protect an injured bird.

Stone-curlews or thick-knees (Family Burhinidae)

The several species of this family share a common physical trait: swollen heels. The type bird is the Stone-curlew or Thick-knee (*Burhinus oedicnemus*), which has a wide breeding range that includes western Europe and parts of Asia and Africa. Plumage is reddish brown with black spots. The beak is shorter than the head and, since it is a nocturnal bird, its eyes are large. Its hind toe is atrophied, as in many other terrestrial species. It has a harsh cry, somewhat like that of the Curlew, but not so melodious. Usually solitary, the Stone-curlew readily takes wing when approached. It feeds on insects, worms, snails, lizards and voles, and occasionally it attacks other birds. It nests, as its common name suggests, on bare stony ground. Other species are found in Africa, southern Asia, Australia and South America.

Pratincoles and coursers (Family Glareolidae)

The pratincoles are a subfamily of brownish shore birds with long wings and an easy flight that often leads to wrong identification as terns. They are, however, waders and not swimmers. Their common names, sea-partridge and sea-swallow, demonstrate the unreliability of observers. Pratincoles hunt on the wing, skimming across the grass to catch dragonflies and grasshoppers, and rising into the air to survey their hunting grounds. In South Africa they are known as locust birds. Their true domain is the sky, where they circle tirelessly. The Common Pratincole (*Glareola pratincola*) ranges mainly over southern Europe, Africa, and southern Asia and occasionally wanders farther north.

The coursers are a subfamily of long-legged, terrestrial birds that live in arid or semi-arid regions and generally lack the hallux or hind toe. They are insectivorous, like the related pratincoles. Plumage is cryptic. The colouring of the Cream-coloured Courser (*Cursorius cursor*) of Africa, for example, is a perfect camouflage in the sandy and desert-like terrain which is its favourite habitat. The male and female of this species run with incredible speed, about fifteen paces apart. Its commonest nickname is 'Desert Runner'. It also flies well and takes advantage of this to range from district to district. It is sometimes found on the sand dunes of southern France and other European coasts as well as south-west Asia.

Seedsnipe (Family Thinocoridae)

This family of short-legged little shore birds includes only four species, all confined to South America. Plump, with short bills and pointed wings, seedsnipes live on stony ground at all altitudes, feeding on buds and seeds.

Sheathbills (Family Chionididae)

The two species of sheathbill (*Chionis alba* and *C. minor*) are primarily terrestrial in habit, though they fly and swim fairly well considering the small size of the wings and the unwebbed feet. They are confined to Antarctic and subantarctic shores, and

The Black-winged Stilt (*Himantopus himantopus*) has a worldwide distribution with five distinct subspecies being recognised. Its extraordinary long legs enable it to feed in fairly deep water where it picks water bugs and insects off the surface. On dry land, however, its long legs sometimes compel it to bend its knees when feeding.

Yellow-billed Sheathbills (*Chionis alba*) with a group of Chinstrap Penguins (*Pygoscelis antarctica*). These Sheathbills breed on islands in the north-west of Antarctica. They build their nests in crevices in the rocks around colonies of Adélies and Chinstraps.

The Stone-curlew (*Burhinus oedicnemus*) at its nest. In Europe its numbers have been considerably reduced owing to changes in its habitat induced by agriculture. Each pair of birds needs a fairly large, isolated breeding territory well away from human disturbance.

The Great Skua (*Stercorarius skua*) is unique in that races breed in the north, mainly on Iceland, the Faeroes and Scottish islands, and in the south, around the coasts of Antarctica, subantarctic islands and southern South America. The skuas are fish eaters which have also taken to piracy.

are the only bird without webbed feet to be found in southern seas. Plumage is unbroken white, and the bill has a horny case. They feed on eggs and chicks of sea birds, seaweed, molluscs and small crustaceans.

Skuas and jaegers (Family Stercorariidae)

Their strongly hooked bills distinguish the four species of the family from the closely related gulls and terns. Outside the breeding season they are solitary and oceanic. During this period they probably eat mainly fish which they catch for themselves or steal from other birds. During the summer they prey on small birds and mammals and also eat carrion. There has been much misunderstanding of the feeding habits of skuas in the past.

The commonest species, the Arctic Skua or, in America, the Parasitic Jaeger (*Stercorarius parasiticus*), is a pirate that will suddenly appear in the middle of a flock of terns and harass them until they disgorge. The species is found on coasts and islands throughout the Arctic.

The Great Skua (*S. skua*), sixty centimetres long, is found in both polar regions, off Scotland, the Faroes and Iceland, and most abundantly, in the Antarctic and subantarctic regions, where it preys on the penguins' eggs and chicks. This is the species known simply as the Skua in North America.

Two other species are the Pomarine Skua (*Stercorarius pomarinus*), known in America as the Pomarine Jaeger, and the Long-tailed Skua or Jäeger (*S. longicaudus*), both of the northern hemisphere.

Gulls and terns (Family Laridae)

Like the plovers and curlews these web-footed hook-billed or pointed-billed birds have green, speckled eggs and more or less nidifugous chicks similarly speckled. Their flight is superbly effortless. In a stiff breeze they make economic use of their long, supple wings. A few slow measured beats and wings become rigid again and the birds soar and glide almost at will, maintaining height by using the force of the winds.

Gulls swim well but they never dive. They are rarely found far out at sea. Many come inland, where they walk without difficulty in a hurried gait. Sometimes they rob the nests of other birds. Distribution of more than forty species is cosmopolitan, with a marked concentration in the northern hemisphere.

Gulls live in noisy colonies even during the breeding season, when they nest side by side on ledges or in hollows in rock or sand dunes. Two to three heavily spotted brownish eggs are laid in a seaweed nest. The chicks are only semi-altricial. They are fed by their parents until, at five or six weeks, they are strong enough to fly and fend for themselves. Adult plumage, which in some species may take three years to acquire, is typically white with grey or dark wing and back variations between species.

There are more than a dozen species of European and American gulls. The commonest are the white-headed gulls which include the Herring Gull (*Larus argentatus*), the Lesser Black-backed Gull (*L. fuscus*), and in Europe only, the Common or Mew

A mixed flock of gulls following a fishing boat in the North Sea. Although their main food is fish, many European gulls come inland each day during the winter months, feeding on waste food on rubbish dumps around the towns or searching for insects on playing-fields and farmland.

The Arctic Tern (*Sterna paradisaea*) in flight. It breeds in the Arctic and then crosses the equator to spend the southern summer in the Antarctic, a migration of some 17,500 kilometres. By making this long migration the Arctic Tern enjoys continuous summer for eight months of the year

The Black Skimmer (*Rynchops nigra*) skimming along the surface of the water hunting for small fishes swimming just below the surface. It is the largest of the skimmers, about fifty centimetres long. The plumage is distinctively black and white with orange legs and a bright red bill. Although skimmers are related to gulls and terns they do not form such tightly-packed breeding colonies but come together loosely as pairs.

Gull (*L. canus*). Other gulls found only in America include the California Gull (*L. californicus*) and the Ringbilled Gull (*L. delawarensis*). There are also the hooded and masked gulls, so-called because they acquire dark-coloured heads in the mating season; among them are the Black-headed Gull (*L. ridibundus*), the Laughing Gull (*L. atricilla*), the Red-billed or Silver Gull (*L. novaehollandiae*) of Australia and the Mediterranean Gull (*L. melanocephalus*).

The Black-headed Gull (*L. ridibundus*), about thirty-eight centimetres long, is a small gull. In the spring it assumes a hood of black feathers. The Common or Mew Gull (*L. canus*), which can be used as the type bird, has an ashen-grey back and white front and lower parts. The tail is rounded when spread, whereas in other species it is very slightly forked. The bill is generally shorter than the head, but strong and hooked at the tip. Both sexes are exactly identical.

The two extremes in size are found in the Great Black-backed Gull (*L. marinus*) and the Little Gull (*L. minutus*), which are about the size of a small Golden Eagle and a Domestic Pigeon respectively. There are two exceptional types: the Kittiwake (*Rissa tridactyla*), in which the hind toe is atrophied, and Sabine's Gull (*Xema sabini*), which has a forked tail.

Most gulls are sedentary round the northern European coasts, but their numbers are increased in winter by migrants from the north. Through ringing, the migration routes of some, such as the Black-headed Gull, are well known. We know, for example, that in Europe the gulls of north Germany and Denmark mostly migrate to Gibraltar and Morocco following the coasts of Holland, Belgium, France and Spain. The gulls of central Europe separate strangely and inexplicably: some head straight for the south-east to reach the Adriatic and continue via Italy, Sicily and Tunisia, while the rest, for no clear reason, first fly north to the Baltic and then take one of the routes taken by the gulls of Denmark and northern Germany.

Terns (sometimes called sea-swallows for their forked tails) are markedly different from gulls, though general colouring patterns are similar. They are slightly smaller. Their bills are pointed, not hooked; their pointed wings are very long and narrow; and their legs are very short. They seldom alight on water and walk with dificulty on land. Small feet make them poor swimmers, but they are tireless, wonderful flyers, skimming the surface of the waves, seizing prey from the water as they pass, or soaring high, cleaving the air like arrows. In a flash they will dive headlong towards the sea, stopping just short of the surface to inspect the water, then wheeling and climbing again to repeat the manoeuvre. Some species settle on the surface to feed, others make a noisy dive below surface to catch their prey. The gregarious terns are ground-nesters, laying two or three eggs in an unlined scrape or among small heaps of plant stems.

Three groups make up the subfamily: the black-capped terns, the noddies and the monotypic Inca Tern (*Larosterna inca*) of South America.

Possibly the most widely distributed is the Common Tern (*Sterna hirundo*), which has a white body, a light grey mantle, a black cap, red bill and red feet. Its shrill incessant cry is easily identifiable. The Little or Least Tern (*S. albifrons*), almost cosmopolitan, is the smallest. It is scarcely larger than a Swift but no bird is more active. Its bill and legs are yellow and it has a white patch on its forehead. Otherwise its habits are those of other terns, as are those of the inland nesting Black Tern (*Chlidonias nigra*) which used to breed in parts of England, but now does so only occasionally. It breeds fairly commonly in eastern North America.

The noddies are tropical species, of which the dark-plumed Common Noddy or, in America, the Noddy Tern (*Anous stolidus*) is the commonest, and the white Fairy Tern (*Gygis alba*) the smallest.

Skimmers (Family Rynchopidae)

This is principally a tropical family of three species, larger than the terns but smaller than the gulls. There is the African Skimmer (*Rynchops flavirostris*), the Indian Skimmer (*R. albicollis*), and the Black Skimmer (*R. nigra*) of America. The main peculiarity of the adult birds is a lower mandible much longer than the upper which is flattened laterally to almost knife-blade thinness at the tip. Skimmers fish in the estuaries, mainly in the evening and at night, flying close to the water—as the common name suggests—with the lower mandible dipped below the surface to flip fishes into the mouth, and the short upper mandible ready to close on them. By day they roost by open beaches, lakes and rivers, their vertical slit pupils protecting the eyes from the sun's glare. The American species is confined to coastland and the shore itself.

Auks, guillemots, puffins (Family Alcidae)

The Alcidae are the northern counterparts of the southern hemisphere's penguins. These short-winged birds of northern seas have several features reminiscent of grebes and superficially resemble the penguins: legs at the back of the body, short wings, indifferent flight and great skill at swimming and diving. They use wings rather than feet to propel them while swimming underwater. On land they stand upright and walk rather quickly. Flightlessness accompanies simultaneous moulting of the flight feathers in most species. As in the gulls, black, white and grey are the predominant colours.

The northern seas would be depressingly bare if their great wealth of fishes and plankton did not support huge colonies of terns, gulls, kittiwakes, fulmars, gannets, razorbills, guillemots and puffins in hundreds and thousands on rocky islets. At a distance a vague murmur tells of their presence and at closer quarters it becomes a deafening uproar of raucous, strident cries from clouds of birds wheeling round the cliffs.

The Little Auk or Dovekie (*Plautus alle*) is a bird with black upper parts, white underparts, and a very short beak. It feeds on plankton which it scoops up from the water as it swims along, beak open. It seldom goes on land except in the breeding season. Its main breeding-grounds are in Greenland and Spitzbergen.

The Guillemot or Common Murre (*Uria aalge*) also has a black back and white belly, but its bill is longer than that of the auks. Though it has bred in Europe as far south as France and Spain, it is essentially an inhabitant of arctic waters. Immense breeding colonies are found in Iceland, the Faroes, Greenland and Labrador. The birds nest on every possible ledge of the cliffs, sitting with their black backs towards the sea. At the slightest noise all turn around, as if to plan, showing their contrasting white front.

Only one egg is laid and both parents share the incubation. When newly hatched, the chick is a little ball of black down quite incapable of looking after itself. It is fed by its parents and flies down to the sea before its wing feathers have fully grown. It then swims out to sea accompanied by its parents.

The Common Puffin (*Fratercula arctica*) has a parrot-like bill laterally compressed, slate-grey at the base and ornamented during the breeding season with vivid red, yellow and black plates. The button-like eyes are red and white and the hood is black. Although its gait is clownish, the Puffin is a good, strong flyer and walks well. But it is at swimming and diving that it excels. In the rookeries of northern Europe the puffins inhabit burrows in which they lay and hatch their single egg. The mouths of these burrows are so close together that the nesting area looks like a honeycomb.

There is a certain similarity in attitude and habit between the Razorbill or Razor-billed Auk (*Alca torda*) of the Arctic and the unrelated penguins of the southern hemisphere. On land, both stand erect on short legs which are placed well back on the body. The gait of both is clumsy and in quick retreat turns rapidly to a slide or crawl. Both swim with consummate ease and are skilled divers, being able to remain submerged up to two minutes and to penetrate ten metres deep, propelling themselves with their wings. Such similarities illustrate common adaptations to environment in unrelated birds.

The Razorbill also has a highly developed social instinct. It normally lives in flocks, and during the breeding season gathers in thousands on cliffs and islets. Its food is mainly fishes, supplemented by aquatic animals. The Razorbill is found all over the North Atlantic and the Arctic Ocean during the summer. In Europe it breeds as far south as Brittany and the Channel Isles. In winter it goes even farther south and has been seen on the shores of the Mediterranean. In North America it seldom breeds south of Canadian shores but usually large flocks can be seen wintering off Long Island. Head

The Razorbill (*Alca torda*), a sea-going auk related to puffins and guillemots. Like the puffin its bill is deep and laterally compressed. In adults the bill is marked by a white line which extends on both sides back to the eye. More than any other auk the Razorbill most nearly resembles the extinct Great Auk.

The Rhinoceros Auklet (*Cerorhinca monocerata*), the largest of the auklets, has a curious short horn projecting upwards from the base of the upper mandible. It is also distinguished by a pair of white plumes on each side of the head, one from above the eye, the other from the corner of the mouth.

and upperparts are black, breast and belly white. The bill is laterally compressed, arched and marked with a prominent white stripe on each side in winter. The cry is low and distinctly raucous.

The Razorbills' courtship is rather grotesque. Male and females rub bills and nibble each other's head and neck, or sit with bills held vertical, rattling their mandibles like castanets. The couples select nesting places on a ledge of rock or in an old burrow or a mere depression in the ground. The female then lays one large brown, pear-shaped egg, six by five centimetres, which both birds take turns to sit on. When hatched, the chick is a mere ball of black down. The parent birds bring it fishes until, at about three weeks, the young bird is strong enough to dive into the sea from its tall cliff.

Although numerous murrelets and auklets throng the northern coasts the ill-fated Great Auk (*Plautus impennis*), was a common, flightless member of the Alcidae until the middle of the century when hunting brought extinction.

Sandgrouse and pigeons (Order Columbiformes)

The columbiform birds, which once included the extinct dodos and solitaires, are mostly of moderate size, the largest being as big as a Swan, but most are about the size of the Wood-pigeon and Stock Dove. The thick-set body is carried on short legs, giving a slow and rather clumsy gait. Long, pointed wings give rapid and sustained flight. The head is small and the neck rather short. Pigeons and doves also have a characteristic bill structure; the basal part is covered with soft skin, and the terminal part is horny. The nostrils open through longitudinal slits in the soft part of the beak. Three toes on each foot are directed forwards; the fourth points backwards. All four toes are set at the same level. The males have no spurs and the claws are short and straight.

A Puffin (*Fratercula arctica*) with food for its young. Puffins feed mainly on sand eels.

Their food is almost entirely seeds and fruit, but unlike other grain-eating birds they have very short rectal caeca which is quite unusual.

The sexes are similar in appearance and, though tending to live in groups columbiform birds are monogamous, the males taking part in nest building and in brooding and caring for the chicks, which are quite helpless when hatched and are fed on 'pigeon's milk' formed in the crop of the adult. The birds of this order produce few eggs, usually two in pigeons and doves, and three in the sandgrouse.

Sandgrouse (Family Pteroclidae)

This family includes about sixteen species which differ from the pigeons in some respects: the newly hatched young are covered with down and they leave the nest soon after hatching. But like pigeon nestlings the young are fed with a milky substance from the adult's crop. The wings are long and pointed, and the first digit on the foot is missing. These birds inhabit desert and steppe, and their plumage is cryptically coloured to blend with the ground on which they spend most of their life. Those living on sand are fawn-coloured, and those from the steppes are striped. When motionless they are almost invisible. The nest is built on the ground at the foot of a bush, or simply hollowed out in the sand. The adults bring water to their chicks by soaking their breast feathers.

The Pin-tailed or White-bellied Sandgrouse (*Pterocles alchata*) is the only species resident in Europe, but it also ranges into Asia as far east as India, and southwards into northern Africa. It breeds regularly in France, Spain and Portugal.

Pallas's Sandgrouse (*Syrrhaptes paradoxus*), a species that looks rather like a turtle-dove, but with wings much longer than the tail, is found from south-east Russia to Mongolia, but occasionally migrates to Europe, sometimes in large numbers.

The extinct dodos and solitaires of the family Raphidae also formed part of the Columbiformes.

Pigeons and doves (Family Columbidae)

Pigeons proper are thick-set and have a relatively small head, the front of which bulges forward over the bill. The bill is somewhat constricted in the middle and membranous at the base. Only the upper parts of the legs are feathered, and the feet are usually quite bare. When folded, the wings border the tail, which may be rounded or straight at the tip.

Distribution is world-wide in tropical and temperate zones, with the greatest number of species in the Far East and Australasia. Apart from certain tropical species, they feed on grain and seeds, which are swallowed whole. Unlike other birds they do not sip when drinking but take long draughts.

The wild variety of the Domestic Pigeon is known as the Rock Dove (*Columba livia*). Whether wild or domesticated pigeons have definite social habits. They move about in flocks during the day and roost together at night. Fighting seldom occurs during the breeding season and when it does it is more of a mock combat. These birds also have regular habits. They begin the morning with a chorus of calls. Then the flock sets out to feed and drink, returning to their perching place, where they stay during the hottest part of the day. In the afternoon they again go off to feed and drink, and finally retire at night to the cover of trees or rocks. Such regular habits make them adapt to captivity.

Courtship takes place during the spring and summer, and in Europe breeding continues from April to late autumn. During courtship the males coo loudly, display before the females, and indulge in display flights. They are monogamous and tend to mate for life, a feature remarkable in birds so strongly gregarious.

For about five or six months before it is fully adult, the cooings of the male have a dull and melancholy sound, these having replaced the feeble and rather nasal calls of the adolescent. The cooings eventually take on a richer quality when the bird is mated. When displaying to the female a sort of bubbling sound seems to come from its crop. At a more advanced stage of courtship the display movements seem more like a bowing to the female and the cooing sounds almost like speech. During the display the female bows her head and points her beak downwards in response to similar movements by the male, which without stopping its song nuzzles her with its beak. When the female submits she crouches by the side of her mate.

A pair of courting pigeons may be silent for hours on end, while one of the pair, usually the male but sometimes the female, gently runs its beak through the head feathers of its mate. Similarly, the intertwining of the beak mandibles is clearly an important part of the courtship displays. At this stage the male regurgitates some of the 'milk', which is swallowed by the female. It was once thought that some of the hormones contained in this secretion stimulated the sex glands of the female and brought her into a comparable breeding condition.

These displays go on for several days and are followed by nest building, in which the male once more plays the leading part. He chooses the nesting site in a tree or gap in the rocks and gathers twigs, roots and other materials, which are then set in place by the female. The nest is a crudely constructed, openwork platform. Although it seems an unlikely structure to withstand wind and rain, it is in fact quite robust.

There are two eggs in each clutch, elliptical in profile and pure white, with a faint bluish tinge. They are brooded by the male and female in turn, but neither seems particularly attached to them. If driven off the nest they may abandon the eggs.

Incubation begins as soon as the second egg is laid and lasts an average of seventeen days. There is an interval of one or two days between the hatching of the two chicks. They are born practically naked, blind and helpless. They are first fed with the 'milk' from the crop, and then with softened seeds and grain. The parents keep them as warm as possible until, after about ten days, their feathers begin to grow. In less than a month the young pigeons can fend for themselves, but they stay on in the nest a little longer with their parents.

The above description of habits and life history are specifically those of the Domestic Pigeon, but in general may be applied to most species of pigeons or doves except for details such as times of breeding and so forth. Many species in the temperate regions are at least partially migratory though the Domestic Pigeon is sedentary.

The Wood-pigeon or Ring-dove (*Columba palumbus*) is the largest of the European pigeons, with a maximum length of nearly forty-five centimetres. The general colour of the plumage is greyish. The breast is wine-red with a metallic sheen, and there are patches of white on the wings and the sides of the neck. Those on the neck form a ring or collar (whence 'Ring-dove'). This species is found throughout Europe and migrates from the northerly parts to winter in northern Africa. It also occurs in western and central Asia. It is called the Wood-pigeon because in the wild state it lives and nests in wooded areas, descending to the ground only to feed.

The Stock Dove (*C. oenas*) is a smaller bird, about thirty cenimetres long. It is bluer than the Wood-pigeon and has no white patches on neck and wings, though the latter have black markings. The two species have much the same habitat and habits. The Stock Dove is found in Europe, North Africa, and western Asia, and is fairly common throughout the British Isles.

The Rock Dove (*C. livia*), the source of domestic breeds, is about the same size as the Stock Dove, but is more varied in colour. The lower part of the back is white or pale grey, there are two black bars across the wings, and the tip of the tail is black. It nests on cliffs on the coast or in mountainous regions and is found in Europe, India, western and central Asia, and northern and western Africa.

Feral pigeons, that is birds descended from domesticated pigeons that have to some extent reverted to the wild state can be seen in many towns, particularly in public squares, as the Europeans have carried them wherever they have gone.

DOMESTIC PIGEONS: Darwin was very interested in evidence that domestic pigeons furnished in sup-

The Wood Pigeon or Ring Dove (*Columba palumbus*) usually only lays two white eggs, but the breeding season is long and several broods may be raised. The unfledged nestling, known as a squab, is fed with pigeon's milk, a curd-like substance produced from the parent's crop.

The Collared Dove (*Streptopelia decaocto*) originated in Asia but since the 18th Century has been steadily spreading across Asia and into Europe. reaching Britain in 1955, and since then spreading as far as the Outer Hebrides and Iceland. In Britain the population built up to a phenomenal 19,000 birds by 1964. The spread results from the dove's association with man, feeding on grain put down for poultry or spilt in railway sidings.

port of his famous theory of evolution. He showed that the races were derived from the Rock Dove by artificial selection of natural variations or of those appearing from breeding. Their common origin was shown by the ease with which the races bred, not only among themselves but also with the wild Rock Dove. That the crosses were fertile, and that the races also showed some tendency to revert to ancestral type, particularly in the characteristic black bands on the wings that are found in the wild Rock Dove, added further support to his theory. In addition, it was unlikely that the various races had come from distinct wild stocks and that the Rock Dove could be the only survivor.

The domestic races differ among themselves and from the Rock Dove in certain features of form, plumage, bill and behaviour.

The Roman pigeons are one of the races closest to the ancestral stock. With a maximum length of nearly fifty centimetres and a wingspan of over a metre, they are the largest of the domestic pigeons and are readily identifiable by the red ring circling the eyes. They are slow breeders and, because they are rather heavy and clumsy, fall a ready prey to cats and raptorial birds.

The tumblers are not a pure race, but a mixture of breeds, with one curious mode of behaviour in common: all are able to turn backward somersaults in flight and on the ground. Such acrobatic behaviour may well be attributable to some deformation of the semicircular canals in the ear or of the cerebellum, the centre for the co-ordination of such movements.

The Jacobin pigeons have a distinctive form of plumage, the feathers of head and neck turn forward in the form of a hood. The necktie pigeons have a tuft of feathers at the base of the bill and their cooing resembles drum beats.

Fantail pigeons have a large tail consisting of as many as forty-two feathers. It can be raised and spread like a fan. At the same time the head is bent backwards until it touches the fan.

Pouter pigeons, particularly the males, have a very large gullet which they can inflate with air. When they do this the head is almost completely lost behind the great swelling of the breast, and in this position they strut about, their long wings and tail trailing the ground. This is a difficult breed to rear since the special structure of the gullet makes it impossible to feed the young on 'milk' regurgitated from the crop.

CARRIER-PIGEONS: These do not constitute an independent race, but are more an assemblage of breeds obtained by various crosses and have little in common except a highly developed sense of direction, which enables them to return unerringly to the nests.

A carrier-pigeon usually flies at somewhere between 180 and 300 metres depending on atmospheric conditions, though in a head wind it may fly close to the ground. Speed varies, but is usually between fifty and 100 kilometres an hour. A fully trained carrier-pigeon taken to a point up to several hundred kilometres from its loft will fly home in a direct line in the shortest possible time. A successful homing flight can be made even on a moonless night. Wind, rain or fog may slow the bird but will not stop it. There is a record of a carrier-pigeon that flew from Ution to its original home in New York City (about 500 kilometres away) after being kept in captivity for two years.

The way in which pigeons and other birds navigate over long distance is not fully understood. Experiments indicate that birds can orientate and fly on a compass course by reference to the position of the sun and stars. It can also calculate its geographical location by reference to the height and movement of celestial bodies and, by comparing these with the equivalent data for its destination, lay off a course for home. This is essentially how a human navigator operates. Recent experiments have shown that some birds can orientate with a magnetic sense by reference to the earth's magnetic field.

Over short distances carrier-pigeons learn to recognise local landmarks and so improve with training. One can only speculate that something similar occurs when birds migrating over long distances year by year return to precisely the same spot to nest, as when a swallow not only arrives at the same stable door in spring but perches nearby waiting for the door to be opened for it to enter.

The whole process of bird navigation is remarkable enough but hardly more so than the feat of memory implied by the behaviour of such birds as swallows.

The Passenger Pigeon (*Ectopistes migratorius*) is now extinct, but was once very numerous. The famous naturalist Audubon relates that flights of these migrating birds used to darken the sky for hours and make a sound like the distant rumbling of thunder. There were millions of individuals. Entire forests were spoiled by their droppings, and the branches of trees were broken as the birds moved among them. While it is true that the pigeon was slaughtered in vast numbers, the survivors appear to have been wiped out in the wild by an epidemic almost within a single year. The species became totally extinct in 1914 with the death of the last known individual in the Cincinnati Zoo.

The Turtle-dove (*Streptopelia turtur*) breeds in the more southerly parts of Europe and also in western Asia and North Africa. In the British Isles it is commonest in southern and eastern England, where the first pairs appear towards the end of April or in May, and are in the habit of nesting on the verges of woods, in bushes and hedges.

This bird is the smallest European member of the family Columbidae. It is also more slender in form and more graceful in appearance than the pigeons, and has a smaller head and longer neck. The bill is straight and slender, and the plumage tends towards a brownish red. On the sides of the neck are three or four black bands on a white background. The remiges and contour feathers of the wings are dark brown with a reddish border. It is attractive in appearance and in its gentle habits.

In September the Turtle-dove leaves Europe for its winter quarters in Africa, returning the following year. If taken when young, turtle-doves soon get used to captivity in aviaries and become remarkably tame. Another species known as the Collared Turtle-dove (*S. decaocto*)) is even more readily tamed it is almost pure cream in colour, with a black collar.

While the turtle-doves, like most pigeons, are tree-dwellers, the ground-doves and the bronze-wings are more terrestrial in habit, and form a transition between the columbiform and gallinaceous birds. They spend most of the time on the ground searching for seed, and sometimes even nest on the ground. The small, sparrow-like Ground Dove (*Columbina passerina*) is peculiar to the Americas. The several genera of pigeons known as bronze-wings are native to Australia.

Closer still in appearance to the gallinaceous birds, the Nicobar Pigeon (*Caleonas nicobarica*) is almost entirely greenish-bronze in colour and is one of the most beautiful birds of the south-east Asian forests, particularly of the Nicobar Islands and New Guinea.

MORE BIZARRE MEMBERS OF THE FAMILY: These include the parrot pigeons, the crowned pigeons, and the Tooth-billed Pigeon. A species of the first group, *Treron abyssinica*, is a pigeon with a heavy, squat body, short wings and tail, and legs almost entirely covered with feathers. The tip of the bill is expanded to form a solid, pincer-like arrangement. The plumage is predominantly green with a brilliant metallic sheen. The name given to them in Africa, parrot pigeons, is rather apt for, like the parrots, they take up curious positions when climbing branches, feed on fruit and nest in holes in trees. There are many species in the genus.

The three crowned pigeons (*Coura* spp.), which occur in New Guinea, are quite different. They are essentially terrestrial in habit, wandering in forests in small groups and gathering up seeds and fruits fallen from the trees. A conspicuous feature is the fanlike crest of feathers on the head, which can be erected or lowered at will. They are large, up to eighty-three centimetres long.

To conclude this survey of the Columbiformes, some mention must be made of the Manumea or Tooth-billed Pigeon (*Didunculus strigirostris*), an almost extinct native of the islands of Samoa. It is about the same size as a Domestic Pigeon and the plumage is a dark shining green. This bird is terrestrial in habit and feeds on roots and bulbs.

Gregarious and brightly coloured, macaws are the largest members of the parrot family, up to a metre long, including the long tail. They live in the tropical forests of South America. This group of Scarlet Macaws (*Ara macao*) and Red-and-green Macaws (*A. chloroptera*) shows up their bright colours, long tails and massive beaks characteristic of the genus.

Parrots and parakeets (Order Psittaciformes; Family Psittacidae)

This distinctive family Psittacidae includes parrots, cockatoos, macaws and lories. All show a high degree of specialisation to arboreal life, using both beak and feet to climb. The feet also serve as 'hands' to husk and hold seeds. These two habits distinguish them from all other birds. Another characteristic is the bill, the two mandibles of which are curved and opposed, so that the lower fits into the larger upper one when the beak is closed. One curious character of the group is that the upper mandible usually articulates (with a movable joint) on the cranium. Being essentially fruit- and seed-eating birds, they have well-developed crops, in which the food is stored before entering the stomach. Lastly, plumage is nearly always very brightly coloured. Green is the predominant colour, and red, yellow and violet are quite common and can occur in the same individual.

Distribution is world wide through the tropics, with the main concentrations in Australasia and South America. The tropical forests in which they live gregariously are brightened with their gay colours and resound with the incessant clamour of their chattering, shrieking calls. In the morning and evening they set out in great flocks to plantations of fruit trees, which are soon despoiled by their raids. During these excursions they prove to be both cautious and wily, displaying remarkable intelligence.

Although parrots never live alone, but move about tropical forests in noisy groups, they are strictly monogamous. In most species the male and female build the nest in a hollow tree, where the young are fed until they are able to fend for themselves.

Longevity is quite common. Some individuals may live to an age of seventy to eighty years, at least in captivity.

The classification of the various members of the order presents certain difficulties. It is sufficient

The Philippine or Red-vented Cockatoo (*Cacatua haematuropygia*), of the Philippines, is only one of numerous kinds of birds of the parrot family found in the Australasian region and the East Indian islands. The name is from the Malay *Kakatua*, which was adopted by the Dutch traders. Its English spelling is influenced by the word 'cock', although this has no relevance.

here to point out the distinction between the typical parrots, the kaka, kea, kakapo, lories and lorikeets, pygmy parrots and cockatoos.

The typical parrots include the macaws, the amazons, parakeets, lovebirds, budgerigars and conures. One of the best known is the African Grey Parrot (*Psittacus erithacus*) particularly prized for its highly developed powers of mimicry.

Almost as well known are the colourful macaws of the New World, strikingly coloured, long-tailed birds with bare cheek patches. Native to the tropical rainforests of Central and South America, they are most commonly represented by the metre long Scarlet Macaw (*Ara macao*), the slightly smaller Blue and Yellow Macaw (*A. ararauna*) and the turquoise Military Macaw (*A. militaris*).

The numerous species of amazons constitute another familiar South American genus. Commonest and most widespread is the large green Mealy Parrot (*Amazona farinosa*). The best talker is the Yellow-headed Amazon (*A. ochrocephala*). A third New World group are the conures, which are smaller than the amazons.

The cockatoos are quickly recognised by the crest of erectile feathers on the head. They are fairly large birds and are generally light-coloured. The most widespread species, the Sulphur-crested Cockatoo (*Cacatua galerita*), is completely white except for its crest of long yellow feathers. Cockatoos are found in Australia, Tasmania, New Guinea, the Philippines and neighbouring islands. Being easily domesticated and trained, they are popular as pets for the home or the aviaries of public zoos.

Small-tongued parrots are represented by a single black-coloured species found in Australia and New Guinea, where its native name is *kasmalos*. Like the cockatoos, the bird is crested, and also has bare cheek patches like the macaws. Its characteristic feature is the shape of its tongue, which is long and cylindrical and ends in a spoon-shaped swelling. When the bird has reduced its food to a pulp with its beak, it gathers it up with its tongue. A projection from the roof of the mouth enables it to empty the 'spoon' in one operation.

The three main species of cage parrots are the African Grey Parrot (*Psittacus erithacus*), the You-you (*Poicephalus senegalus*), and the Orange-winged Parrot (*Amazona amazonica*). The first two live in West Africa, while the third comes from South America. The African Grey Parrot is not entirely grey, for its tail is blood red. the You-you's head is grey, and the rest of the body green and yellow. The South American species is predominantly green. All three parrots are splendid talkers, have good memories, a marked intelligence, and are readily tamed in captivity.

The common name 'parakeet' is applied to small parrots with a long tail. The Carolina Parakeet (*Conuropsis carolinensis*) was one of the more northerly species, since it occurred in the United States, until it became extinct. The Budgerigar (*Melopsittacus undulatus*), which is found in Australia, is another. In the wild state the Budgerigar's plumage is predominantly green with some yellow, and there are small wavy black markings on the head. Several varieties have been produced by selective breeding. In one of the most popular the green coloration is replaced by a sky-blue shade. These birds are quite the most delightful of all parrots.

Their breeding behaviour is also particularly interesting. While the male is always in breeding condition, he never forces his attentions on his mate, as many other birds do. He continues his courtship until she is ready to mate. When they copulate the female lowers her head to the male, who takes her beak in his own and enfolds her in his long wings. When the time comes to feed his mate, he is tireless.

The female builds in a hollow tree. She works away at the opening until it is just the size required. Then she chips off pieces of wood from the sides of the cavity and with these she covers the floor. Over a period of two days she lays from four to eight white, rounded eggs, which she broods for eighteen to twenty days. During the incubation period she is fed by the male, and leaves her nest only in cases of necessity. The young remain in the nest for thirty to thirty-five days and are not left by the parents until they are fully feathered.

The small, short-tailed parrots, particularly those of the genera *Agapornis* and *Psittacula*, are commonly known as lovebirds. The first is found in Africa, the second in India and Ceylon. Schomburgk, an explorer and naturalist of the early nineteenth century, remarked: 'In choosing the Turtle-dove as the symbol of idyllic love, the poets have been quite unaware of the greater affection displayed by a pair of lovebirds. There is complete harmony between male and female. When one eats or takes a bath, the other does the same. If the male calls, the female will join him in song. When one is sick, the other will care for it and feed it. Even when a flock of these birds gathers in a tree, the members of each pair are always together'. The Blue-winged Parrotlet (*Forpus passerinus*), not much bigger than a sparrow, is the smallest of the Brazilian parrots. Its plumage is a handsome green, variegated with blue and yellow. The smallest of all parrots, however, is a species from New Guinea, the Pygmy Parrot (*Nasiterna pygmaea*), which is no bigger than a Canary. Little is known of its habits.

Certain small parrots found in Australia. New Guinea, Malaya and Polynesia are known as lories. These have a feebly developed beak and the tongue usually has a papillose or brush-like tip. (The name of one genus, *Trichoglossus*, is Greek for 'hair tongue'.) As might be supposed, these birds use the tongue for gathering nectar and pollen from flowers. Their mode of life is rather like that of butterflies and humming-birds, but they also feed on fruit and insects. There are about a hundred species, which differ markedly in colour pattern. They include the Black Lory, the Red Lory, the Green Lory and so on. But there is little chance of seeing these attractive birds except in museums as they do not thrive in captivity.

The Kea (*Nestor notabilis*), of the mountainous regions of the South Island of New Zealand, is a large bird measuring about fifty-five centimetres in length. General plumage colour is brownish green; the tail is green with a black bar near the tip, the rump is reddish, and there is some blue on the wings. The upper mandible of the bill is long and sickle-shaped. Its food consists of carrion, insects, berries, buds, and honey. The Kea also feeds on any blowfly larvae living in the wool of sheep, and on occasion inflicts injuries on the sheep themselves with it pecking.

The genus *Strigops* has only one species, the Kakapo (*S. habroptilus*), a curious nocturnal parrot found in New Zealand. It was formerly classified among the owls since its eyes are partly turned forwards and its beak, like that of a typical owl, is hidden in its feathers. Much of its life is spent on the ground, where it hunts for food by night, and during the day retires into a burrow made among the tree roots. The ravages of wild dogs threaten the species with extinction.

Cuckoos and turacos (Order Cuculiformes)

This arboreal order, the most closely related to the parrots, includes cuckoos and road-runners, turacos or plantain-eaters. Cuckoos are sometimes called 'climbing birds that cannot climb', for although the toe arrangement is that of climbing birds, two in front and two behind, they are quite unable to climb. They are perchers which fly from tree to tree, often alighting in a climbing manner and steadying themselves with the wings and elevated tail. Having long wings, they fly well with the direct flight of a Falcon or Sparrowhawk. Their white, dusky-barred underparts also give them the appearance of a Sparrowhawk.

This Black-capped Lory (*Lorius lory*) of the Aru Islands, Indonesia, is seen feeding off tree fruits in the tropical forests. All parrots are gregarious and usually brightly-coloured, moving through the trees with noisy chattering.

Turacos or plantain-eaters (Family Musophagidae)

These members of the cuckoo order look rather like small game birds. They are peculiar in that the outer toe can be turned either forwards or backwards. There are about twenty species, all of which live in small groups in the African forests and, like parrots, are both noisy and frugivorous. Their scientific and common names are both derived from the mistaken belief that they feed on wild bananas (*Musa*, a species of plantain). The plumage is unusual in containing a water-soluble red pigment which may be washed out by rain.

Cuckoos and road-runners (Family Cuculidae)

This is a primarily arboreal group, mainly insectivorous. Some species are social parasites laying their eggs in the nests of other birds, others—like the coucals—build their own nests and brood their own eggs. The American anis even build communal nests.

The widely distributed Old World typical cuckoos of the subfamily Cuculinae are wholly parasitic. The commonest genera are *Cuculus*, breeding throughout the palaearctic region, *Chalcites* found in the Far East and Australasia, *Chrysococcyx* of Africa, and several, including the Koel (*Eudynamys scolopacea*), that used to be placed in separate genera.

The Kea (*Nestor notabilis*) belongs to a small family of parrots found only in New Zealand. Having evolved in isolation for so long they now bear little relationship to other parrots. Outside the breeding season Keas forage in flocks usually in low-level forests but also above the bush-line amongst scree and bare rock.

The Common or Eurasian Cuckoo (*Cuculus canorus*), famous for laying its eggs in other birds' nests. Here a young cuckoo is being fed by a Reed Warbler (*Acrocephalus scirpaceus*). The young Cuckoo has an enormous appetite and consumes all the food its foster-parents can provide, so it grows rapidly and soon becomes far too large for the Reed Warbler's nest.

The Common Cuckoo (*Cuculus canorus*), a lively, agile bird, is a summer visitor to Europe and northern Asia. Its characteristic call is generally first heard about the middle of April in the British Isles, but the bird is very difficult to see because it conceals itself among the foliage of trees. The head and upper parts are ashy grey, becoming darker over the shoulder region. The underparts are lighter in colour, with dusky transverse bars like those of sparrowhawks. This feature, shared with one of the raptorial birds, may help it to assert itself in its chosen territory.

Much has been written on the Cuckoo's parasitic habits, but there is considerable disagreement, even between observers. The female appears to lay an egg directly in the selected nest, then removes one of the host's eggs with her beak, so that the total number of eggs remains the same. Yet it has been reported that, if the nest is too small or to fragile she lays her egg on the ground and then carries it to the selected nest. She then removes one of the host bird's eggs in her beak or crop. She lays four or five eggs in all, each in a different nest.

The choice of host is not a random choice. It is usually a small insectivorous bird, such as a Willow Warbler, a Pipit, a Wheatear, a Sedge-warbler, a Robin or a Wren. If the protective host is a seed-eating bird, a Linnet or a Bullfinch for example, it will be one that feeds its young mainly on insects, which is the only diet suitable for a young Cuckoo. And a Cuckoo that lays brownish eggs, for example will always choose a host that lays a similar colour.

Whatever the nest in which it is laid, the Cuckoo's egg is usually the first to hatch, or at least hatches very soon after the eggs of the host. Although the young Cuckoo is blind, naked and feeble when hatched, it is soon the only occupant of the nest, for it is extremely active, particularly in its efforts to get rid of the host's eggs and chicks. If other eggs are in the nest it wriggles until it gets the offending egg on its back and slowly heaves itself upwards until it topples it over the edge and on to the ground. It repeats this exercise until it is the sole occupant. When it is not the first to hatch it treats the nestlings in the same way as the eggs, though not always with success. This aggressive behaviour is determined by the rapid growth of the young Cuckoo, which is so much bigger than its host's offspring and bigger than the host too. It is a voracious bird and begs for food with greater intensity than its foster-brothers and sisters, and so stimulates the foster-parents to give more food to it than to their own chicks. Within a few days the young Cuckoo thrives while they starve. With this advantage it pushes the weakened chicks out.

Egg mimicry is one of the Cuckoo's remarkable adaptations to parasitism. It is the only bird to match the size and colour of its eggs to those of the host species with varying degrees of success. The most plausible explanation is that an individual Cuckoo always chooses the same species of bird to parasitise. It is therefore not surprising that a young Cuckoo brought up by foster-parents of this species should, when adult, lay its eggs in another nest of the same species.

A female Cuckoo may lay about twenty times during the breeding season, on each occasion placing a single egg in a different nest. Thus in a brief breeding season it is possible to rear a larger number of young than a pair of cuckoos could manage alone. Although the female Cuckoo never leaves her territory she shows no interest in the hatching of her young.

Why these intruders are tolerated by their foster-parents is problematic, except that no special behaviour pattern has been evolved to deal with parasitisation. The instinctive urge to feed a young chick within the nest is so great that the foster-parents continue to feed the parasite even when weakened by their constant search for food to sate its appetite. Even more remarkable is that other birds as well as the foster-parents may feed it with food intended for their own young.

The Common Cuckoo has been blamed for destroying the young of useful insectivorous birds, but it largely makes up for this by the enormous number of caterpillars it eats. Certain of the Asian and African cuckoos have also been similarly accused. But as some of these lay their eggs in the nests of crows the charges are less serious.

The Bronzed or Shining Cuckoo (*Chrysococcyx lucidus*) breeds on islands off New Zealand. It lays its eggs in the nests of flycatchers, and after laying the adults depart. The young brought up by the foster-parents follow a month later, making a non-stop flight of 1,900 kilometres to Australia, and then head northwards, following the path already taken by their parents, another thousand kilometres to the Bismarck and Solomon Islands.

The Yellow-billed and Black-billed Cuckoos (*Coccyzus americanus* and *C. erythrophthalmus*) of North America are non-parasitic and build their own nests of twigs. They winter in South and Central America. The malkohas of tropical Asia, which are related to them, not only build their own nests but are largely non-migratory.

The anis (genus *Crotophaga*), ranging from Mexico to Argentina, with glossy black plumage, long tails and laterally compressed bills, present the antithesis of what is expected of members of the cuckoo family. Although a pair of anis may sometimes build a nest on their own, usually a group builds one large communal nest of sticks, in which all the hens lay their eggs and share the incubating and rearing of the young.

Road-runners are another group of non-parasitic cuckoos which live in the more arid parts of North America; there is one genus found in south-east Asia. The Road-runner or Chaparral Cock (*Geococcyx californianus*) is as large as a Bantam, which it resembles somewhat in having long, powerful legs and a long tail. As the name implies it is chiefly a ground bird and lives among desert scrub, where it feeds on lizards and small snakes. It runs very fast for a small bird and can keep pace with a car travelling at twenty-four kilometres per hour along a rutted desert track.

Another non parasitic genus of ten species of ground-dwelling cuckoos is found only in Madagascar. These are the couas. They build their own nests, feed on insects and fallen fruit on the forest floor, and seek safety by running instead of flying. The Crested Coua (*Coua cristata*) is a large conspicuous bird that moves about in noisy parties.

Other ground cuckoos, ranging from Africa, Australia and southern Asia, are the twenty-eight species of coucals. They are large, slow-flying birds, mainly dark in plumage, with short down-curved bills, rounded wings, long tails and long, strong legs. They build bulky nests of green leaves and grasses. Their call is a deep bubbling note.

The Roadrunner (*Geococcyx californiana*) is a non-parasitic ground cuckoo of the south-western United States, shown here with a lizard in its beak. A bird of desert and semi-desert regions it feeds mainly on lizards, two of its other vernacular names being Lizard-bird and Snake-killer. A distinctive feature is its habit of running fast with its short wings outstretched. It seldom flies and then poorly.

The Smooth-billed Ani (*Crotophaga ani*) of Central and South America inhabits hillsides, plantations and wet pasturelands where cattle graze. Small flocks feed on the ground or more usually on the backs of cattle stripping off the ticks. The generic name means tick-eater.

Owls (Order Strigiformes)

Despite similarities in the bill and strong claws, owls are very different from the diurnal birds of prey. Apart from their nocturnal habits their distinguishing characters are soft feathers and silent flight, feet feathered down to the digits, and a rather large head with the beak almost hidden in fluffed-out feathers. Their eyes, frontally set as in man, are surrounded by very small feathers which fan out to form a disc-shaped mask. There are small earflaps, positioned asymmetrically, which help to focus sound waves into the ears. The ears themselves are very sensitive and supplement the vision, which is very sensitive in dim light. The eyes face forward so that the visual fields overlap to give stereoscopic vision. As the eyes cannot move in their sockets, the owl has to turn its head.

The owl's well-known silent flight gives it a great advantage as it swoops on its prey. The noiseless approach is partly due to the owl's light wing loading. On its broad wings it can glide down, so avoiding the winnowing rush of wing-beats. The sound of its arrival is further deadened by the softness of the plumage and, in particular, by the flexibility of the flight feathers which effectively muffle the sound of the air rushing past them. It has been suggested that this is chiefly achieved by the special construction of the outer vane of the outermost flight feathers of the wing which forms a loose fringe. These form the leading edge which in other orders cuts through the still air when the wing is flapped, producing most of the flapping, whirring sound that is typical of a bird in flight. The modification of these outer feathers causes a thin, slower-moving cushion of air to separate the fast-moving and the stationary air and prevents the noisy shearing effect. Close examination of the outer vanes of these two feathers reveals that the vanes are extremely narrow.

The owl's digestive powers appear to be more limited than those of the diurnal birds of prey, for the pellets they regurgitate consist of bones as well as hairs and feathers. Another difference between the two types is that owls do not build proper nests, but lay their eggs in a hole in a tree, in old crows' or hawks' nests, or in a cleft in a rock. The eggs are always white and usually nearly spherical.

These and other differences have led modern ornithologists to separate the two families making up the order Strigiformes from the Falconiformes. Through anatomical similarities they seem fairly closely related to the nightjars.

A Barn Owl (*Tyto alba*) landing on its nest in a hayloft with prey for its five chicks. It is distinguished by its heart-shaped facial disc and large dark eyes. At night it hunts low over the ground to take small mammals, or snatch small birds roosting in bushes or ivy. Its exceptionally acute hearing enables it to locate prey in total darkness.

The Great Horned Owl (*Bubo virginianus*), one of the largest and most powerful of owls, fifty centimetres long, it is found from Canada right through to southern South America. It sleeps during the day in dense coniferous woods, forests and mountainous areas, hunting by night. It preys on small mammals, birds and snakes. It will take domestic poultry and cats when other food is scarce, earning its name of 'night tiger'.

Barn Owl (Family Tytonidae)

The Common Barn Owl (*Tyto alba*), otherwise known as the White or Screech-owl, but not to be confused with the American Screech-owl (*Otus asio*), is one of the commonest and most handsome of European birds, and has an almost world-wide distribution. In some countries it is called the 'Monkey Owl' as its face looks much like that of a monkey. It differs from other owls in having a complete ruff-like ring of feathers around the head. The feet are bare or covered with only a few soft feathers. The plumage is truly magnificent, golden or reddish above, with brown, grey or white markings. The underparts are whitish with black spots. Its breeding habits are similar to those of other owls, except that it prefers to nest in ruined houses, barns, granaries, pigeon-cotes and so on. It returns to the same nesting place year after year.

Typical owls (Family Strigidae)

The largest species in the order is the Eagle-owl (*Bubo bubo*), whose thick, fluffy plumage makes it look larger than it really is. It is about sixty centimetres in length and has a wingspan of some 170 centimetres. Plumage varies from yellow to red according to age and sex, and there are wavy transverse brown stripes and brown markings running along the body. Above each ear there is a horn-like tuft of black feathers, which usually stick out at an angle from the head. It is a magnificent bird, which, seen in its natural state, cannot be confused with any other owl. It is found in Europe from Spain to northern Scandinavia and also extends over Russia and Asia and in Africa. It has even been recorded as an occasional visitor to the British Isles. In France it is almost entirely confined to rocky and mountainous regions.

The Eagle-owl tends to live in wooded regions with rocky escarpments, where it builds its nest in spring. This usually consists of dried leaves placed in a rocky crevice and here the female lays two or three white rounded eggs. While she is sitting on them the male provides the food. After this both birds share in feeding and bringing up the young.

By day the Eagle-owl perches motionless on rocks and trees, camouflaged by its plumage. With its eyes almost closed, it seems to be half asleep, but the slightest noise will arouse it. It hunts at twilight, at intervals uttering its hooting cry. At times it seems as though it is laughing, howling or moaning, and these sounds are so similar to those made by human beings as to frighten anyone unfamiliar with them.

The Eagle-owl feeds on all manner of mammals, birds, reptiles and amphibians, and it does undoubted service in eating small rodents, hares, rabbits, weasels and stoats.

The Eagle-owl is replaced in America by the Great Horned Owl (*B. virginianus*) which ranges from the tree limit of North America to the Straits of Magellan. The habits and general appearance of the two species are very similar.

The North African Desert-owl is a subspecies of the Eagle-owl. Its biscuit colour blends with that of the surrounding sand.

The Long-eared Owl (*Asio otus*) is about half the size of the Eagle-owl. The greys and browns of its plumage closely resemble bark and thus give camouflage against the background of trees among

The Spotted Eagle Owl (*Bubo africanus*), the smallest and most common and widespread Eagle Owl over most of Africa. It usually lives in rocky areas of bush and savannah or forested areas. In the Kalahari, however, it has adapted to desert conditions. Although it may kill quite large prey it depends to a large extent on insects.

The Long-eared Owl (*Asio otus*) lives mainly in woods and forests and is strictly nocturnal. As it roosts by day in dense cover it is seldom seen. Although owls cannot move their eyes independently like other birds they have good nocturnal vision and their restricted angle of vision is compensated by having a very mobile neck. The Long-eared Owl, for example, can turn its head through 270 degrees.

which it lives. This is the species often heard at night in woodlands, parks and orchards. It is widely distributed through Europe, including the British Isles, northern Asia, North America and North Africa, nesting in some parts and invading others in the summer in flocks of about ten individuals. In years when voles are locally abundant there may be real invasions by the species.

Like most owls, the Long-eared Owl is essentially useful to man and in country districts should be protected. Analyses of its pellets show them to be formed almost exclusively of the bones of rodents. It is only when mice are lacking that the Long-eared Owl will satisfy its hunger at the expense of various small birds.

The breeding season is in spring. The cry of the male may first be heard in February or March, when the female will answer with higher-pitched sounds. From time to time they make a clapping noise with their wings. The nest is a roughly built affair, and is often the abandoned nest of a Rook, Magpie, Jay or Squirrel. The eggs, about six in number, are white and rounded, three to four centimetres in diameter. They are incubated for rather less than a month. When hatched the young are covered in white down and are still blind, but they soon become brown, and when they are five days old their eyes open. Within several weeks their wing feathers are large enough to enable them to flit from bough to bough.

The Short-eared Owl (*A. flammeus*) has much the same powers and general coloration as the Long-eared Owl, but its plumage is marbled rather than barred. It has longer wings and, as its common name suggests, shorter horn-like tufts of feathers than its congener. This owl lives in open country, including marshy areas, where it captures frogs, small rodents and insects. It is essentially a wandering, migratory bird, flocks of twenty to thirty individuals moving from one part of Europe (including the British Isles) to another. It winters in Africa and is also found in North and South America and in northern and central Asia.

Scops or screech owls of the genus *Otus* are also found in Europe and occasionally in the British Isles. In the United States they are the commonest owls. The Scops Owl (*Otus scops*), a useful insectivorous species, is a good deal smaller than the Short-eared Owl, averaging about twenty centimetres in length and fifty centimetres in wingspan. This miniature owl lives in small groups, which appear in Europe in spring and migrate in autumn to the African interior. In the south of France it is a familiar resident in gardens and parks, where its somewhat melancholy but not unpleasing song may frequently be heard at night.

The Screech Owl (*O. asio*) is not, as its scientific specific name might indicate, found in Asia, but only in North America. The Latin meaning of *asio* is 'a kind of horned owl' which is exactly what the little Screech Owl is. Oddly enough its common call is a quavering whistle, not a screech.

Owls without ear-like head tufts include the Tawny Owl and the Pygmy Owl, in addition to the barn-owls, which form a separate family, the Tytonidae. Their habits are much the same as those of the eared or horned owls.

The Little Owl (*Athene noctua*) is a small, handsome-looking bird with greyish-brown plumage. The underparts are lighter in colour and marked here and there with white spots. The legs carry relatively few feathers, and the face or mask is not strongly marked.

The Little Owl is found over Europe and much of Asia and Africa. It is a common resident in England and Wales, mostly in copses, parks, gardens and orchards.

Being much less nocturnal than the other owls, the Little Owl ventures out during the day, but hunts only at night and during the early morning. It destroys an incredible number of rats, mice, voles, field mice and insects. The brood of four or five hungry owlets keeps the parents continually at work providing food. The cries of the Little Owl, and of owls in general, are much more varied than is commonly supposed. The most frequent calls of the Little Owl are sharp, quick cries or shrill whistling sounds, which it utters whenever it is aroused or disturbed.

The Sparrow Owl or Pygmy Owl (*Glaucidium passerinum*) is one of the smaller species. It flies by day and has a flight recalling that of a Swallow. In the ease and rapidity with which it moves it is more like a diurnal bird of prey. But it can also climb trees like a Parrot and may hunt on the ground or in the air. It feeds on small animals such as mice, shrews and insects. It lives in a broad belt from Scandinavia and south-east France across to China.

Some of the small North American owls have a curious habit of living in rabbits' burrows. One such is the Burrowing Owl (*Speotyto cunicularia*). In soft ground it can excavate its own burrow but elsewhere it relies on using the abandoned tunnels of prairie dogs, viscachas, armadillos and others. This commensalism is to the advantage of the owl.

These small, burrow-dwelling species have become so terrestrial in habit that they are practi-

The Burrowing Owl (*Speotyto cunicularia*) seen with its young. It lives on the open plains of western North America and Florida, through Central and South America and the West Indies. It is a small owl with spotted plumage and relatively long slender legs. Although it can fly when danger threatens, it usually runs into its burrow with remarkable speed.

cally flightless and will flatten themselves against the ground rather than fly when disturbed. Their legs are relatively long and adapted for running. About six eggs are laid, which look like those of a pigeon and take about three weeks to hatch.

The Tawny or Wood Owl (*Strix aluco*) is found in forests and wooded regions over much of Europe, western Asia and north-west Africa. It is the commonest of owls in the British Isles. It is difficult to describe the plumage as it varies with age and sex, passing from greys to reds and browns. The characteristic features are the breast markings, which look something like an inverted fir-tree, and the white spots on the shoulder regions. This species is much the same size as the Long-eared Owl.

The Tawny Owl has a number of different calls, the best known being a kind of *kouwitt*. The pitch varies and the cry has a creaking, mewing or shrill quality, and consists of one, two, three or even four syllables. As these calls are made they fall in pitch until the last syllable, which is made on a rising note. Sometimes the cries follow one another in rapid succession, and certain observers believe that this form of cry is peculiar to the female. The male begins calling as early as the end of December and goes on until June. It may begin calling again in the autumn, even in the middle of August, and it may also be heard, less frequently, at other times. The well-known *oo-oo* cries of the Tawny Owl usually consist of two or three syllables, a signal audible a long way off. After listening for about five seconds it utters a short call followed by a brief silence. Then comes a series of discreet sounds, dying away in a trill. After this there is a further silence of five to seven seconds and the whole sequence is repeated.

The Tawny Owl builds in a tree hollow or takes over the old nest of a rook, woodpecker or squirrel. The female lays several white, rounded eggs just over four centimetres in diameter. These she broods for about a month, during which time she is fed by the male. Both birds help to rear the young in common with most birds of prey.

In North America the Tawny Owl is replaced ecologically by the rather similar Barred Owl (*S. varia*). Another member of the genus is the Great Grey Owl (*S. nebulosa*) which is found in the forests of the Arctic regions of America and Eurasia. Its plumage is so thick that it appears larger than the Eagle-owl or Great Horned Owl, but actually weighs much less than either of these.

The handsome Snowy Owl (*Nyctea scandiaca*) of the Arctic sometimes winters in Scandinavia, Canada, the United States and Russia. The plumage is pure white in the male but the female has a varying number of dark barred markings; the younger individuals are more heavily barred. The species feeds on hares, lemmings and ptarmigans, hunting on the ground or in flight according to circumstance. It is skilled in catching fishes, lying in wait on the banks of rivers or lakes to seize one in its claws.

Nightjars and allies (Order Caprimulgiformes)

This order includes the Oilbird, frogmouths, potoos, owlet-frogmouths and the nightjars: all are brownish, mottled, birds with nocturnal or crepus-

The Ferruginous Pygmy Owl (*Glaucidium brasilianum*) of America occurs in two distinct subspecies. One group lives in North America, the other in South America. The picture shows a member of the southern subspecies from Tierra del Fuego. It is a very small owl, little more than fifteen centimetres long, but is a fierce hunter sometimes taking prey larger than itself.

The Tawny Owl (*Strix aluco*) is one of the commonest owls in Eurasia and northwest Africa. It is strictly nocturnal preying on small mammals, and birds up to the size of a Mallard. It will also take earthworms, beetles, snails and slugs. This wide diet together with its tolerance of man has enabled the Tawny Owl to maintain or even increase its numbers over much of its range.

A female Great Grey Owl (*Strix nebulosa*) seen with her chicks. A very imposing owl, its massive head may be fifty centimetres in circumference and its large, heavily-barred facial disc, bordered with a dark ruff, makes an almost perfect circle. It has a wide breeding range on both sides of the Atlantic but its numbers vary enormously with the population of its prey, which are mainly voles.

The Common Potoo (*Nyctibius griseus*), of tropical America, is related to the nightjars. Its distinctive far-carrying call, sad and beautiful, can often be heard on moonlit nights, but during the day it is seldom seen as its plumage blends in so well with the trees on which it roosts.

cular habits. All except the Oilbird are insectivorous in their feeding habits.

Oilbird or guacharo (Family Steatornithidae)

This family has only one species: the Oilbird (*Steatornis caripensis*) or Guacharo of northern South America and the island of Trinidad. Although only thirty-three centimetres long, it has a wingspan of about a metre. It spends the day deep in caves, finding its way through the darkness by using an echo-location mechanism similar to that used by bats. In colouring and form the Oilbird is similar to the nightjars. It nests in colonies on rocky ledges high above the cave floor. From the two to four eggs in each nest are hatched the naked young, which in two to three weeks pass through two downy stages, during which they attain a weight that is half as much again as the parents. As flight feathers form, the excess weight is lost. Probably because its food is mainly the very oily fruit of palm trees, its flesh is very fatty and the natives use impaled carcasses as torches.

Frogmouths (Family Podargidae)

These also resemble the nightjars in appearance. There are a dozen species confined to south-east Asia and Australia. During the day frogmouths roost lengthwise on a tree branch, with head up and eyes closed, their cryptically coloured plumage matching the bark. There is virtually no sexual dimorphism. The nest is a platform of twigs or a wad of their own feathers camouflaged with plants. The one or two eggs are incubated by both parents, the male sitting by day and the female by night. They are terrestrial feeders: insects are not taken in flight but as they rest on the ground.

Potoos or wood-nightjars (Family Nyctibiidae)

There are five species (genus *Nyctibius*) in this family, distributed from southern Mexico to Brazil. Like true nightjars they hunt insects at night, not in uninterrupted flight but in forays from a branch, taking an insect on the wing and returning to the same perch. By day they rest in a vertical posture on a broken branch, with head up, tail down, and eyes closed. They are solitary birds. The single white egg is laid on the top of a broken-off branch or precariously on a ledge of bark. Both parents taking turns at incubating.

Owlet-frogmouths (Family Aegothelidae)

Very little is known about the seven species from Australia and New Guinea known as owlet-frogmouths, owlet-nightjars, or moth owls. They resemble small nightjars but have something of the habits of owls. They perch crosswise on branches, sit upright, and when flying for insects at night pursue a straighter course than nightjars. Like owls they can turn their heads through 180 degrees, and their calls are owl-like. They lay four to five white eggs in tree hollows.

Nightjars (Family Caprimulgidae)

This is the largest family of the order, comprising the subfamilies Caprimulginae, the typical nightjars or goatsuckers, and Chordeilinae, the nighthawks. Large eyes, wide gape for taking insects on the wing, quiet flight, long pointed wings and slight sexual dimorphism are typical.

The European Nightjar (*Caprimulgus europaeus*) of Europe and central Asia is a large bird mottled with brown, red and black, simulating the colouring of dead leaves. This is excellent camouflage, since it lives in woods and forests. During the day it remains perched lengthwise along a branch and is scarcely visible. As evening falls it starts hunting in the clearings, along the forest ridges, or high up in the air. It is then that the penetrating song, a monotonous churring from which the bird gets its name, can be heard. The mouth is huge, wide and deep, and prolonged into a sticky throat that acts as a trap for insects. It makes no nest, merely laying its eggs in a hollow in the ground under a bush where the hen alone sits on them. It is migratory and winters mainly in tropical Africa.

The North American species include the Whip-poor-will (*Caprimulgus vociferus*), very similar to the Nightjar, and the Poor-will (*Phalaenoptilus nuttallii*). The Poor-will is curious for its habit of hibernating in the winter when insects, the principal item of its diet, are scarce. During this period body temperature drops from about 40°C. to 18°C.

Farther south the White-necked Nighthawk (*Nyctidromus albicollis*) inhabits Middle and South America. In Africa the commonest species are the small Pennant-winged Nightjar (*Macrodipteryx vexillarius*) which has several of the inner flight feathers of the wing lengthened into long streamers, and the Long-tailed Nightjar (*Caprimulgus climacurus*).

The subfamily Chordeilinae is confined to the New World and is typically represented by the Common Nighthawk (*Chordeiles minor*) in North America. The Lesser Nighthawk (*Chordeiles*

A female Tawny Frogmouth (*Podargus strigoides*) with its young. It is widely distributed throughout the whole of Australia, common even in the suburbs of large towns. Although a rapid flier it feeds mostly on ground-living insects, grasshoppers, snails and slugs and occasionally mice. This highly-camouflaged species is related to the nightjars.

The European Nightjar (*Caprimulgus europaeus*), of Europe and central Asia, spends the winter in tropical Africa. When nesting the hen lays her eggs on the ground and incubates them there being extremely well-camouflaged by her mottled brown and grey plumage. The male is distinguished by white markings on the wings and tail.

acutipennis) is represented in both north and tropical South America.

Swifts and humming-birds (Order Apodiformes)

True swifts and crested or tree swifts, together with the superficially dissimilar humming-birds, are fast-flying, short-legged, weak-footed, insectivorous birds. They are principally birds of the tropics and subtropics, though one or two nest in the northern hemisphere.

Swifts (Family Apodidae)

This family is unique in two features: individuals of the species belonging to it sometimes spend a whole night on the wing, and frequently copulate in the air. A familiar representative of the genus *Chaetura* is the Chimney Swift (*C. pelagica*) of North America, while the Old World genus *Apus* includes several African species and one—the Common Swift—that reaches the British Isles.

The Common Swift (*Apus apus*) is all black with a light-coloured patch on the throat. It is on the wing from morning to evening, twisting and turning with incredible agility. If it alights, it clings to the face of a wall or trunk of a tree. Its feet are so small and its legs so short that it has difficulty in taking off again if it falls to the ground. Like the other wide-billed birds, it catches insects while in flight. It reaches Europe from Africa later in spring than the apparently similar swallows, and leaves earlier. It is unmistakable because it is one of the noisiest of birds, and all the time it is on the wing it repeats its shrill cry. Its nest is a hole in a tree or crack in a rock, an old tower, belfry, or the roofspace of a house. It usually lays two eggs, but sometimes three or four. The hen sits and the cock brings her food.

The Common Swift (*Apus apus*) breeds in Europe and part of Asia and winters in Africa. It is unique in spending virtually all its life on the wing except when incubating. It feeds only on flying insects caught on the wing but this may be a disadvantage in bad weather when the swift may find it difficult to find food.

All swifts have large salivary glands, but the swiftlets (genus *Collocalia*), of Asia and Oceania, produce saliva in such quantities that they can use it as the principal material for nest building. They nest in colonies on the face of tall sea cliffs or in dark caves. Their cup-shaped nests are made wholly of saliva, or of saliva mixed with moss or feathers, according to the species. When a swiftlet starts to build, it flies to the place selected and literally spits saliva on to the rock. It repeats this ten or twenty times, drawing a semicircle or horseshoe shape in saliva. This dries quickly and provides a solid formation for the nest. Some species use various vegetable substances bound together with saliva; the tiny Edible-nest Swiftlet (*Collocalia inexpectata*) uses saliva only. Once the frame has been laid down, it alights on it and, turning its head alternately to the right and left, builds up the nest wall which, when finished, is marked with undulating stratified lines.

The saliva, which dries very rapidly, is like a strong solution of gum Arabic. A thread of it drawn from the bird's mouth can be wound round a stick until all the saliva in the bird's mouth and in the ducts of the salivary glands has been extracted.

These are the 'swallow's nests' that are considered a delicacy, and the caves of Karang-Kallong in Java yield more than 300,000 a year.

The American Chimney Swift also uses saliva in the construction of its nest, but only to glue small twigs together and to the vertical surface of the interior of chimneys. The nest thus formed is a neat, surprisingly sturdy shelf on which the white eggs are laid. There is no doubt but that the nests were built inside tree hollows or in caves before European man introduced his chimneys though it is very rare to find a Chimney Swift's nest in such a situation today. These birds winter in South America where recently some have been found 'roosting' inside tree hollows in Peru.

Swifts are well-named as their flight speed is faster than that of almost any other bird; some say the fastest.

Crested swifts (Family Hemiprocnidae)

A group of three species related to the true swifts is assigned to this family. All inhabit the forests of south-east Asia (India to the Philippines and Solomons), but they are not as continually on the wing as the true swifts. They feed on insects taken in flight mainly at dawn and dusk, and spend much time perched on bare branches. They have forked tails, strong legs and toes, a pronounced crest, a distinctive white marking above the eye and another well below it. The nest is minute, a few layers of bark on a dead tree limb with the single egg cemented to the floor of the nest.

Humming-birds (Family Trochilidae)

Although they feed on nectar and small insects found in flowers these birds are not related to the sunbirds or the honey-eaters. They are related to the swifts and have the same short legs, which leave them almost helpless on the ground. In some of their habits humming-birds resemble Old World flycatchers, while the structure of their tongue is in some ways comparable to that of woodpeckers. Nevertheless they are very specialised birds and there is no risk of confusing them with any other species in the Americas where they occur. In general, they are tiny birds and their minute legs are almost hidden among their feathers. They have tubular, pointed bills; tubular, fringe-tipped tongues, slightly forked at the tip, and squamous plumage which refracts light.

Over 300 known species and subspecies have been identified, distributed through the western hemisphere from the Magellan Strait to Canada, and from the humid low country and forests of the Amazon to the highest peaks of the Andes. This wide distribution embracing so many different habitats, is perhaps one of the most remarkable things about humming-birds. They seem to be so weak and so specialised in their way of life, yet they are amazingly adaptable and can live as well in a desert as in an equatorial climate, or even among the snows and ice of high mountains.

The northernmost species migrate annually from the confines of North America, where they nest, to Mexico and Central America, where they pass the winter. The greatest migrants are the Ruby-throated Humming-bird (*Archilochus colubris*) and the Rufous Humming-bird (*Selasphorus rufus*), which breed farthest north, the latter going as far as Alaska. When migrating, some follow a Mexican route, while others go by way of Florida, Cuba and the Yucatan peninsula. Almost all avoid the direct route involving the hazardous crossing of the Gulf of Mexico. In addition to these migrations in latitude, there are many others of fairly limited range which take the humming-birds to different places according to the season. The general impression is that these frail-looking birds are really continuously on the move in search of favourable conditions and more varied sources of food.

The largest of the family is the Giant Humming-bird of the Andes (*Patagona gigas*), which is up to twenty-one centimetres long; the smallest is the Bee Humming-bird (*Mellisuga helenae)*, of Cuba and the Isle of Pines, no longer than five centimetres including tail and long bill.

For colourful plumage the humming-bird has no rivals. There are species with crests, collarets, plumes and other ornamental accessories, and in adition their plumage is iridescent, changing tone with the incidence of the light on the structural colour of the feathers and showing rich metallic effects. This is reflected in the popular names given them by travellers: emerald, garnet, ruby, topaz, bluebeard, golden belly, rainbow.

But for all their fine plumes most humming-birds do not have a pleasing song. All are exceedingly pugnacious, however, and even the smallest are so aggressive that they often succeed in driving away much larger birds.

The wings are marvellous structures. The keel of the breastbone, to which the flight muscles are attached, is better developed than in other birds and the humerus is short. Their beat is vibrant and humming and the rate of movement comparable to that of insects. In the tiny *Pygmornis rubra* of Brazil there may be as many as fifty beats per second. The characteristic attitude of the humming-bird is its hovering as it gathers nectar from a flower without alighting. It is amazing that they can stay so still, hanging in the air, yet in continuous flight. They are so expert in this that they are able to visit a large number of flowers in a relatively short time, flitting from one to the other at lightning speed, their wings never for a moment ceasing to vibrate. They are the only birds that can fly backwards.

Humming-birds use only the beak and tongue for feeding. Their bills vary in length and in degree of curve towards the tip, but they are always slender and pointed. The longest bill is that of *Docimestes* where it is the length of the bird's body, and the shortest is that of *Opisthoprora*.

Inside the bill is a cylindrical tongue, seemingly forked but actually with the outer edges rolled upwards and inwards in two half-cylinders joined over most of their length. Together they form a pair of tubes well adapted for sucking up nectar, pollen and tiny insects, for humming-birds are not solely nectar-eaters. Although nectar itself provides them with sufficient food to replace the energy they expend, it is insufficient for growth and repair of tissues, and so insects and spiders are taken as a source of protein. They find these inside the flowers and hunt them in the air like flycatchers, and they will also rob spiders' webs of flies that have been caught in them and even take the spiders themselves.

The Broad-billed Hummingbird (*Cyanthus latirostris*), one of only two species in the genus, is characterised by a long, straight bill broadened at the base. The male, shown here, is perhaps the most attractive of all hummingbirds, with a brilliant viridescent green back and a bright blue throat and upper chest. It breeds in the southwestern United States and Mexico.

The mating habits of the male humming-birds are simple. They usually live apart from the female, except for a brief courtship followed by a swift mating. In most species courtship display consists of the males performing intricate aerial dances and displays before the perching female. The cock gives no help to the hen in building the nest, incubating, and rearing the young. In this respect the male humming-birds generally resemble the gallinaceous birds more than they resemble the related swifts.

The strangest of all the humming-birds, Loddige's Racket-tailed Humming-bird (*Loddigesia mirabilis*), known from a single valley 2,200 to 3,000 metres above sea-level in Peru, has only four tail feathers instead of the usual ten. The two outer tail feathers are long, supple and sinuous, and with these it displays before the female, making first one then the other undulate, or striking them one against the other like whiplashes. The males of the Long-tailed Hermit (*Phaethornis superciliosa*) forgather at the mating season and, far from fighting, embark on a protracted series of displays.

The Narina Trogon (*Apaloderma narina*) is the commonest and most widespread of the African Trogons, living in forests up to 1800 metres, but it is not often seen except in the rainy season. Then the male displays, inflating a blue-green bladder in its throat and calling with a deep cooing. Little is known about its nesting behaviour.

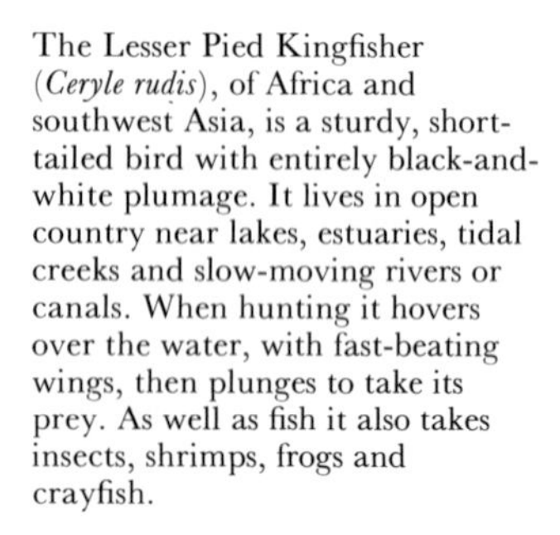

The Lesser Pied Kingfisher (*Ceryle rudis*), of Africa and southwest Asia, is a sturdy, short-tailed bird with entirely black-and-white plumage. It lives in open country near lakes, estuaries, tidal creeks and slow-moving rivers or canals. When hunting it hovers over the water, with fast-beating wings, then plunges to take its prey. As well as fish it also takes insects, shrimps, frogs and crayfish.

By contrast, the females of these two species have no comparable claims to distinction. They build their nests and bring up their young in a straight-forward manner. The typical nest is a small cup of regular shape set at the intersection of two branches or astride a branch. It is made of the finest fibres from the vegetable and animal kingdoms, including spiders' webs, and saliva is usually used to hold it in position. Sometimes coarser materials are added, but the inside of the nest is always fine and delicate.

There are two eggs in each clutch and the hen may lay two or three clutches a season, especially in tropical regions. They are the smallest of all birds' eggs, and always a uniform matt white. The chicks are very weak when hatched and remain in the nest for several weeks, fed with insects by the mother, or with nectar from her gizzard, as she thrusts her beak into the chick's oesophagus before regurgitating. Female humming-birds are most attentive and seldom abandon their eggs or young.

Colies (Order Coliiformes)

The colies or mouse-birds are small birds (twenty-eight to thirty-five centimetres) of southern Africa. Anatomically the six species of the single family (Coliidae) seem to resemble the woodpeckers (Piciformes) and the kingfishers and hornbills (Coraciiformes). They have short legs, strong curved claws and a reversible outer toe on each foot. This is an adaptation to climbing trees. The bill is rather like the finch's but fleshy around the nostrils. The body plumage, including a crest on the head, is soft and hair-like, but the tail feathers are long and stiff. They creep about trees and bushes rather like mice, feeding on berries and fruits and move in bands of twenty to thirty, keeping in contact with one another by whistling. Their mouse-like appearance is exaggerated by the dun colours of their feathers, but there is blue and white in the plumage of some species.

Trogons (Order Trogoniformes)

These birds have a unique foot structure: the first and second toes are turned backwards, while the third and fourth point forwards, an arrangement described as heterodactylous. Because of this marked difference from all other birds they are placed in a separate order, which consists of a single family, Trogonidae.

The trogons are essentially forest-dwelling birds and are rarely seen, even in the districts of Africa, Asia and America where they are most common. They lead solitary lives, making little noise and apparently concealing themselves in the densest and darkest places. They feed mainly on insects, which are taken in flight during the morning and evening. Their soft and downy plumage makes very little noise in flight. The songs are both monotonous and weak in quality. The short, strong beak bears stiff bristly feathers at the base, is hook-tipped, and sometimes denticulated. Like many arboreal birds, some species have a long, rather stiff tail which serves as a counterpoise and as a brace when digging their nest in soft rotting-wood, termite or ants' nests.

Species of *Harpactes*, in which the male and female are distinctly and beautifully coloured, live in Malaysia. Sexual dimorphism is also found in the African genus *Hapalodermes*, and is even more marked in the species of *Calures* from America; most species are sexually dimorphic.

One American species is particularly well-known, the Quetzal (*Pharomachrus mocinno*) which extends from Nicaragua to Mexico. It is a beautiful bird, nearly 120 centimetres long. The male in particular is brilliantly coloured, with greenish-gold tints on the head, back and breast, with carmine shades on the underparts. The eye is encircled with black feathers, the bill and feet are yellow, and there is a rounded crest of hair-like feathers on the head. The tail bears extremely long, flowing feathers. The Quetzal is the national bird of Guatemala.

Kingfishers, hoopoes, hornbills and allies (Order Coraciiformes)

Most members of this cosmopolitan order are tropical Old World species. Long bills, short legs, short wings, bright plumage and hole-nesting are the characteristic features shared by many of the order. Most groups have two or more of the forwardly directed toes fused along the sides for parts of their length and one group is able to reverse one of its toes to the rear, becoming zygodactylous. The fusion of toes is referred to as syndactyly.

Kingfishers (Family Alcedinidae)

This is a particularly bright-plumed group of three subfamilies, the Alcedininae, the Daceloninae and the Cerylinae. The typical kingfishers, the Alcedininae, have their most commonly known European representative in the Common Kingfisher (*Alcedo atthis*), a small solitary bird frequenting peaceful streams in Europe and the East. Perched on an overhanging willow branch it waits, motionless, until it plunges headlong to take its fish. The catch is then taken back to the bough, where it is always swallowed head first.

The Common Kingfisher has brilliant plumage of metallic green combined with azure blue and coppery red. It is squat and its extremely short tail contrasts with its long, wedge-shaped bill.

Like many other members of the family, the Kingfisher's nest is a burrow in the river bank and consists of a long entrance passage terminating in a roomy chamber, usually strewn with fishbones. The eggs are incubated by both parents. When the eggs are hatched the parent birds share the task of feeding and otherwise caring for the young. The nestling's feathers develop in waxy sheaths which protect them from the filth which gathers in the nest.

There are several related insectivorous species in the same family, including the Pygmy Kingfisher (*Ceyx picta*) of Africa and the numerous brightly coloured three-toed kingfishers of south-east Asia.

The Daceloninae, the tree, forest or wood kingfishers, are arboreal species of Australasia and Africa that eat insects, reptiles and even small birds or mammals. They have slightly longer tails than the typical kingfishers. The lower mandible is enlarged and the bill hooked at the end. The best-known species is the Laughing Jackass or Kookaburra (*Dacelo novaeguineae*), which owes its popular name to its cry. It is the largest representative of the family, attaining the size of a Raven. This species is often seen in towns, where it scavenges and eats snails and slugs. It makes its burrow in termite nests. The Racket-tailed Kingfisher (*Tanysiptera galatea*) of the Moluccas and New Guinea is a magnificent bird with elongated median tail feathers ending in rackets.

The Cerylinae are fishing kingfishers and the only members of the family found in the New World. The commonest is the Belted Kingfisher (*Ceryle alcyon*) with blue-grey back and white underparts with a blue-grey band across the breast of both sexes and a tawny band below this on the female, and a penetrating rattle of a call. The largest of the New World tropical genus *Chloroceryle* is the Crested Amazon Kingfisher (*C. amazona*). The Green Kingfisher (*C. americana*) is a small species found from the south-western United States to southern South America. One of the smallest is the Least Kingfisher (*C. aenea*), found through Mexico, Central America, and northern South America, which is only about twelve to fifteen centimetres long. A less colourful species in the Old World is the black and white Pied Kingfisher (*Ceryle rudis*) of Africa and south-west Asia. This species is particularly fond of crayfishes.

Todies (Family Todidae)

The five species of tody are confined to West Indian islands: one each in Jamaica, Puerto Rico and Cuba, and two on Hispaniola. They are wren-sized with broad, flattened beaks, finely serrated at the edges, facial bristles, short tails, and quill-like tongues. All are bright green above and pale below, with bright red bibs (the Jamaican Tody is known as a 'robin'). They sit in pairs on a branch, flying out to catch passing insects with a loud whirring of wings. Their nests are in tunnels in the ground where three to four white eggs are laid.

Motmots (Family Momotidae)

Eight species of this family are distributed from Mexico to northern Argentina. They range from eighteen to forty-six centimetres in length, much of which is tail. The plumage is mainly brownish green, with turquoise blue on the head. The bill is serrated as in the todies, and like them motmots fly out from a branch to take passing insects. They also eat snails, lizards and fruit. The elongated, median feathers of the tail are trimmed as the bird preens until only the racket-shaped ends are left. The nest is in a long tunnel in a bank, where three to four eggs are laid. General nesting habits are similar to those of the kingfishers.

Bee-eaters (Family Meropidae)

The twenty-five species of bee-eater can be typified by the Common Bee-eater (*Merops apiaster*), which usually nests in large colonies, burrowing into a sandy river bank or a cutting in a road. The horizontal passage may be one to two metres long

Two Common Bee-eaters (*Merops apiaster*) perch on a sun-bleached skull in Spain. One of the most brightly-coloured birds in Europe the Bee-eater has pointed wings, long forked tail feathers and a very long beak. It is usually seen in noisy flocks catching insects, particularly bees and wasps, on the wing. It has the rapid circling flight of a swallow.

and ends in a chamber. Sometimes the pair is assisted by non-breeding 'helpers'. The Bee-eater's favourite food is wasps and bees. With its blues, yellows, orange, reds and black, it is as lovely and colourful a bird as the Roller. The family occurs in the Old World from southern Europe and central Asia to South Africa, Madagascar, and Australia.

Cuckoo-roller (Family Leptosomatidae)

The single species is sufficiently different to justify its being placed in a separate family: although it has colours as bright as the true rollers and performs similar aerial acrobatics, it has a reversible fourth toe, powder-down patches on the sides of the rump and a bill overhung by large tufts of feathers.

Rollers (Family Coraciidae)

Sedentary in southern Europe and the northern shores of the Mediterranean, but venturing much farther north in summer, the Eurasian Common Roller (*Coracias garrulus*) is jay-like, has a greenish-blue or aquamarine head and front, yellow back, purplish-blue wing tips and greyish-brown tail. It has a long, straight beak, hooked at the tip, is solitary, flies strongly, and sits waiting for its prey, which it seizes on the wing. It makes its nest in a tree hollow or in a rock, at most adding a meagre amount of grass, straw or feathers.

Ten other species, distributed over Africa, Asia and Australia, make up the family, all noted for their acrobatics in the air, rolling, zigzagging, rocketing up with closed wings and diving.

Ground rollers (Subfamily Brachypteraciinae)

The five species making up this subfamily are confined to Madagascar. They are similar to rollers except that they hunt insects and other small terrestrial animals in the forests, continuing to do so from dusk well into the night. Correlated with this, their legs are stouter and longer and the wings more rounded and shorter.

Hoopoes (Family Upupidae)

The Hoopoe (*Upupa epops*), the only species in the family, has a pinkish-brown plumage, and its wings and tail are black barred with white. On its head is a long crest of chestnut-brown feathers with black tips. Its bill, black and very long, seeks out insects and other animals. It lives a solitary existence in open country and is very timid. The nest is made in a hole in a tree, and this is identifiable by its filthy condition and repellent smell, in striking contrast to the beauty of the bird itself. The excrement of both parents and chicks accumulates, putrefies, and attracts flies.

Wood hoopoes (Family Phoeniculidae)

The six wood hoopoes of Africa have more markedly curved beaks than the Hoopoe and live in large societies in forests. They have a strong, musky smell. They lack a crest and have long graduated tails of metallic colours. They differ from the Hoopoe in certain anatomical details, but some ornithologists place them in the same family.

Hornbills (Family Bucerotidae)

The dark-plumaged hornbills of the tropical forests of Africa and tropical Asia are ungainly looking birds whose bills vie with the toucans' in size. In most species the bill has a 'helmet' or a rough protuberance above it, and in many species this is an air-filled hollow and in some rather solid and ivory-like. The sounds uttered by the birds are loud and raucous. With the exception of the Ground Hornbill, all hornbills, which mate for life, have a common pattern in their behaviour: once the nest is made in a tree hollow, the cock immures the hen in it, blocking the opening with clay until only the tip of her bill emerges. Thereafter he feeds her and, later, the chicks, as long as they are inside. The young birds grow slowly and take several months to mature. When they are about half grown one of the parent birds enlarges the hole in the nest so that the female can emerge to help the male search for the fruit, berries, and insects which habitually form their diet.

The Great Hornbill (*Buceros bicornis*), found in South-east Asia, is 150 centimetres long.

The European Roller (*Coracius garrulus*) breeds in Europe, northwest Africa and northwest India and winters in the East African savannah regions. Its flight is strong and graceful but on the ground it moves clumsily. The name 'roller' comes from the male's beautiful courtship display when he tumbles and rolls down through the air from a great height, often continuing the rolling in level flight.

Woodpeckers and allies (Order Piciformes)

Plainly birds of the woodlands with second and third toes directed forwards, while the first and fourth point backwards. (Such pairing of the digits is termed zygodactylous.) Some families are primarily vegetarian, but most are insectivorous, all nest in holes. One family is parasitic.

Jacamars (Family Galbulidae)

These are graceful birds up to thirty centimetres long that range in humid forest regions from Mexico to Brazil. They have long, tapering bills and iridescent plumage, and in these respects they are not unlike humming-birds. They are noisy and full of activity. Frequent sallies from a tree perch to take brilliantly coloured insects are typical. They nest in burrows in a bank or hillside, where they lay three to four white eggs. The young are covered in a heavy white down, quite unlike the majority of naked piciform hatchlings.

Puffbirds (Family Bucconidae)

Thirty species constitute this family found in the tropical forests of Central and South America. The puffbird's head is disproportionately large, the plumage of most species is drab grey or brown, and its tail short. The overall effect is of a squat 'puffy' bird. A habit of raising the feathers until the bird looks rather like a huge powder-puff strengthens this impression. When alarmed, the birds immediately flatten the feathers against their bodies. They are quiet birds, rarely found in flocks. Nesting is of two types: in holes dug in termite nests, and ground burrows. Two or three glossy white eggs are incubated by both birds. One of the commonest species is the White-necked Puffbird (*Notharchus macrorhynchus*) of Central and South America, which is about twenty-five centimetres long.

Barbets (Family Capitonidae)

The sturdy, non-migratory barbets get their common name from the bristly nostril feathers round their bill. They are noisy and markedly arboreal, rarely descending from their perches at treetop level. All are weak in flight. Some species live on a vegetarian diet, others take insects. Distribution is pan-tropical, with high development in Africa. Asia, Africa, America, each has species peculiar to it. No genus or species occurs in more than one of the continents. Most are brilliantly coloured and active, but others, cryptically coloured merge inconspicuously into a background of dead leaves, are much slower in their movements. All are cavity-nesters, pecking out hollows in dead tree-trunks.

Honey-guides (Family Indicatoridae)

Like cuckoos, the honey-guides are social parasites and lay their eggs in the nests of other birds, where the young are raised by foster-parents. They are small birds found in the tropical forests of Asia and Africa. One species, the Greater Honey-guide (*Indicator indicator*) is particularly well known for its remarkable skill in finding the nests of wild bees. Its fluttering and calling in the bushes attracts the attention of any interested party, man, honey-badger or other mammal, and reveals the position of the nest. The birds wait for the comb to be left behind in the opened nest. Unique secretions in the stomach enable them to digest the wax. The honey-guides are insectivorous too.

The Hoopoe (*Upopa epops*) is widely distributed in Europe, Africa and Asia. Although it flies strongly it has a wavering, irregular flight. On the ground it runs and walks about with its head bobbing up and down. The name 'Hoopoe' comes from its cry of *hoop-hoop-hoop-hoop*.

Toucans (Family Ramphastidae)

A large, ludicrous, brightly coloured bill, serrated at the edges and in some species as long as the body, makes the arboreal Toucan one of the most striking of the piciforms. But the bill size is deceptive: its apparent solidity and weight are broken by a honeycomb of fibres within the bulky outer case. There is some doubt about the adaptive origin of the large bill. Certainly the bird's frugivorous habits do not explain its massive structure. The long tongue is bristled at the tip.

The largest species, with the largest bills, are those of the genus *Ramphastos*, inhabitants of lowland forests. The black of their bodies is relieved with gaudy throat patches, bright bills and tail coverts. Species of the genus *Pteroglossus*,

The Yellow-horned Hornbill (*Tockus flavirostris*) eating a snake. This is one of a number of small hornbills that live in savannah and thornbrush regions of Africa. They are usually seen in small groups feeding on the ground. Apart from small reptiles they eat fruit and insects and may take eggs and young birds.

The Keel-billed or Sulphur-breasted Toucan (*Ramphastos sulfuratus*), one of the most conspicuous of the toucans that inhabit the dense low-lying forests of Central and South America. They live in noisy flocks feeding on fruit and berries. In spite of its size the bill is very light and useless in defence against hawks, the toucans' main enemies.

The Great Spotted Woodpecker (*Dendrocopos major*) of Europe and Asia showing its striking black and white plumage. Typically a woodland species, it is also seen in parks and orchards, and is becoming a frequent visitor to bird tables where it will feed on household scraps. Its main food, however, is insects and the fruits of trees.

usually called aracaris, are smaller and the most gregarious. Other species inhabit the higher altitudes of the mountain forests.

Woodpeckers (Family Picidae)

This is a widely distributed family over two hundred species subdivided into three main groups: the Picinae or true woodpeckers, the Picumninae or piculets, and the Jynginae or wrynecks. General characteristics are large head, short legs, long, sticky tongue, insectivorous feeding habits, and harsh cries. The true wookpeckers are essentially tree-climbing birds. The wrynecks, on the other hand, are perching rather than climbing birds. The piculets perch and climb.

The Green Woodpecker (*Picus viridis*) of Europe and the Great Spotted Woodpecker (*Dendrocopos major*) of Europe and Asia are typical examples of the Picinae, clinging to a tree trunk with their claws, using the stiff, spiky tail feathers as additional support. In this position, using the large robust head, they hammer away at the bark with their strong wedge-shaped bill to extract insect larvae. The prey is then probed from the crevices with the long, sensitive, pointed tongue, which is cylindrical in cross-section. Its entire surface is sticky and bears small hooks at the tip. It is used as an organ of touch and taste. The tongue of the Green Woodpecker can be protruded for a length of twenty centimetres, five times as long as the bill itself, to explore cavities for insects. The anatomical structure of a woodpecker's tongue is curious in that it is prolonged to the back of the head by two ligaments which then curve upwards and forwards over the top of the skull to terminate, according to species, near the base of the bill, in the upper mandible or, more rarely, behind or below the eye.

The hunt for food is usually over a restricted territory, which is scoured daily. The entire surface of each tree is examined from top to bottom. The flight from tree to tree is both jerky and noisy. On the ground the bird has an ungainly way of hopping after insects and worms. The holes it drills in search of food are wrongly supposed to damage trees. In fact it attacks only wood that is already riddled with the borings of wood-eating insects. Its stomach is always crammed with the pests of cultivated lands and forests.

Woodpeckers' cries are short and resounding. In the Green Woodpecker the call resembles a crazy laugh, which has earned the bird the nickname 'yaffle'. During the mating season characteristic drumming sounds are made with the bill on a tree branch or a resonant, dead stump.

Woodpeckers lead markedly solitary lives, but come together in pairs for the breeding season. Male and female remain together throughout the entire period of nesting, incubation and the rearing of the young. The nest is hollowed out in the heart of an old tree and is lined with chips of wood. Some six eggs are produced, brown spotted or white.

North America has numerous species of typical woodpeckers: the Yellow-bellied Sapsucker (*Sphyrapicus varius*), the Red-headed Woodpecker (*Melanerpes erythrocephalus*), the Golden Fronted Woodpecker (*M. aurifrons*) and—one of the best known—the Yellow-shafted Flicker (*Colaptes auratus*) which is an ant-eating species common in the eastern United States. Further west this last species is replaced by the Red-shafted Flicker (*C. cafer*). A singular habit is found in one species, the Acorn Woodpecker (*Melanerpes formicivorus*): it gathers acorns and stores them for the winter in individual holes dug into the boles of trees, telephone poles, agave, and yucca stems. The method of storing is very systematic. The first hole is made near the base of the plant and then filled with an acorn. The second hole is made a little higher up, again packed with an acorn, and so on to the top of the stem. One wooden, electric power pole contained over 2,000 acorns stored in this manner.

European coasts have three spotted species, the Great Spotted Woodpecker (*Dendrocopos major*), the Lesser Spotted Woodpecker (*D. minor*), the Middle Spotted Woodpecker (*D. medius*); and also the Green Woodpecker (*Picus viridis*), the Grey-headed Woodpecker (*P. canus*), the Black Woodpecker (*Dryocopus martius*) and the Three-toed Woodpecker (*Picoides tridactylus*). The last-named species also occurs in North America where it is called the Northern Three-toed Woodpecker as there is a closely related species there, the Black-backed Woodpecker (*P. arcticus*). Black, white and red are the dominant colours in the plumage of *Dendrocopos*.

There are marked geographical variations in colour and size within this widespread group. Yellows and reds predominate in the warmer regions, while in humid conditions the darker colours are commoner because warmth and high humidity lead to excessive development of pigment and a reduction in size of the birds. Cold and dry conditions seem to have the opposite effect, producing bigger birds and brighter colours. This is an interesting example of the direct influence of the environment on living creatures.

Two species of wrynecks complete the family: the Eurasian Wryneck (*Jynx torquilla*) and the African Wryneck (*J. ruficollis*). Unlike the true woodpeckers these less specialised birds neither climb nor drill holes in trees though they do nest in cavities or holes in trees. They are, rather, perching birds, finding their food on the ground not in the trees. Ants form the staple of their diet. They take their common name from their habit of twisting their neck when disturbed. Plumage is a cryptic mottle of greys and browns. It is supposed that the wrynecks are primitive woodpeckers.

Perching birds (Order Passeriformes)

About 5,100 of the 8,700 known species of living birds are classified as perching birds or passerines. This group is currently highly successful. Other groups have been dominant in the past, each in turn replaced by a more successful form. Passerines owe their success to adaptation to a wide variety of habitats and to exploiting different ways of feeding. Their evolution has been so rapid and so diversified that the order contains about sixty-five families.

The true inter-relationships of many of these families are largely unrecognisable, particularly as parallelism and convergence are common; that is, unrelated birds with similar habits have come to resemble each other. For example, the American orioles and blackbirds (Icteridae) share their habitat preferences with the Old World starlings (Sturnidae) and have much the same build. More striking, they have the same kind of bill, a factor once regarded as a reliable basis for classification, but now known to be extremely plastic from an evolutionary point of view. Among the flowerpeckers (Dicaeidae) many different bill-shapes are found, some almost conical like a seed-eater's, others slim like a warbler's. Apart from a few reasonably well defined groups such as larks (Alaudidae), it seems that behaviour, especially nest building, provides a better clue to relationship than the structure of the birds themselves.

The passerines are all land birds, and the principal features common to the whole order are the four toes, all at the same level and never webbed. The hind toe is highly developed but not reversible. Song, too, shows remarkable development, particularly in the suborder Oscines, the true song birds.

All passerine birds are altricial and are hatched with only a trace of down on the feather tracts of the dorsal surface. At its fullest development this natal down presents a soft, fluffy appearance over the helpless nestlings. It is gradually pushed outwards by the tips of the feathers of the juvenile plumage, and portions of the down may frequently be seen adhering to the young birds when they leave the nest. Although the flight feathers are hardly discernible when the chick hatches some passerines are ready to fly in less than ten days.

The Yellow-shafted Flicker (*Colaptes auratus*) one of the best known woodpeckers in North America, widespread in the eastern United States, where it is also known as the Yellowhammer or Goldenwing. It has distinctive yellow markings on the wings and tail feathers, in contrast to the Red-shafted Flicker (*C. cafer*) in the western states which has red markings. Most authorities, however, now regard all flickers as one species.

Primitive perching birds (Suborders: Eurylaimi, Tyranni, and Menurae)

Broadbills (Family Eurylaimidae)

The broadbills are brightly coloured insectivorous birds inhabiting the tropical forests of Africa and Asia. The greatest number of species is found in the islands of the Malayan archipelago. One of the commonest in this area is the Green Broadbill (*Calyptomena viridis*), which is largely frugivorous. It is a dark grass-green colour with black bars on

The Black-headed or Hooded Pitta (*Pitta sordida*) of tropical southeast Asia, like all pittas has brilliantly-coloured plumage. Pittas feed on the forest floor and, in spite of their showy appearance, are more often heard than seen. They build large, untidy nests of sticks and roots on or near the ground.

the wings. The feathers are soft but look slightly waxy, so that the bird harmonises with the wet shiny leaves of its habitat. It sits silenty for hours in the shadows of a tree and only occasionally makes short foraging flights for insects, after which it returns to its perch. In contrast, the Black-and-yellow Broadbill (*Eurylaimus ochromalus*), of the same area, is whitish, with black wings with yellowish-white barring, and rather vinous-coloured underparts. The males perch for long periods singing a loud melodious song. Broadbills build a long, hanging nest of woven grasses and fibres, suspended from a branch by a slender rope of the same materials.

Kingbirds and allies (Suborder Tyranni)

Woodcreepers (Family Dendrocolaptidae)

Woodcreepers, or woodhewers as they are often called, are about fifty species of small neotropical birds, twenty to thirty-eight centimetres long, and predominantly brown in colour. They range throughout the forests and brushlands of Mexico, Central America and all but the southern tip of South America. They resemble woodpeckers in having a long bill and stiff-shafted tail feathers, and they lay white or whitish unspeckled eggs in tree cavities, although they do not excavate the nest-hole themselves. The Ivory-billed Woodcreeper (*Xiphorhynchus flavigaster*) is a typical species. It is a solitary bird, cryptically coloured in brownish tones, and never seen away from the woods. It invariably utters a loud, melancholy cry as it passes from tree to tree. It always alights on the trunk close to the ground, clinging to the bark in a vertical position, supported by its tail and with its head thrown back to give the extremely long beak free play. Thus positioned, it progresses upwards by short hops, exploring the crevices in the wood for small insects and spiders. When it reaches branch height, it flies off to the next tree. Its manner of seeking food is very similar to that of the Old World tree creepers. It is especially fond of the very large carpenter ants which live in the decaying parts of trees.

Ovenbirds (Family Furnariidae)

Chiefly renowned for the unusual clay, oven-shaped nests they build, ovenbirds, of which there are some 200 species, are found in most habitats in southern Mexico and Central and South America from forests to semi-desert, and from rocky mountain slopes to the sea shore. The so-styled North American Ovenbird is actually a wood warbler.

The Red Ovenbird or Hornero (*Furnarius rufus*), which is extremely widespread, is a stout little bird with a slender, slightly curved beak nearly two centimetres in length, and strong legs suited to its terrestrial habits. The upperparts are a uniform rufous brown, the tail slightly redder, and the underparts pale brown. Its food consists of insect larvae and worms, for it is an exclusively terrestrial feeder.

In favourable seasons a pair begin nest building in the southern autumn and continue sporadically in mild spells during the winter. Otherwise nest building starts in early spring. The site selected may be a stout horizontal branch, the top of a post, the roof of a house or even the ground. The nest is made of mud, to which root fibres are added to make it more durable. When finished it has the shape of a kiln or old-fashioned baker's oven, but with a deeper and narrower entrance. There is an inner nesting chamber so walled off that, while a man may get his hand into the entrance, he cannot twist it to reach the eggs in the inner cavity.

The inner compartment is lined with dry soft grass, and five white eggs are laid. The 'oven' is thirty centimetres or more in diameter, and sometimes weighs as much as four kilograms. Both birds share the incubation. The young are extremely noisy and, when half-fledged, can be heard although they are still within the nest. After emerging from the nest the young remain with the parents for up to three months. Only one brood is raised each year, and a new oven is built for each, although old deserted ovens will survive for two or three years.

Ant-thrushes (Family Formicariidae)

This family contains over two hundred species confined to the area between southern Mexico and central South America. The birds range in size from that of a Wren to as large as a Jay, but most are about the size of chats and thrushes, which they resemble. They tend to skulk in the undergrowth of the forests and brushland and in some respects have the same ecological preferences as the pittas of eastern tropical forests. Their name reflects the common habit of accompanying ant-armies in order to feed on the insects the well-organised ants flush from the litter on the forest floor. The nest, unlike that of the ovenbirds, is usually a simple cup, semi-pendent on a low branch or in a bush near the ground. A few species build a covered nest on the ground and some line a tree-cavity. Ant-thrushes are usually solitary, sometimes occurring in pairs, and are somewhat sombre in appearance, with black, greys and browns predominating. They are strongly terrestrial birds and consequently have very weak flight.

Ant-pipits (Family Conopophagidae)

Also known as gnat-eaters, the ten or eleven species of this family belong to the Amazonian rainforests. Small, stocky and wren-like, they keep to thick impenetrable cover, and little is known of their habits.

Tapaculos (Family Rhinocryptidae)

The ground-dwelling tapaculos related to the antbirds, may be found throughout South America and in Central America, in grassland, scrub or forest, from sea-level up to 3,000 metres. Most species are inconspicuous browns and greys, stout-bodied and up to twenty-five centimetres long. They feed on insects and seeds, scuttling for cover as soon as disturbed, and seldom flying. At most they flutter a few metres. Their breast muscles are poorly developed and their legs strong. For example, the Barrancolino (*Teledromas fuscus*), of Argentina, is only seven centimetres long but is capable of taking fifteen centimetre strides. A special feature of the family is that each nostril has a movable flap, the function of which is unknown. Nesting habits are varied: some species are cavity-nesters, others are tunnel-burrowers, yet others build with grasses.

Pittas (Family Pittidae)

Known also as jewel-thrushes, the pittas inhabit the tropical forests of the Old World, particularly in the islands of the Malayan archipelago, including New Guinea, and the rainforests of Queensland in Australia. They are brightly coloured birds of the forest floor, where they live on insects, grubs and land molluscs. They resemble thrushes in their skulking habits, their size and even the brown-speckled young, but differ in having bright plumage, stubby tails, fairly long, strong legs, and only a piercing whistle instead of a melodious song. One of the most widespread species is the Red-breasted Pitta (*Pitta erythrogaster*), which ranges from the Philippines throughout the Moluccas to New Guinea and its associated islands. Most species of pitta are sedentary and seldom fly. The African Pitta (*P. angolensis*), however, breeds as far south as the Transvaal and outside the breeding season is found as far north as Uganda.

Asities and false sunbirds (Family Philepittidae)

There are four species of these birds on the island of Madagascar. Two are plump long-legged fruit-eaters, the Velvet Asity (*Philepitta castanea*) and Schlegel's Asity (*P. schlegeli*), which look like pittas. They inhabit the humid forests on the eastern and western sides of the island. The other two species, the Wattled False Sunbird (*Neodrepanis coruscans*) and the Small-billed False Sunbird (*N. hypoxantha*), are so like sunbirds they were originally classified with them. They have a habitat similar to that of sunbirds but they are of more slender build, with shorter legs and a long down-curving bill with which they sip nectar and take small insects. The Small-billed False Sunbird is known only from seven skins in museums and appears to be in danger of extinction, as its forest habitat is disappearing rapidly.

New Zealand wrens (Family Acanthisittidae=Xenicidae)

Only three of the four known species of these wren-like birds are left. Two are now rare, the Bush Wren (*Xenicus logipes*) and Rock Wren (*X. gilviventris*) having been preyed upon by introduced rats, cats and stoats. The third is the Rifleman (*Acanthisitta chloris*), which is yellowish green, and feeds on insects and spiders in much the same manner as tree-creepers. There was a fourth species, the Stephens Island Rock Wren (*X. lyalli*), but the lighthouse keeper's cat exterminated them. All three extant species are insectivorous.

Tyrant flycatchers or kingbirds (Family Tyrannidae)

The tyrant flycatchers are common throughout the New World, about 365 species being currently recognised. They destroy many insects in gardens and orchards. In America these are commonly referred to as 'flycatchers', but since the flycatchers of the Old World, quite a different family, have prior claim to the name the Tyrannidae are better known as tyrant flycatchers to avoid confusion.

The Vermilion Flycatcher (*Pyrocephalus rubinus*), a tyrant flycatcher of Central and South America, is easily identified by its bright red and black plumage. The male is seen to best advantage during his beautiful courtship flight. For a small bird he is often surprisingly bold in defending his territory.

The Superb Lyrebird (*Menura novaehollandiae*) lives in the rain forests of eastern Australia. The male builds circular mounds on which he sings and dances, displaying his lyre-shaped tail feathers, during the breeding season. The female builds the nest, incubates the single egg and rears the chick which stays in the nest for at least six weeks.

Nesting habits are varied, with a general emphasis on cup-shaped nests set in trees or bushes, but hole-nesting and ground-nesting is the pattern in some species.

Plumage is olive-green, grey or brown, black and white; a few species are brightly coloured. There is little sexual dimorphism. Wings are pointed and tails slightly forked. Bristles at the base of the beak are prominent. Some species, like the Scissor-tailed Flycatcher (*Muscivora forficata*), have a deeply-forked tail. This species owes its name to the habit of opening and closing its long outer tail feathers while in flight. These feathers are ten centimetres longer than the neighbouring two. The total length of the adult male is thirty-five centimetres, of which the tail contributes twenty-five. The head and back are pearly grey and the crown and wing-linings salmon pink. The underparts and all the tail feathers are white, with the exception of the black-tipped central pair. The Scissor-tail is found usually in open, sparsely wooded country, where it watches for insects and catches them in flight like an Old World flycatcher. It also feeds on small fruits.

The Eastern Kingbird (*Tyrannus tyrannus*) is a large black and white tyrant flycatcher, and is the best known of this family. It is very much in evidence during the summer in American orchards and farmyards. These noisy birds, always ready for a quarrel and usually coming off best, seem to delight in driving off crows, even when they have no eggs in the nests on which the crows might prey.

Many species are crested, particularly those of the genus *Myiarchus*. The best known is the Great Crested Flycatcher (*M. crinitus*), mainly of eastern North America but also found in Texas, and in the winter in South America. In has a prominent crest, grey throat and breast, yellow underparts and a rufous tail, and it nests in cavities in trees, laying four to six buff-coloured eggs scratched and spotted with a variety of rich shades of brown and lavender.

Other common species of Canada and the United States are the Eastern Phoebe (*Sayornis phoebe*), Say's Phoebe (*S. saya*) which breeds as far north as central Alaska, the Least Flycatcher (*Empidonax minimus*), the Eastern Wood Pewee (*Contopus virens*), the Western Wood Pewee (*C. sordidulus*), and the bright red species with a black back, wings, and tail, the Vermillion Flycatcher (*Pyrocephalus rubinus*).

Sharpbills (Family Oxyruncidae)

A few skins, gathered from tropical America and deposited in various museums, represent nearly all that is known of the single species of Sharpbill (*Oxyruncus cristatus*). About the size of a starling, olive-green above, yellowish with dark spots below, and with a yellow and scarlet crest, the Sharpbill has a straight, sharp-pointed bill and feeds on fruit.

Manakins (Family Pipridae)

In some of the fifty-nine known species there is a curious and unexplained modification of the wing primaries. In shape and appearance this group of small, brightly coloured birds of South America resembles the tits, although the two families are unrelated. The wing feathers of many species are so modified as to produce a rattling noise in flight, so that the first intimation of the presence of one of these birds is a sharp whirring sound, followed by two or three sharp snaps. There is marked sexual dimorphism and an elaborate lek courtship pattern that varies according to genus. In one species, *Chiroxiphia linearis*, sometimes called the Fandango Bird, the central pair of tail feathers is very long. At the time of courtship a number of males assemble at a given point, where each prepares a display ground for itself. Then the birds placidly await the arrival of a female, when each male indulges in astonishing acrobatics in its own area. The competition continues until the hen selects one for a mate. The female builds the woven nest, slung in a low fork, and cares for the young completely by herself.

Cotingas (Family Cotingidae)

Also known as chatterers, the cotingas are distributed from northern Argentina to the southern border of the United States. Bellbirds, fruit-crows, tityras, becards, cocks-of-the-rocks and the strange Umbrella-bird are all embraced in this group as diverse in colour as it is in size and form.

The sexual dimorphism marked throughout the family is well demonstrated by the male Umbrella-bird (*Cephalopterus ornatus*), a jet black bird the size of a crow with a long feathered lappet and a huge umbrella-like crest on its head that projects beyond the lip of the bill. Another ornamented species is the White Bellbird (*Procnias alba*) of the Guianas. This snow-white bird has a black fleshy caruncle about seven centimetres long rising from its forehead. When excited, it erects the spike-like caruncle and utters a sound like a bell.

In the genus *Rupicola* or cocks-of-the-rock, living in the Amazon basin, both sexes have an erectile crest that covers the whole of the top of the head and extends right to the tip of the bill. The cocks are a bright orange, and the females are brownish. The cock birds perform in turn a dance on a prominent clearing, around which the hens gather to select mates.

Plant-cutters (Family Phytotomidae)

The three species of plant-cutter are pests to agriculture, for a reason unusual in birds: they damage far more than they eat. Sparrow-like in appearance, they live in the open woodlands of South America, from Peru to Argentina. They not only feed on vegetation, but with their finely toothed saw-like bills they cut off leaves, buds and shoots, and even sever small plants at the base.

Lyrebirds and scrub-birds (Suborder Menurae)

Lyrebirds (Family Menuridae)

There are two species, the Superb Lyrebird (*Menura novaehollandiae*) and the smaller Prince Albert's Lyrebird (*M. alberti*). The first is the largest of the passerines and looks very like a pheasant. It lives solitarily in the eucalyptus forests of eastern Australia, where it is rigorously protected. The species is terrestrial and rarely takes wing. The male is plainly clad in grey and rufous, but possesses a long tail made up of sixteen plumes, each of the outer pairs curved in the shape of an 'S'. When the bird displays it spreads the tail feathers fan-wise forward over its body. The inner tail feathers lack barbules and resemble the strings of a lyre stretched between the S-shaped outer pair. The male builds a mound of twigs on which he sings and displays. The female builds the nest unaided and she broods the single egg while the male remains nearby and sings to her. The single youngster stays with the parents for up to three years, and as one egg is laid each year it means that a family party may consist of both parents, a young chick, another one year old, and a third two years old. It is believed that the birds mate for life. The males are renowned for their powers of mimicry, and can imitate the songs of other birds, the screeching of parrots, and the sounds made by dogs and man. They have even been known to reproduce the sound of a train-whistle.

Scrub-birds (Family Atrichornithidae)

Although related to the lyrebirds, the scrub-birds resemble large wrens. There are two known species, both unique to Australia. The Noisy Scrub-bird (*Atrichornis clamosus*) of western Australia is the larger, measuring twenty-two centimetres long. The Rufous Scrub-bird (*A. rufescens*) of eastern Australia is eighteen centimetres long. This is a rare species, decimated by the destruction of its habitat, and survives mainly in the Lamington National Park. In 1961 the Noisy Scrub-bird, thought to be extinct, was rediscovered. Scrub-birds are near-flightless and rarely show themselves, although the ringing whistle of the male can be plainly heard. Their mimicry is almost as skilled as the lyrebird's.

Higher perching birds or song birds (Suborder Passeres=Oscines)

Larks (Family Alaudidae)

Larks differ from all other song-birds in that the posterior surface of the tarsometatarsus (the longest part of the exposed 'leg') is reticulate. They have conical beaks and are mainly insectivorous. One obvious and well-defined character is a hind toe with an immense straight claw. This makes perching difficult but walking easy. Other predominant features are the superb song and colour adaptation to environment. In a ground-dwelling family the second feature has particular importance in evading predators. The best examples are found in Africa where species living in red sand areas have reddish plumage, those living in pale desert are appropriately paler, while those in dark lava areas are very much darker plumaged. The species rarely enter the 'wrong' colour zone.

The well-known Skylark (*Alauda arvensis*) of the Old World has been introduced several times unsuccessfully into the eastern United States and successfully on Vancouver Island, British Columbia, as well as New Zealand and Hawaii. It soars vertically to a great height and hovers there singing for a long time, a mere speck in the sky, but still audible. It is while the bird is in flight that the song reaches its best. Suddenly it drops like a stone, and the next moment begins another soaring ascent towards the sun. On the ground it walks and runs quickly. It feeds on insects and seeds.

Normally sociable, the Skylark becomes pugnacious in the breeding season, the male birds fighting each other and behaving almost like gamecocks. After mating, the birds build simple nests in depressions in the ground. They may have two or three broods each year, with normally three or four eggs in a clutch. Both cock and hen share the duty of sitting on the eggs and feed the nestlings with worms, and insect larvae.

Four other species of lark are very closely related to the Skylark, but belong to different genera. The Woodlark (*Lullula arborea*) is smaller and, with the Short-toed Lark (*Calandrella brachydactyla*), inhabits waste ground, lightly tree-clad slopes and woods. The other two are larger; these are the Crested Lark (*Galerida cristata*), with an erectile crest, and the Calandra Lark (*Melanocorypha calandra*), recognisable by the dark patch on either side of its neck. The former likes the verges of roads, while the latter prefers bare, dry ground.

In North Africa there is the Desert Lark (*Ammomanes deserti*), which has a long, frail bill and sandy-grey plumage harmonising with the ground,

The Woodlark (*Lullula arborea*) feeding its chicks. It is a summer visitor to the south and west of Britain. Less territorial than most larks, it inhabits open spaces with trees where it can perch. Both sexes are alike, having a flattened crest and a pale eye-stripe. Its thin beak is adapted to an insectivorous diet and contrasts with the short finch-like beaks of the seed-eating African larks.

The Swallow (*Hirundo rustica*) or the Barn Swallow, as it is known in America, at its nest. The nest is made of mud lined with grass and is usually built on a roof beam or against a wall. Usually two clutches, of four to six eggs, are laid, very occasionally three. Swallows migrate to Africa in the autumn, returning the following April, quite often to the same nest-site.

in which it scratches like the gallinaceous birds, and there are bush larks (genus *Mirafra*), and finchlarks (genus *Eremopterix*).

Although there are many species of lark in the Old World, there is only one in America: the Horned Lark or the Shorelark (*Eremophila alpestris*). This also occurs in Eurasia and northern Africa. It has two small black 'horns' formed from crown feathers, and a black collar below a light throat. In flight it looks light-bellied with a black tail. There are slight differences in colour in the various regional subspecies found throughout North America. Being birds of prairies and open spaces that were once separated by continuous forests, their movements have tended to change as the forests have been cleared. Thus during the winter when the birds migrate from the interior to the warmer coasts more than one subspecies may be seen together. In the more southern states and in Britain and Europe they are sometimes known as shorelarks because when they visit these areas they are frequently found on the shore.

Swallows and martins (Family Hirundinidae)

This is a really cosmopolitan family of small, insectivorous birds, about ten to twenty-two centimetres long and highly gregarious. Only the polar regions and New Zealand are excluded from this distribution. Long, pointed wings, darkish plumage and forked tails are the general outward characteristics. They are well adapted to an aerial life. Flight is strong, swift and graceful, and food is taken on the wing through the very wide gape. This makes migration inevitable for most of those species living in temperate climates, for in winter their wholly insect diet is not available; one American species in northern areas during the winter subsists on the waxy fruit of the bayberry.

Three genera are cosmopolitan, the barn swallows (genus *Hirundo*), the cliff swallows (*Petrochelidon*) and the sand martins or bank swallows (*Riparia*). Some are confined to the Old World: the palaearctic House Martin (*Delichon urbica*), the Red-rumped Swallow (*Hirundo daurica*) of southern Europe and Africa; others, mostly hole-nesters, belong to the New World: the Tree Swallow (*Iridoprocne bicolor*), the Purple Martin (*Progne subis*) of temperate areas, the Golden Swallow (*Kalochelidon euchrysea*) found in Jamaica; the Grey-breasted Martin (*Progne chalybea*) ranging from Texas south to Argentina.

In Britain, during March or April, the first swallows and martins return, and by May all are preparing to breed. Most nests are made of mud, sometimes mixed with saliva, and lined inside with soft materials. In them are laid four to six white eggs (speckled in some species). Incubation lasts about twelve days, during which the cock feeds the sitting hen. When the chicks hatch they are first fed with insects.

In autumn the swallows assemble in flocks on roofs and telephone wires. They leave during the night, the European birds to Africa, and some American populations to Mexico and central South America. They fly by night and rest by day to escape predators. They appear to have a delicate sense for atmospheric changes. Often flocks fly off at the onset of a cyclone and escape storms that might be fatal. Swallows ringed in Great Britain have been recovered in Senegal, Guinea, Egypt, and even at the Cape of Good Hope. Few swallows or martins cross the Mediterranean on a wide front, but follow one of three routes: via Spain and Morocco, Italy and Tunisia, or the Balkans and Asia Minor. They cross the Sahara using the oases as staging posts. They reach their destination in October, winter in their second homeland and return to the first the following spring. Throughout southern Europe swallows are becoming unaccountably rare. In Paris 100 years ago, 2,000 nests were counted on roof-tops in a single street, but today not one is to be found there.

The Swallow (*Hirundo rustica*) which breeds in Eurasia and North America and winters in Africa, southern Asia, and South America, is known in America as the Barn Swallow: the Tree Swallow (*Iridoprocne bicolor*) is very common through most of North America. It is a hole-nester and winters as far north as it can find ample bayberries.

AFRICAN RIVER MARTIN (*PSEUDOCHELIDON EURYSTOMINA*): This is a single aberrant species of martin. It differs from typical swallows and martins in having complete bronchial rings, and there are other peculiarities. A large black swallow with red beak and red eyes, it is highly localised. It was believed to be rare, but in 1921 its breeding ground was discovered on sandy shoals in the middle reaches of the Congo River, where the water level is low in the dry season. There the colonies nest, each nest being a chamber lined with dead leaves and twigs, at the end of a downward-slanting tunnel, where three white eggs are laid. Later, as the waters rise again, the birds migrate 800 kilometres to the Nyana River. Their food is mainly winged ants. The species is presently recognised as a subfamily, Pseudochelidoninae, of the true swallows.

Pipits and wagtails (Family Motacillidae)

The pipits have the same brown plumage speckled with black as the larks, but they are distinguished by more slender bodies, longer, thinner legs, finer bills, and by being more strictly insect eating. The commonest British species are the Meadow Pipit (*Anthus pratensis*) and the Tree Pipit (*A. trivialis*). The former is more common in fields and marshy land, the latter on heaths, trees and bushes. The Meadow Pipit spends most of its time on the ground, whereas the Tree Pipit is most often seen in the branches of trees. Both, however, nest on the ground. There is also the Rock Pipit (*A. spinoletta*), which is not so common, for it normally breeds on the coast, less frequently inland in the mountains, and comes down to the wet lands of the valleys only in winter. In the western hemisphere this same species is known as the American Water Pipit. It breeds in the Canadian arctic, winters in open spaces as far south as the Gulf of Mexico, and is the most common member of the family.

Another American species is Sprague's Pipit (*A. spragueii*), which is mainly a bird of the plains and prairies, although it winters throughout most of the southern United States. It is distinguished from the Rock or Water Pipit by its straw-coloured legs, its striped back and less active tail.

Several pipit characteristics are exaggerated in the wagtails of the Old World, so called because of the movement of their tails when they walk. There are three very widespread species: the Pied or White Wagtail (*Motacilla alba*) with black and white plumage, slender legs, and a long tail; the Yellow Wagtail (*M. flava*), which has yellow underparts; and the Grey Wagtail (*M. cinerea*), which has a very long black tail. There are few birds so pleasant to watch. A wagtail runs very quickly along the water's edge, and even in the water, provided that the water does not rise above the tarsus. It walks with its body horizontal, the tail often held aloft for fear of wetting it. When perching, it straightens its body and lets the tail hang. When walking it wags its tail up and down. Its flight is easy and swift, undulating, jerky; often it will cover a considerable distance at one unbroken stretch. Its song is simple and pleasant; its food insects and aquatic molluscs. It makes its nest at the water's edge.

Cuckoo-shrikes and minivets (Family Campephagidae)

Many of the seventy-two species of this family have superficial resemblances to both shrikes and cuckoos. All have a shrike-like bill with bristles at the base, and all have the rump feathers matted, partly erectile, and with rigid and pointed shafts. Ranging from sparrow- to pigeon-sized, they are distributed from Africa, across southern Asia, to the Solomons. They live mainly in forests, where they feed mainly on insects and berries.

The Barred Cuckoo-shrike (*Coracina lineata*), of Australia to the Solomons, is twenty-four centimetres long, and mainly grey with underparts barred in black and white, recalling the Common Cuckoo. The Red-shouldered Cuckoo-shrike of Africa (*Campephaga phoenicea*) is slightly smaller, and mainly black with a red shoulder patch.

The Flamed Minivet (*Pericrocotus flammeus*), of India to the Philippines, is similar in size. It is black but has scarlet underparts, rump, outer tail feathers, and scarlet patches on the wings.

Bulbuls (Family Pycnonotidae)

The bulbuls are moderate-sized birds that live in the forests, open country or gardens of tropical Africa and Asia. There are about one hundred and twenty species, predominantly brown to olive in colour, few species having bright plumage. For their size they have remarkably small feet and legs, a feature that has no disadvantages, however, since bulbuls seldom come to the ground. Bulbul nests are cup-shaped. The chief item of diet is

The Red-eyed Bulbul (*Pycnonotus nigricans*) of southern Africa. The African bulbuls are mostly green or yellow with slender bills and rounded tails. They live in thick forest and undergrowth and feed much more on insects than do other bulbuls. They are sometimes called Greenbuls or Brownbuls.

The Grey Wagtail (*Motacilla cinerea*) seen at its nest with young. It has slate-grey plumage with contrasting yellow underparts. In summer the male has a black throat and a white eye-stripe and white moustachial stripes. This wagtail is widespread in Europe, parts of Asia and Morocco. In Europe it is mainly a resident or only a short-distance migrant but over part of its range the population winters in Africa and Arabia.

The Red-backed Shrike (*Lanius collurio*) is the only shrike to breed in the British Isles. The male is seen here feeding the young. The female lacks the male's black face. Like many members of the family it impales its catch on thorns earning it the name of 'butcherbird'.

fruit, although insects are frequently eaten. Some species resemble flycatching birds and these have well-developed bristles around the gape, but in the main these bristles are poorly developed, as would be expected among frugivorous birds. They are noisy birds, and according to species, the voice may be harsh or pleasant, but the most famed songsters of the orient belong to this family.

One of the best songsters is the Yellow-crowned Bulbul (*Pycnonotus zeylanicus*), which approaches the size of a Eurasian Jay. It has a straw-coloured head with a black line through the eye, a white throat, brown upper parts and mottled underparts, and it makes an attractive pet. It lives in scrub country, sometimes gardens, and along watercourses in Malaya, Sumatra, Java and Borneo. Another bulbul very common in the same area is the Yellow-vented Bulbul (*P. goiavier*). This is a thrush-sized bird, brown above, whitish below, with white eyebrows, face and throat, and a black stripe through each eye. As its name implies it is characterised by a sulphur yellow vent and under tail coverts. It also has a crest which is variously developed among the family.

Fairy bluebirds, ioras, leafbirds (Family Irenidae)

These very colourful birds from the size of a thrush to that of a pigeon, are fruit-eaters living in the tree-tops in forests from southern Asia to the Philippines. The male Blue-backed Fairy Bluebird (*Irena puella*) is iridescent black and ultramarine. The Common Iora (*Aegithina tiphia*) is nearly fifteen centimetres long, black above, yellow below, with yellow on the head, a greenish-yellow rump and white wing-bars. The Golden-fronted Leafbird (*Chloropsis aurifrons*) is green above, greenish yellow below, with a golden-red forehead, blue throat and black patches on head and breast.

Shrikes or butcherbirds, and allies (Family Laniidae)

There are about seventy species of these predominantly Old World birds, which are aggressive and carnivorous. The bill is strong, conical and hooked, with a notch on either side of the tip of the mandible. Together with their strong, sharp-pointed claws this gives them a predatory look. Like pipits and wagtails, they have three toes in front and a hind one which is separate. The shrikes or butcherbirds are well equipped for hunting, though much of their diet is insectivorous. The largest of them are about the size of a European Blackbird or American Robin but sturdier. They resemble birds of prey when attacking other small birds or mammals, but unlike the birds of prey they carry their prey in their beaks not in their claws. They have short wings, long tails and their colouring varies. A shrike's nest is an intricately made bulky, cup-shape built in a tree or bush. The parent birds tend their chicks over a relatively long time, a feature suggestive of birds of prey.

Among the European species the Great Grey Shrike (*Lanius excubitor*) has an ash-grey hood, the Woodchat Shrike (*L. senator*) is black with a rufous nape, and the Red-backed Shrike (*L. collurio*) is entirely rufous. All three have a pinkish-white belly and black wing feathers edged with white or chestnut. They inhabit olive groves, woods, hedges and isolated trees. They are generally solitary outside the breeding season and jealously guard their territory. They perch motionless in a tree, waiting to hurl themselves at their victims, killing them with blows of their beaks and carrying them off into a bush. The Red-backed Shrike, like many members of the family impales its catch on thorns, and in these 'larders' may be found dead beetles, grasshoppers, mice, lizards and frogs, which the birds eat at their convenience.

The Great Grey Shrike (*L. excubitor*) is one of the two species found in America, where it is known as the Northern Shrike. It breeds in southern Canada and migrates to the United States each winter. It is essentially a northern bird and is replaced in the south by the Loggerhead or Migrant Shrike (*L. ludovicianus*). Generally, the commoner of the two in the United States in winter is the Northern Shrike, and in summer the Loggerhead. The Northern Shrike is slightly larger than the Loggerhead and its breast is faintly barred instead of plain grey. The feathers at the base of the bill are grey rather than black.

The Bornean Bristle-head (*Pityriasis gymnocephala*), is twenty-five centimetres long, greyish black with red on the head and throat. This strange species is now considered a subfamily of the true shrikes Laniidae. Its head is partially naked and warty, the rest of it clothed with bristle-like feathers.

Helmet-shrikes (Family Prionopidae)

An exclusively African group is formed by two genera and several species of helmet-shrikes or wood shrikes. They are shrike-like birds found mainly in Africa, south of the Sahara, living in forests and feeding mainly on insects. Most are black above, white or buff below, and their distinctive features are the stiff feathers on the forehead projecting forward over the nostrils and the wattle surrounding each eye. The White Helmet-shrike (*Prionops poliocephalus*) is twenty-two centimetres long. It builds in the forks of trees a nest of grass, rootlets, bark fibres and spiders' webs, and sometimes the nests are in groups. Birds in the flock nesting communally will incubate each other's eggs and feed the chicks at random. It is even said that up to three adults will drive a sitting hen off her nestlings, and each then feed them in turn, the last settling on them to brood them. A group of six Spectacled Shrike (*P. plumata*) has been observed engaged in communal nest building, four bringing nest materials and two making the nest.

Vanga-shrikes (Family Vangidae)

Confined to Madagascar, the vanga-shrikes are closely related to the helmet-shrikes. The eleven species differ more than usual within a family, especially in the shape of the bill. All keep to the trees, feeding on insects, frogs and lizards found among foliage or on bark. The Helmet Bird (*Euryceros prevostii*) has a huge compressed bill, and the Sicklebill (*Falculea palliata*) a long, down-curved bill in marked contrast to this.

Waxwings (Family Bombycillidae)

The Bohemian Waxwing (*Bombycilla garrulus*) differs from the shrike in its soft, thick plumage, its crest, long wings and short tail. It is a fairly uniform rufous colour, lighter on the belly than on the back, and the feathers of wing and tail end in a patch of white or yellow. The secondary feathers have reddish, waxy-looking tips, giving rise to the name 'waxwing'.

The Waxwing nests in the northern forests of the Old and New Worlds, and makes only brief, irregular appearances in more southerly temperate latitudes. In the winter season it subsists almost exclusively on berries and other fruit, but during the breeding season it consumes mostly insects.

During some winters the Bohemian Waxwing is locally common in Great Britain, but these invasions occur sporadically and the number of birds varies. They arrive from Scandinavia in parties of a dozen or so and move around the country stripping bushes of their berries.

In America, in addition to the Bohemian Waxwing, there is a smaller species, the Cedar Waxwing (*B. cedrorum*). It is plainer coloured and has no white in the wing or chestnut red on the under tail coverts. Whereas in North America the larger species is found principally in western Canada, the Cedar Waxwing is common farther south and is seen commonly if somewhat irregularly throughout the eastern United States.

The silky flycatchers are here included in the family Bombycillidae. They are slender birds with crests, and are found from the south-west borders of the United States to Panama. The four species are often placed in a separate family Ptilogonatidae.

The Hypocolius (*Hypocolius ampelinus*) is distributed around the northern end of the Persian Gulf, and feeds largely on figs, mulberries and dates. This rather peculiar bird has been considered the sole member of a separate family Hypocoliidae.

The Waxwing (*Bombycilla garrulus*) known in North America as the Bohemian Waxwing. In winter the Waxwings move south through Europe from their breeding areas in the northern forests, sometimes in enormous flocks of several thousands. They move from one area to another stripping the trees of fruits and berries. At one time these irruptions were looked on with superstitious fear as the forerunners of disaster.

Palm-chat (Family Dulidae)

The single species (*Dulus dominicus*) in this family of starling-sized birds is localised on the West Indian islands of Hispaniola and La Conave. These birds live in flocks in trees, feeding on flowers and berries. Members of a flock crowd close together when perching and this social behaviour is evident also in nesting, a communal nest being built by about four pairs. Some authorities consider this species as a member of the Bombycillidae.

Dippers or water-ouzels (Family Cinclidae)

The five species in this family are all somewhat wren-like in stance, but their habits are unique. They are to be found mainly by mountain streams from Great Britain, Europe, through central Asia to Japan, and in western America from the Yukon to the Argentine. They are the most exclusively aquatic of all the perching birds and swim underwater, even walking on the bottom of streams in search of small crustacea, molluscs, small fishes and particularly insect larvae. A remarkable adaptation is that the 'third eyelid' (the nictitating membrane) is transparent, so that a dipper can close its eyes underwater and still see. It is something of a mystery how these lightweight birds can stay underwater, especially as air is inevitably trapped in their plumage when they dive under the surface. Yet they manage to do so and without the plumage becoming waterlogged, which would prevent the birds emerging and flying off. Their nests are always built close to

A Common Wren (*Troglodytes troglodytes*) coming to its nest with food for its young ones. The cock builds a number of nests, one of which is chosen by the hen, who lines it before laying her eggs. In severe weather as many as forty-six wrens or more have been seen roosting together in a hole or nestbox. Even so in hard winters the wren populations become seriously reduced.

water, usually behind a waterfall, in hollows, under walls or banks, even on a rock or fallen tree in the middle of a stream. They have even been seen to fly through a waterfall to get at the nest. The European Dipper (*Cinclus cinclus*) has an undeservedly bad reputation among salmon fishers, for it is thought by many to rake over redds (troughs in which the female salmon lays her eggs) to eat some of the eggs or fry.

Wrens (Family Troglodytidae)

About sixty-three wren species are currently recognised. They are essentially American and are all dull-coloured birds in shades of olive, brown and black, a few having a little white in the plumage. The bills are slender, often somewhat longish and curved. In most species the tail is short and frequently cocked over the back. The most widespread species is the Common or Winter Wren (*Troglodytes troglodytes*), occurring in the Old World. Long ago, it or its ancestors succeeded in crossing the Bering Straits and it gradually spread westwards to Britain and southwards to North Africa. Nowadays it is found wherever there is low cover and is frequently seen darting from shrubbery or a hedgerow. The song of most species is highly developed. In many the female joins the male in song, and antiphonal singing has been recorded. Some build nests in hollows, but others build bulky, ball-shaped nests out of sticks, moss and grass, lined with feathers.

The best known American species, the House Wren (*T. aedon*), ranges from southern Canada to the southern United States and in winter extends into south central Mexico. It has taken to constructing a neat cup-shaped nest atop a mass of twigs in bird houses and in any natural hollow. It sets up its summer home in almost every garden where the owners supply the house, and in return supplies continuous, rollicking song and vigorous action against any insect pests that there might be.

Mockingbirds, catbirds, thrashers (Family Mimidae)

Ranging from southern Canada southwards to all but the extreme south of South America, these are mainly solitary birds, or occur in pairs. Although most are arboreal they usually feed on the ground, and some are largely terrestrial. The Common Mockingbird (*Mimus polyglottos*) is as large as a thrush but more slender and longer-tailed. These birds not only have a well-developed song of their own but, as the name implies, they can mimic or mock nearly any other bird song or call. They will sing all day and even at night, without seeming to take time to hunt for worms or insects. The Catbird (*Dumetella carolinensis*) does not repeat its song. Its chief call is a distinctive, cat-like mewing note, usually heard issuing from thickets. The Brown Thrasher (*Toxostoma rufum*) is a slim bird. It is larger than a thrush and its underparts are not spotted. It also has a longer tail and yellow eyes. Like the Catbird it is found mainly in thickets, and even its song resembles that of the Catbird, although it is more musical and is repeated once.

Accentors or hedge-sparrows (Family Prunellidae)

The accentors are a family of North African, European and mainly central Asian birds. Because of the similarity between the plumage of the House Sparrow and that of *Prunella modularis*, this species, common in most of Great Britain, is generally known as the Hedge Sparrow, and less frequently by the more distinctive name, Dunnock. It is in no way related to the sparrows, but has a close affinity with the Old World flycatchers and thrushes. The bill is more slender than that of the House Sparrow and the head, throat and neck are greyish, the underparts greyish-white.

Babblers, Old World warblers, thrushes, bald-crows, Old World flycatchers, gnatcatchers, etc. (Family Muscicapidae)

All the subfamilies listed below have been, and still are, considered by many ornithologists as full families. There are, however, so many species so intermediate between these groups that the divisions have merely served as convenient size aggregations enabling the experts to discuss and study them more easily. They are listed here as subfamilies and one has but to substitute '*idae*' for the *-inae* in order to raise them to full families should the need or desire arise at any time.

Babblers (Subfamily Timaliinae)

The babblers, or babbling thrushes, have a distribution rather similar to the bulbuls, but also extend to Australasia. However, like the bulbuls some species in this subfamily closely resemble birds of other families, particularly the Old World flycatchers (Muscicapinae) and the Old World warblers (Sylviinae). Consequently some are dificult to identify as one cannot always be certain to which family the bird one sees really belongs. A good example is provided by the Malay Nun-babbler (*Alcippe poiocephala*), which apart from its slightly rounder, more slender bill, cannot be distinguished in life from the Olive-backed Jungle Flycatcher (*Rhinomyias olivacea*) unless the observer is familiar with the behaviour of these two species. Babblers further resemble the more unrelated bulbuls by being poor flyers, with short, rounded wings. There the similarities end, for as a rule the legs and bill are very stout and the birds are entirely insectivorous. Moreover, many live on or near the ground, particularly in thickets and dense jungle undergrowth. They have one characteristic which clearly separates them from the flycatchers and the thrushes, which many resemble, and that is the unspotted plumage of the young.

The ground-babblers are almost entirely terrestrial and are somewhat like small rails. the Malay Rail-babbler (*Eupetes macrocerus*) lives in the dense Malayan jungle and behaves very much like pittas, it moves fast on the ground and is difficult to spot. The jungle babblers are mainly dull-covered birds of Africa and Asia and some look very much like warblers. A widespread Asiatic species, Abbotts' Jungle Babbler (*Trichastoma abbotti*), which is olive brown above and pale below, is a common lowland bird, particularly along the sea coast, even entering wooded gardens. The ball-like nest is built close to the ground.

Then there are the scimitar- and wren-babblers. The former, which have scimitar-shaped bills, occur in Asia, Australia and New Guinea. The latter are small birds with long, strong legs and feet. Another group is the tit-babblers, small, almost tit-like birds, found almost entirely in trees, bamboos and long grass. These often have hair-like feathers on the back that give them a soft, fluffy look. The last group is the song-babblers, some of which are known as laughing or jay-thrushes. They are noisy birds and, unlike other babblers, their plumage is often brightened with scarlet, green, yellow and other colours. Many of them have a pleasant song. The Silver-eared Mesia (*Leiothrix argentauris*) is one of the most attractive. It has an orange forehead, black crown, eye stripe and moustache, silvery-grey ear coverts, orange-red shoulders, olive back, scarlet throat, rump and upper breast, brownish abdomen, and dark grey wings and tail marked with yellow and some red. This species ranges from the Himalayas to Indo-China and Malaysia, where it moves around the mountain undergrowth in parties.

Bald crows (Subfamily Picathartinae)

The two species of *Picarthartes* have not been seen by Europeans. Their native haunts in West Africa

The Common or Northern Mockingbird (*Mimus polyglottos*) is probably the best-loved songbird in North America. It usually sings from a high perch and its song is said to rival the Nightingale's. Mockingbirds will attack any intruder that enters their territory, even humans. Outside the breeding season they live in noisy flocks.

The Hedge Sparrow or Dunnock (*Prunella modularis*) feeding its young. It is common throughout Europe and the Near East but is often overlooked because of its unobtrusive appearance and habits. It is typically a bird of open woods and forests and of scrubland but in the British Isles it is found in parks, gardens and hedgerows.

Male Asiatic Paradise Flycatcher (*Terpsiphone paradisi*) seen on its nest. It breeds from Russian Turkestan eastwards through India to China and south and east to Malaysia and Borneo. Plumage varies in colour considerably in the various sub-species. The vernacular name comes from the long tail-feathers recalling the plumes of the birds of paradise.

are difficult to find and the birds are of uncertain relationships. Originally classified with the crows they resemble starlings anatomically, while in their build, nesting habits and method of progressing by long hops they recall the babblers. They are the largest birds to build a mud nest which they construct on the face of a rock. The Grey-necked Rockfowl or Bald Crow (*Picarthartes gymnocephalus*) and the White-necked Rockfowl or Bald Crow (*P. oreas*), up to thirty-five centimetres long, differ largely in the bare yellow skin of the head in the former and the pink skin of the latter.

Parrotbills (Subfamily Paradoxornithinae)

There are fourteen species of parrotbills, also known as suthoras, living in central and south-east Asia. They have no clear relationship with other families. Smallish with inconspicuous plumage, they inhabit scrub or grassland, feeding on insects, seeds and berries. Their feature is their parrot-like bill, yet they are probably near relatives of titmice.

Wren-tit (Subfamily Chamaeinae)

A single species of Wren-tit (*Chamaea fasciata*) is placed in this separate subfamily largely because its relationships are not clear. Many authorities feel it is definitely a babbler of subfamily Timaliinae. Small, brown, with a long barred tail, and living in low scrub on insects and fruit, it recalls both wrens and titmice. Wren-tits remain in pairs throughout the year, and probably for life. They are found only in western North America.

Old World flycatchers (Subfamily Muscicapinae)

This subfamily comprises 300 or 400 species, distributed over the forests, woods and orchards of the Old World. Most flycatchers are about the size of a sparrow, but have a bill somewhat similar to a swallow, that is, short, flattened, wide-split, and equipped with bristles, which act as a funnel for scooping insects through the open gape. Flycatchers keep watch for insects, especially flies, which they seize in flight, but towards the end of summer, when insects are less plentiful, some take to eating a little soft fruit. Then they leave for the south, and from September to March none is to be seen north of the Mediterranean. Convergent evolution in food habits leading to very similar methods of capturing insect food led the early Europeans in America to consider the tyrant flycatchers as belonging to the same group.

Two flycatchers are common in Great Britain. The Spotted Flycatcher (*Muscicapa striata*) is a dull grey-brown, somewhat paler below with brown-black streaking on the throat. It is usually seen from May to August in trees and bushes in reasonably open country, particularly parklands. It sits upright on the outer branches of a tree, occasionally flitting outwards after an insect and returning to the same perch. The way the bird flutters up to a swarm of gnats, takes an insect, then returns, only to repeat the performance, could give the impression that it is incapacitated in some way. The nest is usually built in the hollow of a tree and may consist of little more than a lining of moss, wool and feathers. Generally six blue-green eggs are laid and both parents share the incubation.

The other common British species is the Pied Flycatcher (*Ficedula hypoleuca*), which is found mainly in wooded valleys in Wales, northern England and southern Scotland. This species is black above and white below and has white also on the forehead and wings. Although one of the commoner flycatchers, it is not very numerous in comparison with some other summer visitors.

Many more species of flycatcher are found in the tropical forests of Africa and Asia, some brightly coloured. In Asia there is a large number of species with predominantly blue upperparts. The male Verditer Flycatcher (*M. thalassina*), apart from a black forehead and throat, is entirely verditer blue. This species lives in fairly open forests from northern India and Burma to Indonesia.

Another group is the monarch flycatchers, which also belong to the Muscicapinae. They differ from other true flycatchers in taking their insect prey from the branches of trees instead of sallying forth on wing. Although strongly territorial in behaviour in the breeding season, they often roam in small flocks in the winter. There are many species throughout the tropical forests. One of the most striking is the Black Paradise Flycatcher (*Terpsiphone atrocaudata*). Although only about fifteen centimetres long, the males of this species have tails thirty-eight to forty-three centimetres in length. Mainly black with purplish maroon-coloured shoulders and a white abdomen, this bird breeds in Japan and in winter flies south along the south China coast to Malaya and Sumatra.

Two groups of flycatchers are centred mainly in the Australasian region. First, the fantails (genus *Rhipidura*), which are easily distinguished by their small bills and feet, short but wide wings and their long broad tails which they cock up and partly open, flitting from branch to branch. Secondly, the whistlers (genus *Pachycephala*), which have a round, stout head and a short, thick, shrike-like bill and a robust body. They are brightly coloured with yellow, white and grey predominating. They are usually to be found singly or in pairs searching the lower levels of the forests for insects.

Old World warblers or true warblers (Subfamily Sylviinae)

The warblers are a large subfamily of perchers that includes the birds known in America as gnatcatchers. They are small birds with straight, conical bills that have a few feathers at the base and are slightly notched towards the tip. They are mainly insectivorous though they eat some fruits, especially in winter. Big trees do not tempt them, and they tend to be clumsy on the ground. As they have short wings, their flight is not strong and they are seen mostly in bushes or reeds, creeping about in search of their favourite food. There too they nest and sing. Their nests vary in shape, but they are always built with skill and grace.

The Sylviinae are divided into many genera, some containing numerous species. It is easiest to divide them into two biological groups: the bush or leaf-warblers, and those that prefer the reeds or marshy ground, the reed-warblers.

The warblers are mainly brown and grey, and male and female often have differently coloured crowns. The species are so numerous that only a few can be mentioned: the commonest in Europe are the Garden Warbler (*Sylvia borin*) and the Blackcap (*S. atricapilla*). The former is a reddish brown with lighter underparts; the latter has a brown back, grey-blue belly and head, and the cock has a fine crown of deep black. Both have a sweet song. Their nests are cup-shaped, made of dried grasses and hung from the lower branches of a hedge or bush. The warblers are sedentary in the south of Europe, only migrating north to nest from April to September.

Warblers of the genus *Phylloscopus*, a name which means 'inspector of leaves', have shorter bills that are also 'pinched' towards the tip. The plumage is a uniform green for the upper parts and yellowish underneath. In habits they differ little from birds of the genus *Sylvia*, except that they are more often seen in tree-tops and that their nests are spherical with an opening in the side. Their song is not as musical. Another species is the Willow Warbler (*P. trochilus*), which is a migrant in northern Europe, though sedentary further in the south.

Bush-warblers (genus *Hippolais*) are experts at imitating other birds' songs, and sometimes produce a regular potpourri of them.

Reed-warblers (genus *Acrocephalus*) generally have a reddish-brown plumage. The several species, including the Reed-warbler (*A. scirpaceus*) and the Marsh-warbler (*A. palustris*), haunt ponds, marshes and the banks of rivers, where they climb up and down the stems of reeds and water-plants. Their call is not pleasant, being rather like a croak. Their nest, which is in the shape of a purse, is of woven reeds. Both cock and hen sit on the eggs. The related Sedge-warbler (*A. schoenobaenus*) has black markings on its back, and the Fan-tailed Warbler (*Cisticola juncides*) also has black markings on a reddish back. Finally, the grasshopper warblers (genus *Locustella*) live on the ground rather than amongst vegetation and build crude nests.

Another group of species include the kinglets or goldcrests, from both Old and New Worlds. The Goldcrest (*Regulus regulus*), the smallest European bird, is a dull green above and pale greenish yellow below. It receives its name from the bright golden-orange streak edged with black along the centre of the crown. It is an inconspicuous bird with a rather plaintive, high-pitched call and is commoner in pine woods than elsewhere. A similar bird is the Golden-crowned Kinglet (*Regulus sapatra*) of the spruce belt of southern Canada and the northern United States. It differs from the Goldcrest mainly in having a white streak above each eye extending to the black edging of the orange along the crown.

The tailor-birds (genus *Orthotomus*), of which there are several Asiatic species, are also warblers. They owe their popular name to the way they sew together several leaves of the tree in which they nest, edge to edge, to make the walls of the nest. An Australian genus, *Malurus*, includes several small birds, some with brilliant, metallic colouring, mostly black, blue, green and violet. They are known by a variety of names: Australian wrens, emu-wrens, grass-wrens and bristle-birds.

The Spotted Flycatcher (*Muscicapa striata*) is a common summer visitor to Eurasia. Their reliance on flying insects for food prevents these flycatchers from remaining in Europe for the winter so they start leaving for Africa at the end of July, returning the following spring.

The Sedge Warbler (*Acrocephalus schoenobaenus*) seen at its nest in the reeds. It breeds over much of Europe and Asia and winters in Africa, south of the Sahara. It prefers to nest in reed-beds or in marshy areas on the edges of lakes or rivers but will sometimes use forestry plantations or cornfields if near water.

Others of this subfamily are the American gnatcatchers, the Blue-grey Gnatcatcher (*Polioptila caerulea*) being common in the woodlands of the United States. It is smaller than a Blackcapped Chickadee, blue-grey above and whitish blue, and has a long, black tail with white outer feathers.

Wren-thrush (Subfamily Zeledoniinae)

The Wren-thrush (*Zeledonia coronata*) lives in deep forests in Costa Rica and western Panama, 1,800 to 3,000 metres above sea-level. Although the size of a Wren, and having much the same habits, it also recalls the babblers of south-east Asia and Australia in its habit of skulking on the ground in inaccessible forests. Many authorities consider it a thrush of subfamily Turdinae.

Thrushes, nightingales, robins, Old World blackbirds (Subfamily Turdinae)

Representatives of this large subfamily are found in all parts of the world, especially in the temperate areas, where it occurs in fields and open country as well as in woods, arid regions and along the water's edge. In Europe and North America most are migrants that come north to breed and spend the winter in warmer countries. They eat mainly worms and insects and their larvae, but many species also feed on berries and fruits. The song is usually highly developed. It is difficult to find distinct common characteristics. Their toes are not joined; they tend to have slender rather than conical bills; and they are more insectivorous than frugivorous. Their affinities are with the Old World flycatchers and warblers. The Turdinae comprise the European Blackbird, thrushes, Nightingale, robins, bluebirds, Blue-throated Warbler, redstarts, wheatears and chats.

The European Blackbird (*Turdus merula*) is one of the most common European birds. It is seen everywhere and heard whistling from morning to evening during spring and early summer. Distinctive by reason of its all-black plumage and yellow bill, the cock cannot be confused with any other European bird. The hen is brown with mottled underparts. Partial albinos are not infrequent. Another species, more common in mountainous districts, the Ring Ouzel (*T. torquatus*), is distinguished by a broad, white crescent on its breast. These two build their nests low down and with great care, using moss, blades of grass and dry leaves, which they weave together. They then line the inside wall with damp earth, making a smooth waterproof covering. They lay four to five greenish eggs on which the cock and the hen sit in turn, whereas the hen Blackbird normally does all the incubating. Both species generally have two broods, one in March, the other in May, and it is not unusual for a Blackbird to have three, or even four, broods in a season, for they are prolific birds.

The thrushes differ from the European Blackbird in that both cock and hen are conspicuously marked on the underside with dark spots on a light ground. The Mistle-thrush (*T. viscivorus*) is the largest and perhaps the most common in Europe, where it gets its name from its predilection for the white viscous berries of the mistletoe, and on the Continent it sometimes roosts in mistletoe. By evacuating the seeds with its droppings, the Mistle-thrush helps to spread this parasite.

The Song-thrush (*T. philomelos*) is somewhat smaller than the Mistle-thrush. It sings short musical phrases, often a series of variations on or around the distinctive song of the species. It is sometimes called the nightingale of the north.

The smallest of the European thrushes is the Redwing (*T. musicus*). It is the only one with a buffish-white eye stripe, but gets its vernacular name from its chestnut-red flanks. Unlike the other thrushes, the Mistle-thrush and Song-thrush, the Fieldfare (*T. pilaris*) and Redwing belong to the higher latitudes, migrating south in autumn, and are most numerous in Britain in autumn and winter. The cock takes little part in building the nest except to help choose the site and to transport some of the materials, but even that is not the rule.

The Rock-thrush (*Monticola saxatilis*) and Blue Rock-thrush (*M. solitarius*) live in open rocky areas and on bare mountainsides of Europe and south-western and central Asia, though they have been known to nest in niches in towers and tall buildings. They are wary, solitary birds. The plumage of the Blue Rock-thrush is deep blue-grey, except for the wings and tail, which are deep black. It has a lovely song, though not the equal of the Nightingale or its close relatives.

Another member of this group is the very common American Robin (*T. migratorius*), very like the Song-thrush except for its grey back and its brick-red breast, which is its sole similarity to the European Robin. In the male the head and tail are blackish; in the female, paler. It breeds from the tree-limit in Canada southwards to southern Mexico. It is partially migratory and many winter in the southern United States.

Other American thrushes that resemble birds of this group, but are a little smaller, belong to the genus *Catharus*. The Veery (*C. fuscescens*) is the most uniform in colour, rusty above, pale below with indistinct spots on the breast. Its song is a distinctive breezy whistle. Common in damp woods from Canada to the central United States, it migrates to South America during the winter.

A similar bird is the Hermit Thrush (*C. guttatus*), which has more distinctive spotting on the breast and a conspicuous reddish tail. It breeds in the evergreen-hardwood forests of southern Canada and the central United States and winters in the more southern States. The song is clear and flute-like, consisting of a key note followed by four or five phrases at different pitches. Another similar bird is the Wood Thrush (*H. mustelina*), but this has conspicuous spotting on the breast and sides and a reddish head instead of a reddish tail as in the Hermit Thrush. It also has a wider range in North America, where it is found in deciduous woodlands. It usually winters in places like Florida.

Another group of European Turdinae comprises four main species, all small in size, sombre in colouring, and easy to distinguish by their markings. The Nightingale (*Luscinia megarhynchos*) is of a uniform reddish brown, deeper on the back than on the underparts. The European Robin (*Erithacus rubecula*) differs from the latter in having a bright red throat and breast. These same parts are of a lovely azure blue in the Bluethroat (*Luscinia svecica*), which also has a central white patch and tri-coloured collar. Finally there is the Redstart (*Phoenicurus phoenicurus*) with its distinctive red tail and black throat. The top of its head and its back are of an ashen blue.

All four live in woodlands, parks and heaths. They are solitary and not sociable, quarrelling and fighting among themselves in the breeding season. Each cock then selects a territory which it will defend most energetically. They make rather crude cup-shaped nests on or near the ground.

In addition there are a number of small, brightly coloured members of the thrush family. One of several similar species, the Eastern Bluebird (*Sialia sialis*) is common in semi-open country and is found throughout most of temperate eastern North America. It is a little larger than a Sparrow and the male is blue above with a red breast. In Asia there are other similar birds, usually known as robins or shortwings. The Siberian Blue Robin (*Luscinia cyane*), which is slaty blue above and white below, breeds in Siberia and Japan and winters principally in the islands of the Indo-Australasian archipelago.

In these same islands live a group known as shamas. One of the commonest is the White-rumped Shama (*Copsychus malabaricus*), which is black with a chestnut abdomen and a white rump. Its tail is longer than its body and is black, apart from the outermost feathers which are white. It lives in thickets in the forests and is regarded as one of the best song-birds in the world.

Another group in the subfamily Turdinae is the forktails found throughout the Orient. They can be distinguished by their deeply forked tail, which is opened and closed repeatedly like a pair of scissors. Their size is about that of wagtails, particularly the Pied or White Wagtail (*Motacilla alba*), which they resemble not only in continuously flicking the tail as they walk but in being mainly black and white in colour. One of the most widespread species is the White-crowned Forktail (*Enicurus leschenaulti*), which extends from the Himalayas to the China Sea. This bird is black but has a white crown, rump and abdomen, and a white bar on the wings and white tips to the long, black tail feathers. It is usually to be found along fast-flowing streams flying from boulder to boulder, searching the water for insect larvae.

The last group of the Turdinae comprises the wheatears and the chats, most of which live in stony, rocky or sandy parts and make their nests in a hole in the ground. Like the Nightingale, they are fairly strictly insectivorous and thus of help to farmers. There is nothing remarkable about their song. An example is the Wheatear (*Oenanthe oenanthe*), which has a white rump and white sides to its tail. Then there is the Stonechat (*Saxicola torquata*) with a black head, white half-collar and an orange breast contrasting with the deep brown of its upperparts.

Titmice and chickadees (Family Paridae)

The members of this family are small birds with stocky bodies and short, conical bills. Their nostrils are covered by feathers, and they have strong claws, especially on the hind toe.

In the woods and copses they are never still, constantly flying from tree to tree, examining the branches, and swinging and hanging like acrobats to do so. No corner, however remote, escapes them as they seek out insects as well as their larvae and eggs. A fly passing by is caught as it goes. Enormous quantities of insects must be eaten to feed their broods, which are always large.

The Paridae build strong, intricate nests, which are usually spherical with a round opening near the top. Moss, lichen, feathers, hair, and spiders' webs are some of the materials with which they weave. Each of their two clutches comprises six to fourteen finely speckled yellowish-white eggs.

The plumage patterns in the Paridae are variable, but with grey, black and white predominating in many species. Among the European birds there are first the two tits with greenish upperparts and yellow belly: the Great Tit (*Parus major*), which has a black head and white cheeks; and the Blue Tit (*P. caeruleus*), which has a white head with

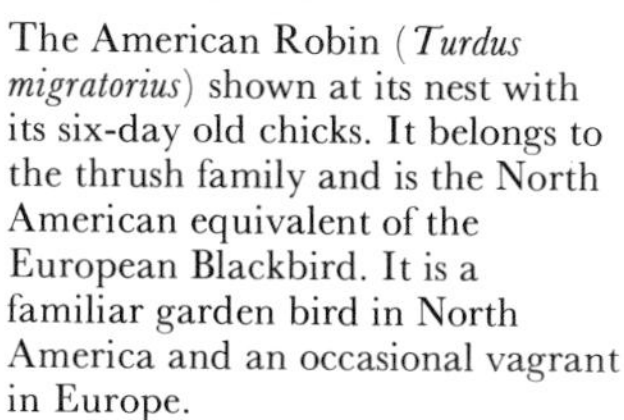

The American Robin (*Turdus migratorius*) shown at its nest with its six-day old chicks. It belongs to the thrush family and is the North American equivalent of the European Blackbird. It is a familiar garden bird in North America and an occasional vagrant in Europe.

The European Robin (*Erithacus rubecula*) is a familiar and popular bird of gardens and parks in Britain but on the Continent it is a shy bird frequenting woods and forests. It is a resident bird in Britain but Robins breeding in many parts of northern Europe migrate to the Mediterranean region in winter.

The Blue Tit (*Parus caeruleus*) is largely confined to central and western Europe. It is a familiar and popular bird at the bird table showing great enterprise and ability in reaching hanging coconuts and fats and taking peanuts from meshbags. The Blue Tit's normal diet is insects of all kinds, as well as the larvae and eggs.

The Long-tailed Tit (*Aegithalos caudatus*) shown here feeding its young. The nest, often built in a gorse bush, is a beautiful and compact domed structure made of mosses and bound together with hair and spider's webs. The species is widely distributed across Europe and Asia.

The Whinchat (*Saxicola rubetra*) is a migratory species breeding throughout most of Europe and western Asia, as far north as the Arctic Circle, and wintering in tropical Africa. It nests on the ground in open grassland, marshes and heaths. It can be distinguished from the similar Stonechat by its pale eye-stripe and white sides to the base of the tail.

blue crown and a black collar. Then come those that are less common, the Coal Tit (*P. ater*), the Marsh Tit (*P. palustris*), and the rare Willow Tit (*P. atricapillus*), all of which are more sombre with brownish upperparts and black crowns. The last two are almost indistinguishable, but the head of the Willow Tit is duller. There is also the Crested Tit (*P. cristatus*), which has a crest of black feathers edged with white, and in Great Britain is confined to Scotland. Finally, one that looks almost like a little ball of feathers, the Long-tailed Tit (*Aegithalos caudatus*), has a coat of black and pink, a white apron, white head, and black eyebrows. There is, too, the Penduline Tit (*A. pondulinus*) of southern Europe, which has red upperparts and white belly and which makes a purse-shaped nest hung from reeds.

The Willow Tit of Europe also occurs in North America, where it is known as the Black-capped Chickadee. In America it is one of the most common and beloved birds at home feeding stations. A similar species, but somewhat smaller, is the Carolina Chickadee (*Parus carolinensis*). These two species replace each other geographically. The former range across Canada and parts of the northern United States, while the latter extends southwards throughout the more southern United States to the Gulf of Mexico. The Brown-capped or Boreal Chickadee (*P. hudsonicus*) is similar but its plumage is brown or brownish where it is black or grey in other species. Finally in North America is the Tufted Titmouse (*P. bicolor*) with a grey, crested crown and grey back. The name chickadee is derived from the songs of the Black-capped Chickadee, or Willow Tit of Europe (*P. altricapillus*), and the other 'chickadees'.

Another branch of the Paridae consists of a number of Asiatic forms, as well as one European species, the Bearded Tit (*Panurus biarmicus*). It is an attractive bird with ashen grey head, vivid red underparts, and the sides of its head are graced with a pair of black 'moustaches'. It lives in secluded reed beds. The pairing bond between the sexes appears to be very great.

Tree creepers and nuthatches (Families Certhiidae and Sittidae)

These two families belong to the same ecological group as the true climbers like the woodpeckers. However, while the woodpeckers have two toes in front and two behind, tree creepers, wall creepers and nuthatches have three in front and one behind. Their form of adaptation for climbing consists of an extraordinary development of the claw of the thumb, which is strong and hooked. It is a veritable climbing iron which supports them when climbing vertically and enables the nuthatch to climb head downwards. The creepers particularly have long slender bills for searching out insects and spiders. All are mainly insectivorous and spend their lives climbing about the trunks of trees or rock faces inspecting all the cracks and crannies in search of food. They have long tongues which end either in a tuft of hair-like filaments or in little hooked papillae which help them to catch larvae and insects.

The Certhiidae and Sittidae are not sociable, living alone except during the breeding season. They further resemble the woodpeckers by building their nests in a lined tree or rock cavity, which they pad with moss, lichen and feathers; but they do not excavate the hole themselves.

There are three European species of Certhiidae. The first is the Treecreeper (*Certhia familiaris*) which is similar to the Brown Creeper of North America (*Certhia americana*). The Short-toed Treecreeper (*C. brachydactyla*) is more common on mainland Europe. The Treecreeper and Brown Creeper are small birds with long down-curved beaks, reddish-brown plumages with black and white streaks on their upper parts and a light grey belly. The creeper's hunting technique is most interesting: beginning at the foot of a tree it climbs in straight lines and spirals, but in such a way as to leave no part unexplored. Each branch is similarly inspected. When the bird reaches the top of the tree, it glides down to the foot of the next tree, where it starts climbing again. Ivy-clad walls are also good hunting grounds for it. The whole business is performed in silence. The Treecreeper has a very brief and unremarkable call, which sounds like a weak, high-pitched *seeee*. The mating and nesting season is from March to June. There are two successive broods, the first containing from six to nine eggs and the second from three to six. The eggs are white and brown.

The third species is the Wall Creeper (*Tichodroma muraria*), a bird common only in the mountains from the Alps and Pyrenees to the Himalayas. It has a grey-black plumage with crimson patches on its wings, and is said to prefer bare rocks and harsh, arid Alpine regions. It visits the long trails of plants growing down the rocks, but only to look for insects, and always seems to be in a hurry to get back to the bare places. The Wall Creeper never climbs in trees and does not like the ground, living only in the air or on the rocks. If it sees an insect on the ground, and cannot reach it from its rock, it will take off, fly down, and alight for an instant just to seize its prey, and the next moment it will be back on its wall of rock looking for a suitable place in which to eat its prey. It eats the small beetles that feign death and let themselves roll down the rock and into some inaccessible place, and the spiders that try to escape by letting themselves down on their thread. These it catches as they fall through the air.

Included in the family Sittidae are two groups formerly considered separate families: the Australian nuthatches (subfamily Neosittinae) of about five species restricted to New Guinea and Australia and the Coral-billed Nuthatch (*Hypositta corallirostris*) of Madagascar, the only member of the subfamily Hyposittinae.

The European Nuthatch (*Sitta europaea*) is common in the woods and copses of much of Europe. Unlike the creepers it has a straight beak. Its plumage is grey on the upper parts, the underparts are rufous, and it has a long, black eye stripe. Like the Tree Creeper, the Nuthatch darts about the trunks and branches of trees, climbing up and down incessantly, being the only bird to descend head first, which the woodpeckers never do, and ceaselessly uttering its little cry of *tait tait*. Children, being more forthright, generally call nuthatches 'upside-down birds'. The Nuthatch is not as completely insectivorous as the Tree creeper. In addition to insects and larvae it will eat seeds, even those of conifers, which it knows how to extract. In fact the name is derived from an old English word meaning 'nut hacker' because they hack hard-shelled seeds open with their bills. Having selected a hole in a tree and enlarged it, if need be, the hen Nuthatch lines the opening with mud worked with her beak, and so makes it narrower.

There are four species of nuthatches in North America. The White-breasted Nuthatch (*Sitta carolinensis*) has a black cap, and its black eye is set in a white cheek. It has a wide range and is found in most woodlands and orchards. In contrast the Red-breasted Nuthatch (*S. canadensis*) has a broad, black stripe through the eye and prefers the evergreen forests. It breeds from the limits of spruce trees in Canada to north Minnesota, Michigan and in the Appalachian Mountains to North Carolina. The Brown-headed Nuthatch (*S. pusilla*), with a brown cap coming down to the eyes and a white spot on the nape, has a more restricted range. It is a resident only of the open pine woods

The Short-toed Tree Creeper (*Certhia brachydactyla*) seen feeding its young in the nest usually built behind loose bark on a tree trunk. The species is much less widely distributed than the Common Tree Creeper, being restricted mainly to south western and central Europe and a narrow coastal strip in North Africa. It inhabits open deciduous woodlands, parks, gardens and hedges.

The White-breasted Nuthatch (*Sitta carolinensis*) lives in deciduous woodlands in North America from southern Canada to northern Mexico. It nests in hollows in trees or stumps, even in nestboxes. Like the European Nuthatch and Tree Creeper it searches the bark of trees for insects.

from Florida and the Gulf of Mexico, as far north as coastal Delaware and southern Missouri. Finally there is the Pygmy Nuthatch (*S. pygmaea*), small as the name implies, similar to the Brown-headed Nuthatch, which is found in the mountains of western North America.

Australian tree creepers (Family Climacteridae)

This is a group of six species, all in the genus *Climacteris*, found in Australia and New Guinea. They were formerly placed in the true tree creeper family Certhiidae, but some basic differences have led to their being considered a separate family. The bill is longer and more decurved, the legs and toes are long with strong claws, the tail feathers are not stiffened, and there is noticeable sexual dimorphism not present in Certhiid species. Species included are the Red-browed Tree Creeper (*Climacteris erythrops*) and the White-throated Tree Creeper (*C. leucophaea*) both of eastern Australia.

Flowerpeckers (Family Dicaeidae)

About fifty species of flowerpeckers are found only in the oriental and Australasian regions. Those of the genus *Anaimos* look rather like kinglets (or goldcrests). Others, such as the Scarlet-backed Flowerpecker (*Dicaeum cruentatum*), which is mainly black with buffish-white underparts and a brilliant scarlet head and back, look somewhat like a sunbird, but with a short bill. Unlike the sunbirds the flowerpeckers feed on seeds as well as insects. The Scarlet-backed Flowerpecker has a wide Asiatic distribution and can be found wherever the tropical parasitic mistletoe *Loranthus* grows, the berries of which form its favourite food.

Sunbirds are tiny, brilliantly-coloured birds with a tubular tongue adapted for nectar feeding. They are found in the tropics of the Old World. This male Firetailed Sunbird comes from Nepal but most sunbirds are concentrated in Africa.

The Yellow-tinted or Pale-yellow Honeyeater (*Meliphaga flavescens*) lives in open country with scattered trees and scrub in tropical northern Australia and New Guinea. It is never found far from water as it likes to drink and bathe frequently in the heat of the day. It feeds on honey from flowering eucalyptus and also takes insects.

Sunbirds (Family Nectariniidae)

Most sunbirds are very small and are usually seen fluttering around flowers. There are over one hundred species. They look very like humming-birds, having an iridescent plumage and long, curved bills. They are found throughout the tropical parts of the Old World and are the counterpart of the humming-birds in the New World. Like them they feed on nectar, but will also eat small insects found inside blossom. Indeed, insects trapped in the nectar are an essential part of their diet. The nests are usually purse-like structures hanging from a branch. In many species the males lose their brilliant plumage in the non-breeding season, and have an eclipse plumage resembling that of the immature males or even that of the female.

One widespread Asiatic species is the Yellow-backed Sunbird (*Aethopyga siparaja*), which is a brilliant, metallic scarlet above and on the breast, with a bright yellow rump, the abdomen being greyish. In some areas these birds have a metallic blue tail and forehead.

White-eyes (Family Zosteropidae)

Superficially resembling the unrelated American vireos, these small warbler-like birds are predominantly olive-green above, with a yellow throat and white abdomen, although some species have varying amounts of grey, brown or black. With the exception of a few aberrant species they are all characterised by a ring of white feathers around each eye. The white-eyes extend from Africa south of the Sahara eastwards to Asia and southwards to Australia, where they live particularly on the edges of the forests, in secondary growth, plantations and mangroves. They feed on insects, and small fruits, and will probe flowers for nectar with their brush-like tongues.

Honey-eaters (Family Meliphagidae)

There are 160 species of honey-eaters, distributed over the south-west Pacific from Australia to Hawaii. Small, with slightly down-curved bill, honey-eaters have a highly specialised tongue. It is extensile and brush-like just behind the horny, pointed tip, and can be used as a probe, brush and sucking-tube for taking nectar and the insects assembled to drink it. The birds also carry pollen as they brush past the flowers and are believed to play a major part in pollinating the Australian eucalyptus forests. The Parson-bird or Tui of New Zealand (*Prosthemadera novaeseelandiae*) has two white feathers on either side of its throat. The New Zealand Bell-bird (*Anthornis melanura*) is insignificant except for its bell-like call. Other honey-eaters, however, are more richly coloured, and one, the Moho (*Moho nobilis*) of Hawaii, was wiped out through being trapped for its feathers.

Buntings and allies (Family Emberizidae)

This family includes many species which were formerly placed in the family Fringillidae. Recent behavioural and anatomical studies have shown that the grouping followed here is most natural. It includes many species especially in America, referred to as sparrows as well as the buntings, some grosbeaks, towhees, juncos and longspurs, etc. The birds in this family are generally sparrow-like but it also includes many brightly coloured species. There is still much disagreement as to whether or not some species belong in this family or in the Fringillidae; possibly one hundred species or more make up the Emberizidae. To agree with the old arrangements the subfamilies listed below, except for Emberizinae and Pyrrhuloxiinae which would maintain their subfamily rank but in the Fringillidae, should be raised to family status and the tanagers placed closer in order to the Fringillidae. It is one of the most numerous (over 500 species) and widespread of the families.

Buntings and Cardinal grosbeaks (Subfamilies Emberizinae and Pyrrhuloxiinae)

The Yellowhammer or Yellow Bunting (*Emberiza citrinella*) of Europe and the Ortolan Bunting (*E. hortulana*) are likewise not distinguished for their song. None-the-less the Yellowhammer is a beautiful bird with its head and neck a fine lemon yellow. The habitat of both Yellowhammer and Ortolan Bunting is farmlands, roadsides and open country.

In addition to the large number of North American members of the Emberizidae called 'sparrows' there is another group known as juncos. The relationships between some of the species are so close, owing to interbreeding, that it is not always possible to know to which species an individual actually belongs. For this reason the birds are sometimes merely known by field observers as juncos. One common bird of the coniferous and mixed forests of North America which may be more readily identified is the Dark-eyed Junco (*Junco hyemalis*). It is greyish above with a white underside and outer tail feathers. In winter it migrates to the warmer parts of the United States.

One of the best known of the American finches is the Cardinal (*Cardinalis cardinalis*), which is smaller than a thrush, but has the typical conical bill of a finch. The males are red all over except for some black around the base of the bill. The Cardinal can be readily distinguished from some of the tanagers which it superficially resembles, by its characteristic crest and heavy red bill. It is non-migratory and is found chiefly in the states south of the Great Lakes. Another American species is the Painted Bunting (*Passerina ciris*) which is probably the gaudiest of all the birds of the United States. It is about the size of the House Sparrow and the males have a bluish-violet head, green back and red rump and underparts. It breeds mainly in central United States and winters further south.

Many American members of the Emberizidae are known as sparrows. They look very much like House and European Tree Sparrows, although these belong to the unrelated weaver-bird family Ploceidae. One of the best known is the Vesper Sparrow (*Pooecetes gramineus*). It differs from a House Sparrow by having white outer tail feathers, a whitish eye-ring and a chestnut-coloured patch at the bend of the wing. A bird of meadows, fields and prairies, it breeds in southern Canada and the more northern United States, wintering further south to the Gulf of Mexico.

Tanagers (Subfamily Thraupinae)

This subfamily comprises over 200 species of New World birds extending throughout the North and South American continents except for the extreme north and south. The Scarlet Tanager (*Piranga olivacea*) is a common representative of this family in eastern North America as well as being a popular cage-bird in Europe. The male in his breeding plumage is handsome, bright scarlet, with black wings and tail; in autumn and winter he moults into one resembling the females. Like all tanagers the bill is short and conical, rather like that of a sparrow. The female is a dull green above, yellowish below with brownish-black

The Little Bunting (*Emberiza pusilla*), little more than twelve centimetres long, breeds in the tundra regions of Siberia and part of northern Finland and Sweden. In the autumn it migrates south-east to winter in northern India and China. It is an inconspicuous little bird feeding mainly on the ground on seeds and insects. It builds its nest in a depression in the ground.

The male Common Cardinal (*Cardinalis cardinalis*) of North America is unmistakable with its bright red plumage and black throat. The Cardinal is a favourite at the bird table eating a wide variety of food put out. The male sings throughout the year and in the breeding season mated birds may be heard singing antiphonally.

wings. Birds of this family vary in size from being smaller than a sparrow to as large as a jay, but the North American species are all about the same dimensions, that is, a little larger than a House Sparrow. Most feed mainly on small fruits but will also take flowers and insects. Although the males of the different species are brightly coloured in a variety of hues, those of the northern species are predominantly red, the Summer Tanager (*P. rubra*) being a uniform rose-red all over. One exception is the Western Tanager (*P. ludoviciana*), which breeds in the mountains from British Columbia to southern California. In this species the male is yellow with black shoulders, wings and tail, and a red face in the breeding season. The nest is usually a shallow cup built upon horizontal branches of trees at varying heights from the ground. Three or four bluish-grey eggs spotted with brown are laid in the nest. All these northern species are migratory, most of them wintering in central South America. The tanagers include some of the most vividly coloured species known: the Blue-crowned Chlorophonia (*Chlorophonia occipitalis*) and the Paradise Tanager (*Tangara chilensis*) are among the more notable examples.

Plush-capped finch (Subfamily Catamblyrhynchinae)

The sole member of this subfamily, *Catamblyrhynchus diadema*, ranges over much of tropical South America. Finch-like fifteen centimetres long, it is remarkable for its erect, golden-brown crown feathers which are like a stiff velvet pile. Almost nothing is known of its habits. Present-day systematists consider this is an aberrant tanager of the Thraupinae subfamily.

Swallow-tanager (Subfamily Tersininae)

The Swallow-tanager (*Tersina viridis*) is the sole member of this subfamily. It is a colourful, starling-sized and tanager-like bird that ranges over much of tropical America, feeding on insects and fruit. It is remarkable for its bill and its swallowing capacity. The bill is broad, hooked at the tip and has sharp edges. When eating fruit the Swallow-tanager cuts it up with its bill and swallows large lumps, its elastic throat pouch taking on strange shapes in consequence.

Wood-warblers (Family Parulidae)

Some species look very much like vireos, other resemble kinglets, and some species of wood-warblers differ so little from each other that it takes years of experience to be able to identify them in the field. The problem is complicated as many species wear a more sombre dress in the fall than in the spring and therefore resemblances are accented in autumn when even the songs, usually reliable identification guides, are stilled.

Before the birds reappear from their wintering grounds, mainly in tropical America, they have moulted into bright, distinctive plumages and are singing. One of the most distinctive in spring is the Black-and-white Warbler (*Mniotilta varia*) named for its stripes of black and white. It may be seen creeping along trunks and branches in the leafy woodlands of most of Canada and the United States. In winter it migrates to Florida or to the tropics. It is sometimes confused with the Blackpoll Warbler (*Dendroica striata*), although the latter has no white stripe on the head and has white instead of black cheeks. It breeds in spruces chiefly in Canada and winters in South America. One of the brightest of this family is the Myrtle Warbler (*D. coronata*), which is grey, striped with black above, white below, and has a bright yellow crown, wing-patch and rump. Normally it breeds in the conifer belt of Canada and in the northern United States, wintering in the southern United States. This species has achieved fame in recent years because one spent the summer in England. Stragglers of American species do occur from time to time in Europe but this bird was unusual because of its small size and good condition. It may have been swept across the Atlantic by a gale, or it may have rested in the rigging of an eastbound ship and so crossed the Atlantic with comparative ease. Nevertheless, this tiny bird somehow managed to reach Europe, and spent the whole summer in the garden of a house at Exeter in Devon. Generally when birds from America reach Europe they are so physically exhausted that they die shortly after arrival.

There are about one hundred and twenty species of these generally small, often bright-coloured birds of the Americas. Most North American species are migratory, breeding in the more temperate regions and returning to the tropical areas for winter. Spring migration in the United States is often spectacular with myriads of these birds passing through in relatively few days. Common names are very confusing as not all species are called warblers. There is the Yellow-throat (*Geothlypis trichas*) and the Yellow-throated Warbler (*Dendroica dominica*); the American Redstart (*Setophaga ruticilla*), not at all related to the Eurasian Redstart; the water-thrushes of the genus *Seiurus* which are vaguely thrush-like; and the related Ovenbird (*Seiurus aurocapillus*) which looks thrush-like but builds an oven-shaped nest of grasses. Well-known, widely distributed species in the United States include the Tennessee Warbler (*Vermivora peregrina*), Nashville Warbler (*V. ruficapilla*), Yellow Warbler (*Dendroica petechia*), Magnolia Warbler (*D. magnolia*), Black-throated Green Warbler (*D. virens*). and the Yellow-breasted Chat (*Icteria virens*).

Hawaiian honeycreepers (Family Drepanididae)

There are twenty-two species of honey creepers peculiar to the Hawaiian islands. All are small with inconspicuous plumage and with tongues specialised for taking nectar. They differ in details of wing, tail and leg, but above all in the shape of the beak. In some it is finch-like, in others slender and curved, or parrot-like, even crossed at the tip. The assumption is that ancestral birds crossed the 3,200 kilometres from America, and that their descendants have become adapted and altered to the many contrasting habitats on the islands, a parallel with Darwin's finches on the Galapagos Islands.

Vireos (Family Vireonidae)

The vireos are confined to the New World, ranging throughout North America and into central South America. They are very similar to the Old World white-eyes and, like them, many have an eye-ring,

The Chestnut-backed Tanager (*Tangara laviniga cara*) is confined to Central and South America. Most of the small tanagers of the *Tangara* genus live in the tops of tall trees in the tropical forests. They move around in small troops, quite often in the company of honeycreepers, feeding on berries and fruits. Little is known of their breeding habits.

usually white in colour, but normally a white spot links this ring with the base of the bill. They are usually solitary, hunting for food among foliage where they move around rather deliberately. Six species are fairly widespread in the United States. Although difficult to distinguish, they can be identified by a process of elimination. Three of these species have two distinct wing bars, while the other three have none. Of the species with wing bars, the Blue-headed or Solitary Vireo (*Vireo solitarius*) with it blue-grey head is probably the easiest to recognise. It is usually the first vireo to be seen in the spring when it returns from the coast of the Gulf of Mexico to breed in the evergreen-deciduous forest belt of the northern United States and southern Canada and higher altitudes in the Appalachians.

Another species with two wing bars is the readily identified Yellow-throated Vireo (*V. flavifrons*), which is the only American species with a bright yellow throat and breast. It breeds in most deciduous forests in the United States. In winter it migrates south to southern Mexico or into South America. The last species with two wing bars is the White-eyed Vireo (*V. griseus*) which differs from the Yellow-throated Vireo mainly in having a whitish throat and breast and a white iris. It breeds in a broad belt across the centre of the United States and winters further south.

Of the three species without wing bars, the Red-eyed Vireo (*V. olivaceus*) is most readily identified because it has a grey cap and a black-edged white stripe above each eye, the red iris being difficult to see except at close quarters. Its range and habitat are much the same as those of the yellow-thoated Vireo. The Warbling Vireo (*V. gilvus*) is very similar but lacks the grey cap, and the stripe above the eye is less distinct. It breeds in tall shady trees from southern Canada southwards to all but the southernmost parts of the United States, and spends the winter in the tropics. The next species without wing bars is the Philadelphia Vireo (*V. philadelphicus*), which differs from the Warbling Vireo chiefly in having a yellow breast and, to a lesser extent, abdomen. The eye-ring is almost absent. The identification of this species is dificult save by observers who know it or its song well and can differentiate between the vireos and the wood-warblers which this species resembles. It breeds in deciduous forests and edges of clearings in a zone across the temperate parts of North America, wintering in South America. There are six other species in the United States, including the two species of pepper-shrike and four species of shrike-vireo, formerly placed in their own families. In all there are forty-five known species.

American blackbirds and orioles (Family Icteridae)

The vastly different kinds of plumage pattern in this family make it difficult to make any general

The Red-eyed Vireo (*Vireo olivaceus*) lives high up in the trees of the deciduous woodlands of central and eastern North America and winters in northern South America. Although a common little bird it is not often seen because of its inconspicuous rather drab plumage and its secretive ways. Its distinctive song is monotonous and made up of short, whistled phrases.

The Ovenbird (*Seiurus aurocapillus*) of North America belongs to the American wood-warbler family, not to the Furnariidae, a family noted for building oven-like nests of mud. It is seen here bringing food to its young in the domed oven-shaped nest of leaves and grasses which is built in an open place on the forest floor. Ovenbirds live in the undergrowth of woods and thickets feeding on insects, worms, spiders, centipedes and other small ground-living creatures.

statements. They usually have long, sharp-tipped bills and many resemble starlings. They are found throughout the New World, except in the extreme north, and are as varied in habits as in appearance. Some are gregarious, others solitary; some have harsh calls, others have a well-developed song. There is hardly a source of food that is not exploited by some member of the family: nectar, fruit, seeds, fishes, amphibians, crustaceans, insects, small birds and mammals. There are over ninety species recognised.

One of the commonest American blackbirds is the Common Grackle (*Quiscalus quiscula*), which is about thirty centimetres from bill to tail. Its

The Red-winged Blackbird (*Agelaius phoeniceus*) of North America and Cuba, originally bred only in marshes but as these were drained it adapted to drier areas, although never far from water. Its numbers have now grown so rapidly that it has become a serious pest causing much damage to grain crops.

plumage is an iridescent blackish-purple colour, which gives it an oily appearance like that of a starling in summer plumage. Its tail appears to have a crease along the centre, giving it a keel-like structure. Brewer's Blackbird (*Euphagus cyanocephalus*), the male of which is black with a purple sheen on the head and greenish over the rest of the body, somewhat resembles the grackles but has a shorter, more normal-shaped tail, and the male has white eyes. This species is essentially a bird of the prairies and meadows, particularly of the western United States. It nests either in bushes or the lower branches of trees, and even on the ground. The nest is made of sticks, roots and grasses and in it are laid three to five dull white eggs with brown speckling. By far the most abundant land bird in America, possibly in the world, is the Red-winged Blackbird (*Agelaius phoeniceus*) which breeds in reedy marshes from northern Canada to Cuba and Costa Rica.

Many species resemble the Old World orioles. For example, the Baltimore Oriole (*Icterus galbula*) is very similar in size and markings. It is about the size of a starling, and the male has a black head and shoulders, wing and inner tail feathers; otherwise it is orange in colour. This species breeds in groves of trees such as elms in the eastern parts of southern Canada and the eastern United States, and winters in Central America. A common grassland species is the Eastern Meadowlark (*Sturnella magna*), which is brown with speckles on the back, conspicuous black and white streaks on the crown, and bright yellow below with a black 'V' across the breast; the three outer pairs of tail feathers are white. It is a long-legged bird, which walks on the ground looking very much like a Lark or Pipit. It lives and nests in the open fields and in grassy areas, usually in small flocks. The almost indistinguishable species, the Western Meadowlark (*S. neglecta*) replaces it in western North America.

One species found over most of North America is the Bobolink (*Dolichonyx oryzivorus*). The male is black below with white patches on wings and back and a yellowish nape. During the breeding season it is hard to find any other bird that sings so continually. It is sociable and several pairs may be found nesting in the same piece of meadowland, filling the air with their sweet, wild music. They build their nest in a shallow depression in the ground; it is lined with grass and frequently so covered as to be almost arched over to conceal the eggs. Four to five greyish-white eggs speckled with lilac are laid. The bill of this species is rather short and conical.

Some members of this family, the oropendolas, troupials, and some of the orioles, build more complex nests than the Bobolink. These are called 'hangnests' and build large, complex nests that hang from the branches of trees. In contrast a number of species build no nest at all, but are parasitic like the Eurasian Cuckoos. The most common species is the Brown-headed Cowbird (*Molothrus ater*) of southern Canada and most of the United States. The males are black with a brownish head, while the females are a uniform grey; the bill is short and conical, like that of a sparrow. Like the female Cuckoo the hen Cowbird lays one or occasionally two eggs in the nest of a smaller bird. The foster-parents brood and rear the young, which never know their true parents.

Finches, Darwin's finches (Family Fringillidae)

With about 125 species, this family is one of the more widespread and common of the Passeriformes, being absent only from Madagascar and the Australasian region. These are small birds with stocky bodies, free toes and short, conical bills. They eat chiefly seeds, and their nests are generally basket-shaped. Some are migrants, and some, such as the Canary (*Serinus canaria*), have a beautiful song.

The type genus of this family is *Fringilla* of which two species, the Chaffinch (*F. coelebs*) and the Brambling (*F. montifringilla*), are fairly common in Britain and Europe. Both may be frequently seen in woods, orchards and farmlands. The former is undoubtedly the more lovely, with its pinkish-brown front, blue-grey hood, brown wings with double white bars, brown tail, and greenish rump. As well as being handsome it is lively and has a fine song.

The Hawfinch (*Coccothraustes coccothraustes*) is found in the cooler parts of the northern Old World from Ireland to Japan. It is quite a large bird with a huge bill that occupies most of its face. Its main colour is a rich brown with metallic tints, and it has bold white shoulder patches. During the summer it will crack open cherry-stones with its bill and eat the kernels. This is a remarkable feat for it usually requires a force of about thirty kilograms.

As its name suggests, the Greenfinch (*Chloris chloris*) is green except for its wings, which are a mixture of grey, black and yellow. It is a partial migrant and its habitat is gardens, shrubberies and farmlands. The characteristic note of the cock is like someone whistling with indrawn breath.

Very close to these is the Bullfinch (*Pyrrhula pyrrhula*), which is always easy to recognise by its grey back, the fine red of its underparts, and by its lustrous black head. It is rather a shy bird that spends most of its time in woods and its song is noted for its melancholy.

Another of the Fringillidae, which although resident in Britain is more typical of northern Europe, is the Red or Common Crossbill (*Loxia curvirostra*), which irrupts when larger numbers than usual come south every few years. It has red plumage and the tips of its mandibles cross. It is found in coniferous woods, where it picks open cones and eats the seeds. Its habitat is the vast extent of the spruce, pine and larch forests of Europe and North America. There is a second species that occurs in America, the Two-barred Crossbill (*L. leucoptera*) with similar habits and habitat to those of the Red Crossbill.

The European Goldfinch (*Carduelis carduelis*), which has been introduced into parts of eastern North America and Bermuda, gets its name from the Latin word for thistle (*Carduus*), for seeds of which it shows a preference. The main characteristic of its colouring is its scarlet face. The Siskin (*C. spinus*), on the other hand, which is as common in North America as in Europe, is yellowish and quite close to the Serin (*Serinus serinus*) with which it would easily be confused but for the top of the head being far darker. The Serin has recently begun to breed in Britain, while the European Goldfinch is a partial migrant. The Canary is closely related to the Serin, and comes from the islands of that name. The American Goldfinch (*C. tristis*) is common in eastern North America where it is often called the 'wild canary'.

The Linnet (*Carduelis cannabina*) has a pinkish breast and a red crown. Its habitat is open country with hedges. It is a partial migrant, as is another species, the Mountain Linnet or Twite (*C. flavirostris*), which is similar but distinguishable in winter by its yellow bill. Their habits are little different from the rest, and their basic diet is seeds.

The Greenfinch (*Carduelis chloris*) breeds over much of the western half of Eurasia. In Britain it is a familiar finch of parks and gardens and breeds regularly in inner London. It feeds on seeds of wild plants and grasses but also on cultivated grain. During the winter large flocks of Greenfinches gather, some are resident but some migrate up to several hundred kilometres.

The Woodpecker-Finch (*Camarhynchus pallidus*) of the Galapagos Islands has a long stout bill which it uses to probe into bark for insects. It is unusual among birds in being a tool-user. If it cannot reach a particular insect it will use a cactus spine or a thin twig to poke out or impale the insect.

The House Sparrow (*Passer domesticus*) must be one of the most familiar birds in the world as it has become more or less completely dependent on man and his buildings. Although a native of Europe and Asia it has been taken by man to North and South America, southern Africa, Australia and New Zealand. In many places it has become a pest.

The Black-headed Weaver (*Ploceus cucullatus*) is one of the most familiar and widespread weavers in subsaharan Africa. It nests in colonies in trees usually near water and often in association with other species of weaver. All weavers build oval or spherical nests expertly woven from grasses and vegetable fibres.

Darwin's finches of the Galapagos, usually placed in a subfamily, the Geospizinae, are adapted for a variety of ways of life. They presumably evolved from an ancestor from the American mainland.

Waxbills, grassfinches, mannikins and Java sparrows (Family Estrildidae)

This family contains 107 species of small seed-eaters which were formerly assigned to the families Fringillidae and Ploceidae. They are all found in the Old World, and are distinguished by their complicated nests with a spout-like entrance to one side in which white eggs are laid, the young from them maturing in a year. In the Ploceidae, which have equally complicated nests, the eggs are bluish and the young take two years to mature.

Some of the Estrildidae are favourite cage-birds, like the Zebra Finch (*Poephila guttata*) of Australia, barred black and white with a chestnut ear-patch.

The parrot-finches also belong here. Another cage-bird is the Java Sparrow (*Padda oryzivora*) which, with the mannikins, such as the Moluccan Mannikin (*Lonchura molucca*), both of Indonesia, live either near human habitation or on the edge of the forest. They are commonly seen in gardens eating seeds, but have achieved notoriety because they persistently plague the paddy fields. When the rice is ripening large numbers of these birds are to be seen in the fields, often eating half the yield.

One group of birds formerly included in the family Ploceidae and now placed in the Estrildidae is the waxbills. These are small, Old World birds, best known in northern countries as attractive cage-birds, particularly those of the genus *Estrilda*. The males are predominantly a buffish grey with white spots, often with scarlet back, head or bill.

Sparrows and weaver-birds (Family Ploceidae)

The 136 or more members of this family, the sparrows, weaver-birds and widow-birds, closely resemble the finches (Fringillidae) in three respects: free toes, conical beak, and a diet mostly of seeds.

The House Sparrow and Eurasian Tree Sparrow are the only European representatives of the family. The way they spread wherever there are human habitations is well known and they have done this even in countries where they have been introduced, as in North America and Australia. The most familiar species is the House Sparrow (*Passer domesticus*) with its ash-blue crown. A black patch from throat to chest distinguishes the male from the female. This patch is not so large in the Eurasian Tree Sparrow (*P. montanus*), the head of which is browner and shinier. Only the House Sparrow is found in towns. In the countryside the House Sparrow is found in villages and the Eurasian Tree Sparrow in fields and copses. The Eurasian Tree Sparrow was introduced into America near the city of St Louis and, thriving there, has spread to southern Illinois.

Buffon described the House Sparrow as being 'uncomfortably familiar and vulgarly lively'. It is justly accused of doing damage to fields and orchards and also—though this is not certain—of hindering the propagation of the insect-eaters by taking possession of their nests. As the Sparrow is both a seed-eater and an insect-eater, the advantages must be weighted against disadvantages.

Sparrows have at least three broods a year. Cock and hen together make the nest, weaving it of all sorts of materials and choosing the most unexpected sites, such as gutters, ventilation holes, old-fashioned street lamps, farm outbuildings, and even roofs of houses. When they build in trees, the nests are spherical and of sound construction. The nest of the House Sparrow is almost invariably a mess of grasses and a wide variety of debris.

An example of seasonal sexual dimorphism is found in the whydahs (*Euplectes*), plentiful over much of Africa, which are all-black outside the breeding season. But during this season (from May to September) the cocks acquire a fiery red breast and a huge tail that makes them clumsy.

Weaver-birds (*Ploceus* spp.) are spread throughout Africa. They are expert weavers and make their nests with vegetable fibres, shaping them into long pendant pouches. The opening is at the top and a long sleeve open at the bottom gives access to the nest. There may be dozens of these nests jammed one against the other in a single tree.

Finally, there are the sociable weaver-birds, whose collective nests are the work of hundreds of individuals. From a distance these nests look like a thatched roof hung from a tree. At close quarters the holes of the individual nests can be seen along the edge of the 'roof', in and out of which there is a continual traffic of birds. One of the most widespread species is the Quelea (*Quelea quelea*), which is sparrow-like and thirteen centimetres long. It is particularly common in East Africa, where hundreds of thousands of birds will suddenly descend on a field and within a short time completely strip the ripening crops. One nest may fill a whole tree and contain hundreds of females rearing their young. The males are polygamous and a large colony may contain only a few males, each with an immense harem. The weight of the nest is sometimes so great that the tree soon collapses.

Starlings and oxpeckers (Family Sturnidae)

Starlings (*Sturnus vulgaris*) go about in great flocks, often with crows, thrushes and even pigeons. Particularly in non-breeding seasons they fly continuously about the fields, and at the end of the day huge flocks of them return to the cities to roost. In recent years starlings have irrupted noticeably. They have spread from Europe southwards to Africa, eastwards to Asia, and some have been found on Pacific Islands. The few originally introduced into the United States have multiplied to such numbers that they are as great a problem in many American cities as they are in Europe. Another member of the Sturnidae to visit south-east Europe, sometimes straying as far west as Britain, is the Rose-coloured Starling (*S. roseus*). It is predominantly pink with a black and violet head.

Members of this family generally live in warmer climates. The mynahs, which live in Asia, tend to live in flocks, like most starlings, and breed in cavities in trees. The celebrated Talking Mynah is the Hill Mynah or Indian Grackle (*Gracula religiosa*), a widely distributed oriental species frequently imported into western countries as a cage-bird. About the size of a Jackdaw, it is black with a white patch on the wings. It has a thick orange bill and short yellow legs. There is bare yellow skin on the face and behind the eye, extending to the nape. It feeds entirely on fruit, and makes an attractive cage-bird, with a long, melodious whistle. Other mynah species may also be taught to talk.

In Africa two species of the genus *Buphagus* are always found in association with large game mammals, especially cattle. They are known as oxpeckers and perch on the back of game, feeding on the ectoparasites in the mammal's coat, and even on the larvae embedded in the skin. As soon as any predator approaches, the birds swirl upwards calling, so giving warning of danger to their host.

Old World orioles (Family Oriolidae)

These birds should not be confused with the American orioles of the family Icteridae. They are sturdy jay-sized birds, arboreal and insectivorous. Their bills are longer and more pointed than those of the finches and sparrows, though less slender than those of the Old World blackbirds or warblers. Distribution is typically tropical in Eurasia, Africa, Indonesia, the Philippines, and Australia.

The family is represented in Europe by the Golden Oriole (*Oriolus oriolus*), a lovely black and yellow migrant, which arrives in May and leaves again in August for Africa. The general colour and pattern are so similar to that of the Baltimore Oriole of the eastern United States that it led to this member and others of the family Icteridae being called 'orioles'. It is wild, noisy and bold, with a sonorous, rather lovely song heard in the morning and evening. The nest is a skilfully woven bowl lined with moss and lichen hung in the fork of two branches for stability and protection.

Drongos (Family Dicruridae)

The twenty species of drongos are noted for their aggressiveness. All but one are black with iridescent green or purple plumage. The tail is long and varies in shape. Most are the size of a jay, with a hook-tipped beak ornamented with rictal bristles. They feed on insects, hunting them in the manner of flycatchers but with a seeming ferocity. Long pointed wings give strong flight. In defence they will take on even hawks and eagles, and such is their success in driving off intruders that a tree containing a drongo's nest is likely to contain those of less stout-hearted birds as well because of the protection afforded. Curiously, these are not attacked by the drongos. Some are also clever mimics of other bird-songs, and will attack snakes, uttering the calls of other birds.

One species, the Papuan Mountain Drongo (*Chaetorhynchus papuensis*), has twelve tail feathers. The remaining species, distributed from Africa, across southern Asia, to the Solomons and southwards to Australia, have only ten. The King Crow (*Dicrurus macrocercus*), which ranges from India to Java and Formosa, is black with red eyes and a forked tail. The forked tail is most marked in the Racket-tailed Drongo (*D. paradiseus*) of India and Malaya, which has a shaggy crest and 'rackets' at the tip of the tail.

Wattled crow, huia, and saddleback (Family Callaeidae)

These three New Zealand species have long tails and legs, a somewhat velvety plumage and brightly coloured wattles.

The Wattled Crow (*Callaeas cinerea*), or Kokako, said to be New Zealand's best songster, lives in the forests and feeds on leaves, buds and berries, holding them under one foot and tearing them with the other. The beak is sharp-pointed and slightly down-curved.

The extinct Huia (*Heteralocha acutirostris*) is noted for the difference between the male with its straight, sharp beak, and the female with her long down-curved bill. It is said that a pair of huias would combine in food-getting, the male chiselling away rotten wood and the female inserting her long bill into the tunnel to extract the grub, but there is no foundation for this in the published literature.

The Saddleback (*Philesturnus carunculatus*) is glossy black with bright chestnut tail and wings.

The Magpie-lark (*Grallina cyanoleuca*) common throughout Australia, has shiny, sleek black and white plumage. It is found wherever there is water and in the autumn large flocks can be seen feeding around the edges of dams and other wet places. It is mainly insectivorous but will eat large numbers of snails when available.

The Satin Bowerbird (*Ptilonorhynchus violaceus*), best known of the bowerbirds, is confined to eastern Australia. The male has glossy black plumage with an iridescent blue sheen. The female is much drabber, a dull grey-green. The male's bower is a platform of sticks and twigs about thirty centimetres long enclosed within two walls fifty centimetres high, decorated with flowers and other, usually blue, objects.

The Saddleback feeds on insects and fruit, and has a straight, sharp-pointed bill.

Magpie-larks (Family Grallinidae)

There are four species of these birds: three in Australia and one in New Guinea. Both the Mudlark of Australia (*Grallina cyanoleuca*) and that of New Guinea (*G. bruijni*) are black and white, and live along the edges of muddy lakes. Their nest is a mud bowl, strengthened with hair or fur, and lined with feathers and grass. The Apostle-bird (*Struthidea cinerea*) is mainly black, but with some white. It is jay-sized and goes about in parties of twelve. The nest is also bowl-shaped and of mud. The White-winged Chough (*Corcorax melanorhamphus*) also makes a mud bowl, several individuals combining to build it, and several females laying their eggs in it when it has been completed.

Wood-swallows (Family Artamidae)

Another group of birds having apparent affinities with the shrikes are the wood-swallows. The ten are found throughout south-east Asia to Australia and even as far as the Fiji Islands. They also have stout bill, legs and feet. Their pointed wings and their habit of taking insects while on the wing make them appear rather swallow-like.

The colour pattern in some species also increases the resemblance to the swallow family. The Greater Wood-swallow (*Artamus maximus*), of the forests of New Guinea, is a dark slate-grey colour with a white rump and underparts, very much like the House Martin. This species is gregarious and several shallow, cup-shaped nests are often built in the same tree. When a young bird clamours for food it may be fed by any of the adults present.

Bell-magpies, Australian butcherbirds, piping crows (Family Cracticidae)

This is a family of about ten species distributed over Australia, Tasmania and New Guinea. All are jay or crow-sized and some have the beaks and habits of shrikes.

The melodious note of the bell-magpies is one of the commonest bird songs in Australia. Three species represent the group: the White-backed Bell-magpie (*Gymnorhina hypoleuca*), the Black-backed Bell-magpie (*G. tibicen*), and the Western Bell-magpie (*G. dorsalis*). Distribution of the three rarely overlaps.

The Western Bell-magpie (*G. dorsalis*), with black and white plumage, has remarkable territorial behaviour. Groups of six to twenty males and females occupy a territory of up to fifty hectares all the year round, defending its boundaries from rival groups of bell-magpies and mobbing intruders, even human beings. Mating is promiscuous. The hens build the nests and care for the young unaided. The male helps to feed them only when they leave the nest. They have a ringing, bell-like call and at the breeding-time groups call in chorus. This dies down as soon as the egg-laying begins.

The piping crows (genus *Strepera*), also called currawongs, are large birds found in wooded habitats, in pairs during the breeding season and at other times in flocks. Plumage is predominately black, white and grey.

The third genus, the Australian butcherbirds (*Cracticus*), share with the true butcherbirds (Laniidae) the habit of impaling insects, lizards and small birds on thorns to anchor the carcasses during feeding. In contrast to this practical but robust behaviour is their very pleasing song, particularly that of the rather distinctive Pied Butcherbird (*C. nigrogularis*), an inland species.

Bowerbirds (Family Ptilonorhynchidae)

Closely related to the birds of paradise, bowerbirds are so called because they build canopies and galleries for courtship. This family of about eighteen species is restricted to the New Guinea/Australia area. These are built on the ground with interwoven twigs and are ornamented with shells, flowers, pebbles, bleached bones and feathers, particularly blue ones. After courtship and mating take place, the female leaves to build her nest, while the male remains near the bower displaying to other females.

Birds of paradise (Family Paradisaeidae)

Birds of paradise, which are found only in New Guinea and adjacent islands, live mainly on insects, although they also eat fruits. They are characterised by a sexual dimorphism, which attains its fullest expression in the breeding season. They are polygamous, as is often the case where there is a marked sexual dimorphism. The Greater Bird of Paradise (*Paradisaea apoda*), found only in New Guinea and the Aru Islands of Indonesia, is a typical example. In full nuptial plumage the male has a velvety black breast with emerald tints; the crown of his head and nape are lemon yellow; the upper part of his throat is emerald green with golden lights; and his tail, wing feathers and belly are chestnut. Long filiform feathers, with separated barbs, grow from the flanks. They are a beautiful orange-yellow, shading into wine red at the extremities, and the bird can curve them in graceful scrolls or press them close to its body. The hen by comparison is dull.

The cock King of Saxony Bird of Paradise (*Pteridophora alberti*) has two feathers springing from its crown. These are twice as long as the body, beyond which they extend in graceful curves. The male Twelve-wired Bird of Paradise (*Seleucidis melanoleuca*) has six feathers growing from each flank that are reduced to mere filaments.

The courtship of the birds of paradise is a colourful sight. The cocks display in such a manner as to exhibit their plumage to its fullest advantage before the hens, fluffing out their feathers and at the same time prancing and bowing, and in some species performing acrobatic manoeuvres on their perches. Only their raucous, guttural cries seem out of place.

Crows, magpies, jays (Family Corvidae)

These large perching birds have free toes and powerful bills. Many Corvidae live in large flocks, and have a loud and sometimes lugubrious cry. The dominant colour of the species in the crow group is black. The jays, as a group, sport brighter colours. The crow is chiefly insectivorous, picking up grubs when the fields are being worked. During harvest-time it is granivorous and in winter it

The Grey Butcherbird (*Cracticus torquatus*) has a wide distribution in much of the Australian bush and also in Tasmania. It is considered to be one of the best Australian songsters. It is a friendly bird and can be enticed into gardens but it has been known to kill pet caged birds and drag them out through the wires of the cage to be added to its 'larder'.

The Raggiana Bird of Paradise (*Paradisaea raggiana*) lives in the wet lowland forests of New Guinea. Like all members of the genus it has long lacy plumes extending beyond the tail. In the breeding season the male calls to the females and starts his courtship dance opening his wings to show the beautiful red feathers. He then arches his body forward so that his tail plumes cascade into an alluring show.

becomes omnivorous, eating seeds, earthworms, grubs of all kinds, birds and even carrion.

Some of the crow family have entirely black plumage and legs. The most impressive of these is the Common Raven (*Corvus corax*), which can be sixty-three centimetres or more from beak to tail. It has become rare in Europe and in America, and is only found on cliffs or in mountains except in the more arctic regions. The Carrion Crow (*C. corone*) lives in woods and fields, and the Rook (*C. frugilegus*) has a pointed and not hooked bill. It is the most widespread of them all, and lives in colonies or rookeries.

In North America the bird known as the Common or American Crow (*C. brachyrhynchos*) is yet another all-black species which is remarkably like the Carrion Crow in appearance, voice and also in its behaviour.

Another North American species, the Fish Crow (*C. ossifragus*), is seldom found far inland, and may be distinguished by its voice. Instead of the loud, clear open 'caw' of the adults of the European and American crows, it utters a hoarser, shorter 'car' as if it were accustomed to talking through its nose.

Other Old World members of this family have black plumage but red feet; these comprise the genus *Pyrrhocorax*. The Cornish Chough (*Pyrrhocorax pyrrhocorax*) has a long red beak, and the Alpine Chough (*P. graculus*) has a short, yellow bill. Both live in mountains, but the Cornish Chough is also found in cliffs and rocks. The Alpine Chough can live at great heights, and one was seen by the Mount Everest expedition in 1953 at 8,100 metres.

The Hooded Crow (*Corvus cornix*) has a grey back and underparts. It is a close relative of the Carrion Crow with which it interbreeds. Nowadays the tendency is to regard both as belonging to the same species (*C. corone*), but forming separate sub-species. The Jackdaw or Belfry Crow (*C. monedula*) has grey only on the nape. It is one of the most common crows and is frequently seen in towns.

Crows and rooks are among the earliest breeders of the year. They mate from January on, build their nests of twigs in February, and lay their eggs at the beginning of March. They seem to be monogamous. While the hen sits on her four or six greenish eggs, the cock stays near her and supplies her with food. Later, when the chicks are hatched, the two birds look after them together.

The House Crow (*Corvus splendens*), common in India and Ceylon, owes its scientific name to the metallic tints of its plumage, and is an expert thief that will steal anything.

The Black-billed Magpie (*Pica pica*), also a member of the Corvidae, is actually pied. It has a black back and pure white shoulders and belly, and its tail is very long. In Europe where there is only the one species, it is the Magpie; in North America there is also the Yellow-billed Magpie (*P. nuttalli*). Unlike crows and rooks, magpies seldom gather in more than small parties, and then only in winter, living in pairs during the rest of the year. Both magpies' flight is heavy and laboured owing to their short wings, and their cries are an incessant chattering. They are even greater thieves than the rooks, with a marked predilection for bright objects. In other habits magpies differ little from other crows.

The Old World Nutcracker (*Nucifraga caryocatactes*) differs from other Corvidae in that its bill is conical and no longer than its head. It is brown speckled with white, and inhabits the colder parts of Europe, including the conifer forests of the Alps, Jura and Pyrenees, where it feeds mainly on nuts and the seeds of pines and spruce. It will also eat insects, worms and small birds. Like the squirrel, it prepares for the winter by burying acorns in the ground, after first literally stuffing its crop with them. In America this genus is represented by Clark's Nutcracker (*N. columbianus*) which has similar habits.

The European Jay (*Garrulus glandarius*), another member of the crow family, has a bill of medium length, and gay plumage. The wing coverts are barred with light blue, dark blue and black and the body is pinkish brown. It lives in woods and eats acorns, beechnuts, berries and fruit, as well as vast numbers of grubs, caterpillars and other pests. It is a great robber of nests.

The numerous jays, in addition to being more colourful, are commonly crested to varying degrees and have proportionately longer tails than do the sombre crows. In America there is the noisy, rather well-named Blue Jay (*Cyanocitta cristata*) common east of the Rocky Mountains

The Jackdaw (*Corvus monedula*) ranges across Europe and much of western Asia. A smallish member of the crow family, it is an inveterate chatterer and a pet Jackdaw will manage to include a number of words in its vocabulary. Strangely, although its song consists of a medley of many natural calls it seldom if ever copies the call of another bird.

from southern Canada to the Gulf Coast; the great-crested Steller's Jay (*C. stelleri*) which is largely blue, but looking as if the fore third of the bird were dipped in black ink; and the crestless Green Jay (*Cyanocorax yncas*) which has a blue head, black cheeks and bib, and yellow outer tail feathers composing its otherwise green plumage. The Green Magpie (*Cissa chinensis*) of southeastern Asia with its red bill and legs is another beautiful representative of the crow family.

USEFULNESS OF BIRDS: We cannot leave the passerines without mentioning their usefulness. Agriculture and forestry have many enemies, the worst being insects and their larvae. The harm done by locusts, Colorado beetles, weevils, different kinds of caterpillars, especially the processionary ones, wood-boring insects, moths and other pests hardly needs stressing and, as Michelet once said, 'Without birds the world would be at the mercy of insects.'

When one considers the quantities of insects and larvae destroyed every year by some of our small birds, the truth of this statement is evident. A Goldcrest, for example, eats more than three million insects every year. A Blue Tit, which is much the same size, destroys more than six and a half million for its own needs and at least twenty-four million to rear its brood of twelve to sixteen young. To obtain them it makes at least 450 sorties a day in the neighbourhood of its nest. Under the same conditions a swallow flies more than 640 kilometres a day and destroys millions of flies in the course of a season. A nestful of wrens consumes 9,000 insects before leaving the nest. A wren has been observed to bring thirty grasshoppers to its chicks in the space of an hour. Young jays consume half a million caterpillars in a season.

It is more difficult to defend the grain-eating and fruit-eating birds which are accused with some justification of being harmful to agriculture. But even most of these birds feed insects to their nestlings and by consuming weed seeds as well as grain are mainly beneficial to man They all have their part in the critical balance of nature with which man is inextricably bound On the whole the few fruits and seeds a bird eats are a small price to pay in view of the general usefulness of birds in protecting crops from the much greater ravages of insects.

Most members of the crow family take readily to human companionship, even to the point of frequenting houses. The House Crow (*Corvus splendens*) of southern Asia is particularly tame and bold when not persecuted and is always found near human habitations, feeding largely on scraps of food thrown out.

The Common or Eurasian Jay (*Garrulus glandarius*). Jays habitually hide food, usually in the ground, and this is especially true of the autumn acorn crop.

Index

Figures in italics refer to captions.

Abbot's Booby 8
Abbot's Jungle Babbler 167
Acanthisitta chloris 159
Acanthisittidae 159
accentors 166–7
Accipiter 105
gentilis *31*, 105
nisus 105
Accipitridae 99–100
Accipitrinae 99, 101–3, 105
Acorn Woodpecker 156
Acrocephalus 169
palustris 169
schoenobaenus 169, *169*
scirpaceus *31*, *142*, 169
Acryllium vulturinum 119, *119*
Actophilornis africana *65*, *111*
africanus 127
Adélie Penguin 74, *74*
Adjutant Stork 87–88, *87*
Aechmophorus occidentalis 76
Aegithalos caudatus 172, *172*
pondulinus 172
Aegithina tiphia 164
Aegypiinae 99, 100–1
Aegypius tracheliotus *57*
Aethopyga siparaja 174
African Fish Eagle *28*, 65
African Village Weaver *27*
African Blacksmith Plover 128
African Darter 81
African Finfoot 125
African Grey Parrot 140
African Jacana 63, *65*, *111*, 127
African Jackass Penguin 74
African Little Bittern *85*
African Open-bill 88
African Pitta 159
African River Martin 162–3
African Skimmer *64*, 65, 134
African Wryneck 157
Afropavo congensis 119
Agapornis 140
Agelaius phoeniceus 178, *178*
Agriocharis ocellata 120
air sacs *13*, 14
Aix galericulata *23*, 94
Alauda arvensis 161
Alaudidae 157, 161–2
albatrosses 13, 16, 66, 77–78
Alca torda 135–6, *135*
Alcedinidae 153
Alcedininae 153
Alcedo atthis *62*, 153
Alcidae 135–6
Alcippe poiocephala 167
Alectoris chukar *114*
graeca *114*
rufa *114*
Alectura lathami *108*
alimentary tract 15–16
Alophen aegyptiacus 92
Alpine Chough 184
Amazona farinosa 140
ochrocephala 140
amazons 140
American Avocet *17*, 130–1
American Bittern 85
American Black Rail 124
American blackbirds 177–78
American Burrowing Owl 50
American Coot 125
American Crow 184
American gnatcatchers 172
American Golden Plover 127, *127*
American Goldfinch 179
American Jacana 126
American Kestrel 52, 106, *107*
American Monk Parrot 48
American orioles 181
American Oystercatcher 127
American Painted Snipe 127
American Purple Gallinule 124
American Redstart 40, 42, 176
American Robin 115, 172, *173*
American Screech-owl 144
American Stint 129
American Sun-grebe 125
American Water Pipit 163
American White Pelican 79
American White-tailed Kite 101
American Wigeon 18
American Woodcock 129
Ammomanes deserti *59*, 161–2
Anaimos 174
Anarhynchus fontalis 128
Anas 92
acuta 92
carolinensis 93
clypeata 92
crecca 92, 93
discors 93
penelope 92
platyrhynchos 92, *93*
querquedula 93
rubripes 92
strepera 92
Anastomus 88
lamelligerus 88
Anatidae 89, 90–5
Anatinae 90, 92
Anatini 90, 92
Andean Condor 96–7, *96*
Anhima cornuta 89
Anhimidae 89–90
Anhinga *80*
anhinga *80*, 81
melanogaster 81
novaehollandiae 81
rufa 81
anhingas 16, 65, 81
Anhingidae 81
Anodorhynchus hyacinthus *48*
Anous stolidus 134
Anser 91
albifrons 91, *91*
anser 91
brachyrhynchus 91
caerulescens 91
canagicus 91
erythropus 91
fabilis 91
Anseranas semipalmata 90
Anseranatinae 90
Anseranatini 90
Anseriformes 89–95
Anserinae 90
Anserini 90, 91
ant-pipits 159
ant-thrushes 158–9
Anthornis melanura 174
Anthropoides virgo 122
Anthus pratensis 163
spinoletta 163
spragueii 163
trivialis 163
Apaloderma narina 152
Aphriza virgata 128
Apodidae 150
Apodiformes 150
Apostlebird 182
Aptenodytes 73, 74
forsteri 74
patagonica 74, *74*
Apterygidae 72
Apterygiformes 72–3
Apteryx australis 72, *73*
haasti 72
oweni 72
Apus 150
apus 150, *150*
Aquila 101
chrysaetos *16*, 101–2
clanga 102
heliaca 102
rapax *102*
Ara 11
ararauna 140
chloraptera *139*
macao *48*, 139, 140
militaris 140
aracaris 156
Aramidae 122–3
Aramides cajanea *123*
ypecaha 124
Aramus guarauna 122–3
Archaeopteryx 8, 120
lithographica *9*
Archilochus colubris 151
Arctic Loon *75*, 76
Arctic Skua 36–7, 132
Arctic Tern *20*, 21, 37, *133*
Ardea cinerea *61*, *82*, 83
herodias 84
purpurea *83*, 84
Ardeidae 82–3
Ardeola ralloides 84–5, *84*
Ardeotis australis 126
Arenaria interpres 128
melanocephala 128
Argus Pheasant 22, 108, 118
Argusianus argus 18
Artamidae 182
Artamus maximus 182
Ascension Frigate-bird 82
Asian Sun-grebe 125
Asiatic Paradise Flycatcher *168*
Asio flammeus 146
otus 146, *147*, 148
asities 159
Athene noctua 146
Atrichornis clamosus 161
rufescens 161
Atrichornithidae 161
auks 28, 32, 126, 135
Australian Avocet 130–1
Australian Bittern 85
Australian Bustard 126
Australian butcherbirds 183
Australian Darter 81
Australian Gannet 80
Australian nuthatchers 173
Australian Satin Bower Bird 47
Australian Striped Honeyeater *30*
Australian tree creepers 174
Australian wrens 169
Avocet 62, 126, 130–1
Aythya ferina 94
fuligula 94
vallisneria 93
Aythyini 90, 93

babblers 167
Baird's Sandpiper 56
Balaeniceps rex *16*, 86
Balaenicipitidae 86
bald crows 167–9
Bald Eagle 102, *108*
Baldpate 18
Balearic Crane 122
Balearica pavonina *121*, 122
Baltimore Oriole 28, 178, 181
Banded Plover 128, *128*
banding 18
Bank Swallows 162
Barbary Duck 94
barbets 155
Barn Owl 52, 144, *144*
Barn Swallow 18, 162, *162*
Barnacle Goose 91, 92
Barrancolino 159
Barred Cuckoo-shrike 163
Barred Owl 147
Bartramia longicauda 130
bat-hawks 99
Bateleur 103
beak 13, 15–17
Bean Goose 91
Bearded Tit 172
Bearded Vulture 101
becards 160
Bee Humming-bird 151
bee-eater 17, 19, 27, 50, 56, 58, 153–4, 154
Belfry Crow 184
bell-magpies 182
bellbirds 160
Belted Kingfisher 153
Bensch's Monia (Rail) 120–1
Bewick's Swan 91
bird ringing 18
birds-of-paradise 22, 48, 49, *49*, 183
birds of prey 95–6
bitterns 82, 83, 85, *85*
Black Curassow *111*
Blackbird 115, 172
Black Duck 92
Black Gooney 78
Black Grouse 112, 113, 114
Black Heron 64–5
Black Kite 100, *100*
Black Lory 141
Black Oystercatcher 127
Black Paradise Flycatcher 168
Black Peacock 119
Black Skimmer *64*, 134, *134*
Black Stork 87
Black Swan 91
Black Tern 134
Black Turnstone 128
Black Vulture 99
Black Woodpecker 156
Black-and-white Warbler 176
Black-and-yellow Broadbill 158
Black-backed Bell-magpie 182
Black-backed Woodpecker 156
Black-bellied Bustard 126
Black-bellied Plover 37, 127
Black-billed Cuckoo 143
Black-billed Magpie 184
Black-billed Tree Duck *91*
Black-capped Chickadee 172
Black-capped Lory *141*
Black-cheeked Waxbill *56*
Black-chested Harrier Eagle 53
Black-crowned Night Heron 85, 86
Black-footed Albatross 78
Black-headed Gull *23*, 134
Black-headed Pitta *158*
Black-headed Weaver *180*
Black-necked Grebe 76, 77
Black-necked Screamer 90
Black-necked Swan 91
Black-poll Warbler 176
Black-throated Diver *75*, 76
Black-throated Green Warbler 42, 176
Black-throated Little Grebe 76
Black-winged Kite 55
Black-winged Stilt *60*, 62, 130, *131*
Blackback Three-toed Woodpecker 157
Blackbirds 23, 157
Blackburnian Warbler 40
Blackcap 23–4, 169
Blood-pheasant 116
Blue-and-Yellow Macaw 140
Blue Bird of Paradise *49*
Blue Jay 184–5
Blue Peafowl *118*
Blue Rock-thrush 172
Blue Tit 43, 173–4, *174*, 185
Blue-backed Fairy bluebird 164
Blue-crowned Chlorophonia 176
Blue-faced Booby 80
Blue-footed Booby 80, *81*
Blue-gray Gnatcatcher 172
Blue-headed Vireo 177
Blue-throated Warbler 172
Blue-winged Parrotlet 141
Blue-winged Teal 93
bluebirds 172
Bluethroat 172–3
boatbill 85–7, 89
Boatbilled Heron 85–7
Bobolink 52, 178
Bobwhite 115
Bobwhite Quail 42, 110
body temperature 14
Bohemian Waxwing 40, 165, *165*
Bombycilla cedrorum 165
garrulus *40*, 165, *165*
Bombycillidae 165
Bonasa umbellus 114
boobies 16, 66, 78, 79, 80
Booted Eagle 102
Boreal Chickadee 172
Boreal Owl 41
Bornean Bristle-head 164
Bostrychia hagedash 88
Botaurus 85
lentignosus 85
pinnatus 85
poiciloptilus 85
stellaris 85, *85*
bower birds 49, 183
Brachypteraciinae 154
Brahminy Kite 100
Brambling 179
Banded Stilt 130
Branta 91
bernicla 91
canadensis 91
leucopsis 91
sandvicensis 91

Brazilian Ovenbird 27
breeding habits 24–5
Brent Goose (Brant) 91, 92
Brewer's Blackbird 178
bristle-birds 169
Bristle-thighed Curlew 21, 130
Broad-billed Humming-bird *151*
Broad-winged Hawk 43
broadbills 157–8
Bronze-coloured Lotus-bird 127
Bronzed Cuckoo 142–3
Brown Booby *68*, 80
Brown Creeper 42, 173
Brown Kiwi 72, *73*
Brown Pelican 16, 79
Brown Thrasher 166
Brown Towhee 24
Brown-capped Chickadee 172
Brown-eared Pheasant 116
Brown-headed Cowbird 178–9
Brown-headed Nuthatch 173–4
Brush Megapode *108*
Brush Turkey 108, *108*
Bubo africanus *145*
bubo 144
virginianus 144, *144*
Bucconidae 155
Buceros bicornis 154
Bucerotidae 154
budgerigar 140
Bufflehead 17
Bulbulcus ibis 84
bulbuls 163–4
Bullfinch 142, 179
Bulweria 78
buntings 175
Buphagus 181
Burhinidae 131
Burhinus oedicnemus 131, *132*
Burmeister's Seriema 125
Burrowing Owl 146–7, *146*
bush larks 162
Bush Wren 159
bush-warblers 169
bustards 126
butcherbirds 164, 183
Buteo buteo 103
jamaicensus *103*
Buteoninae 99, 101, 103
Butorides virescens 83–4
button-quail 25, 121
Buzzard 95, 103, *107*

Cacatua galerita 140
haematuropygia *140*
Cahow 32, 78
Cairini moschata 94
Cairinini 90, 94
Calandra Lark 161
Calandrella brachydactyla 161
Caleonas nicobarica 139
Calidris alpina 129
canutus 129
minuta 129
minutilla 129
temminckii 129
California Gull 134
California Quail 116
Californian Condor *32*, 33, *96*, 99
Callaeas cinerea 181
Callipepla squamata 115–16
Calures 153
Calyptomena viridis 157–8
Camarhynchus pallidus *179*
Campephaga phoenicea 163
Campephagidae 163
Canary 179
Capitonidae 155
Caprimulgus europaeus 149, *149*
vociferus 149
Cardinalis cardinalis 175, *175*
Cariama cristata 125
Carolina Parakeet 140
Canada Goose 91
Canada Warbler 40
Canvasback 93
Cape Barren Goose 92
Cape Cormorant *66*
Cape Gannet 80, *81*
Cape Petrel 78
Cape Pigeon 78
Cape Rail 123
Capercaillie 108, 112, 113, 114
Caprimulgidae 148–50
Caprimulgiformes 147–50
Caprimulginae 148
Caprimulgus climacurus 149
Caracara cheriway 108
caracara 108
Cardinal 175, *175*
Carduelis cannabina 179
cardeulis 24, 179
chloris 179, *179*
flavirostris 179
spinus 179
tristis 179
cariamas 125–6
Cariamidae 125–6
Carmine Bee-eater 55
Carolina Chickadee 172
Carolina Crake 124
Carrier Pigeon 138–39
Carrion Crow 184
Carthartidae 96, 99
Casarca ferruginea 92
Caspian Plover 56
Cassowary 11, 23, 27, *54*, 55, 56, 72
Casuariformes 72
Casuariidae 72
Casuarius casuarius *54*, 72, *72*
Catamblyrhynchinae 176
Catamblyrhynchus diadema 176
Catbird 166
Cathartes aura 99
Cathartidae 96, 99
Catharus 172
fuscenscens 172
guttatus 172
Catoptrophorus semipalmatus 130
Cattle egret 54, 64, 84
Cedar Waxwing 40, 165
Centrocercus urophasianus 113, *113*
Centropelma micropterum 76
Cephalopterus ornatus 160
Cereopsis novaehollandiae 92
Cerorhinca monocerata *135*
Certhia americana 173
brachydactyla 173, *173*
familiaris 173
Certhiidae 172–3, 174
Ceryle aenea 153
alcyon 153
amazona 153
americana 153
rudis *152*, 153
Cerylinae 153
Ceyx picta 153
chachalacas 108, 111
Chaetorhynchus papuensis 181
Chaetura pelagica 150
Chaffinch 43, 179
Chalcites 141
Chamaea fasciata 168
Chamaeinae 168
Chaparral Cock 143
Charadriiformes 126
Charadrius 127–8
alexandrinus 128
debuius 128
hiaticula 128
vociferus 128
chats 172
chatterers 160
Chauna chavaria 90
torquata 89–90, *90*
Chestnut-backed Tanager *177*
chickadees 172
Chilean Avocet 130–1
Chimney Swift 150
Chinese Quail 115
Chinstrap Penguin *132*
Chionididae 131–2
Chionis alba 131, *132*
minor 131
Chiroxiphia linearis 160
Chlidonias nigra 134
Chloroceryle 153
Chlorophonia occipitalis 176
Chloropsis aurifrons 164
Chordeiles acutipennis 149–50
minor 149
Chordeilinae 148, 149–50
Chough 184
Chrysococcyx 141
lucidus 142–3
Chrysolophus amherstiae 116
pictus 116, *116*
Chuck-will's Widow 17
Chukar Partridge *114*
Chunga burmeisteri 125
Ciconia ciconia 86–7, *86*
nigra 87
Ciconiidae 86
Ciconiiformes 82–89
Cinclus cinclus 166
Circaëtus gallicus 102
Circinae 99
circulation 14
Circus cyaneus *52*, 104, *104*
pygargus 104
Cissa chinensis 185
Cisticola juncides 169
Cladorhynchus leucocephalus 130
Clapper Rail 123
Clark's Nutcracker 184
cliff swallows 162
Climacteridae 174
Climacteris 174
erythrops 174
leucophaea 174
Clucking Hen 122
Coal Tit 172
Coccothraustes coccothraustes *16*, 179
Cochleariidae 85–6
Cochlearius cochlearius 86
Cock-of-the-rock 22, 160
cockatoos 139, 140
coelurosaurs 8
Colaptes auratus 156, *157*
cafer 156, *157*
Colies 152
Coliidae 152
Coliiformes 152
Colinus virginianus 115
Collared Dove *138*
Collared Hemipode 121
Collared Turtle-dove 139
Collocalia 150
inexpectacta 150
Columba livia 136–7
oenas 137
palumbus 137, *137*
Columbidae 136–8
Columbiformes 136
Columbina passerina 139
Common Gallinule (Moorhen) 124
Common Grackle 178
Common Gull 132, 134
Common Iora 164
Common Loon 76
Common Murre 135
Common Noddy 134
Common Partridge 114–15
Common Peafowl *118*, 119
Common Potoo *148*
Common Pratincole 131
Common Rhea 72
Common Sandpiper 130
Common Trumpeter 123
Compsognathus 8, *8*
Congo Peafowl 119
Conopophagidae 159
conservation 32, 33
Contopus sordidulus 160
virens 160
conures 140
Conuropsis carolinensis 140
Cooper's Hawk 42–3
Coot 14, *35*, 61, 124–5
Copper Pheasant 23
Copsychus malabaricus 173
Coraciidae 154
Coraciiformes 152
Coracina lineata 163
Coracius garrulus *154*
Coragyps atratus 99
Coral-billed Nuthatch 173
Corcorax melanorhamphus 182
cormorants 16, 64, 65, 66, 80–1
Corncrake 51, 123
Corvidae 183–5
Corvus brachyrhynchos 184
corax 184
cornix 184
corone 184
frugilegus 184
monedula 184, *184*
ossifragus 184
splendens 184, *185*
Coscoroba 91
coscoroba 91
Coscoroba Swan 91
cotingas 160
Coturnix chinensis 115
coturnix 19, 115
Coua cristata 143
couas 143
Coura 139
Courlan 122–3
coursers 131
courtship 22–3, *22*, *23*, 24, *25*
cowbirds 31
Crab-plover 131
Cracidae 108, 111
Cracticidae 182–3
Cracticus 183
nigrogularis 183
torquatus *183*
crakes 123–4
cranes 18, 20, 84, 91, 120, 121–2, *122*
Crax alector 111
mitu 111
rubra 111
Crazy Widow 122
Cream-coloured courser 58, 131
Crested Amazon Kingfisher 153
Crested Coot *125*
Crested Coua 143
Crested Guinea-fowl 119
Crested Lark 161
Crested Screamer 89–90, *90*
Crested Seriema 125
crested swifts 150
Crested Tinamou 73
Crested Tit 172
Crex crex 123
Crimson-rumped waxbill *54*
Crimson Tragopan 116
Crooked-billed Plover 128
Crossbill 9, 15, 17, 19, 39, *40*, 179
Crossoptilon mantchuricum 116
Crotophaga ani *143*
Crowned Crane *121*, 122
crowned pigeons 139
crows 27, 181, 182–3
Crypturellus variegatus 73
Cuban Bee Humming-bird 48
Cuban Finch *11*
Cuban Tree Duck *91*
Cuckoo 29, 31, *31*, 142, *142*, 178
cuckoo-roller 154
cuckoo-shrikes 163
cuckoo 141–3
Cuculiformes 141
Cuculus 141
canorus *31*, 142, *142*
curassows 118, 111
curlews 17, 126, 130
Cursorius cursor 131
Cyanocitta cristata 184–5
stelleri 185
Cyanocorax yncas 185
Cyanthus latirostris *151*
Cygnus 91
atratus 91
bewickii 91
buccinator 91
columbianus 91
cygnus 91
melanocoryphus 91
olor 91
Cyrtonyx montezumae 116

Dabchick *76*
dabbling ducks 92–4
Dacelo novae guineae *56*, 153
Daceloninae 153
Dalmatian Pelican 79
Daption capensis 78
Dark Chanting Goshawk *105*
Dark-eyed Junco 175
darters 16, 80, 81
Darwin, Charles 8, 9
Darwin finch 8, 9, 15, 176, 179
Darwin's Rhea 72
Delichon urbica 162
Demoiselle Crane 122
Dendrocolaptidae 158
Dendrocopos 157
major 156, *156*
medius 156
minor 156
Dendrocygna arborea *91*
bicolor 91
Dendrocygnini 90, 91
Dendroica coronata 176
dominica 176
magnolia 176
petechia 176
striata 176
virens 176
Dendrophagus canadensis *24*
Desert Lark 58, *59*, 161–2
deserts 57–9
Diatryma 8
Dicaeidae 157, 174
Dicaeum cruentatum 174
Dicruridae 181
Dicrurus macrocercus 181
paradiseus 181
Didunculus strigirostris 139
digestion 12, 13, 15–16, *15*
Diomedea 77
exulans *67*, 77, *77*
immutabilis 78
irrorata *25*

nigripes 78
Diomedeidae 77–78
dippers 165–6
divers 16, 61, 74, 76
diving petrels 66, 67, 78
DNA (deoxyribonucleic acid) 9
Docimestes 151
Dodo 32, 136
Dolichonyx oryzivorus 178
Domestic Duck 92, 93
domestic fowls 108
Domestic Goose 91
Domestic Guinea-fowl 119
Domestic Hen 112, 113
Domestic Pigeon 136–7
Domestic Turkey 120
Dotterel 37
Double-crested Cormorant 80
Double-wattled Cassowary *72*
Dovekie 135
doves 26
Drepanididae 176
Dromadidae 131
Dromaiidae 72
Dromaius novaehollandiae *54*, 72
drongos 181
Dryocopus martius 156
Duck-hawk 106
ducks *see* individual species
Dulidae 165
Dulus dominicus 165
Dumetella carolinensis 166
Dunlin 129
Dunnock 31, 166–7, *167*

Eagle Owl 144, 147
eagles 13, *15*, 26, 53, 59, 95, 99
Eastern Bluebird 173
Eastern Kingbird 160
Eastern Meadowlark *52*, 178
Eastern Phoebe 160
Eastern Wood Pewee 160
Ectopistes migratorius 138
Edible-nest Swiftlet 28, 150
eggs 28–9, *29*
egrets 16, 64, 65, 82–5
Egretta alba 84
caerulea 84
garzetta *83*, 84
thula 84
Egyptian Goose 92
Egyptian Plover 65, 128
Egyptian vulture *57*, 59
Egyptian White Vulture 100
Eider Duck 17, *26*, 94–5
Elaninae 99, 100, 101
Elanoides forficatus 100
Elanus leucurus 101
Elf Owl 45
Emberiza citrinella 175
hortulana 175
pusilla *175*
Emberizidae 175
Emberizinae 175
embryonic development 29
Emperor Goose 91
Emperor Penguin 26, 67–8, 74
empidonax minimus 160
Emu *54*, 55, 72
emu-wrens 169
emus 11, 27, 72
Enicurus leschenaulti 173
Ephippiorhynchus 87
senegalensis 87
Eremophila alpestris 162
Eremopterix 162
Erithacus rubecula 172, *173*
Erolia 129
Eskimo Curlew *32*, 130
Estrilda *56*, 180
Estrildidae 180
Eudocimus ruber *64*, 88, *89*
Eudromia elegans 73
Eudynamys scolopacea 141
Eudyptes 73, 74
chrysolophus 74
crestatus 74, *75*
Eudyptula 73, 74
albosignata 74
minor 74
Eupetes macrocercus 167
Euphagus cyanocephalus 178
Euplectes 180
Eupodolis melanogaster 126
Euryceros prevostii 165
Eurylaimi 157
Eurylaimidae 157–58
Eurylaimus ochromalus 158
Eurypyga helias 125
Eurgypygidae 125
Euxenura maguari 87
Everglade Kite 100
evolution 8–9
extinction 32–3
eyesight 12, 13–14

Fairy Bluebird 164
Fairy Penguin 74
Fairy Tern *26*, 134
Falco cherrug 106
columbarius 106
peregrinus 106
rusticolus 106
sparverius 105, 107, *107*
subbuteo 106
tinnunculus 106–7, *107*
vespertinus 107
Falconidae 106–7, 108
Falconiformes 95–6
falconry 107
falcons 53, 95, 100, 106–7
Falculea palliata 165
false sunbirds 159
Fan-tailed Warbler 169
Fandango Bird 160
fantail pigeons 138, 168
feathers 10–11
feeding 15–17
feet 14, *14*
Ferruginous Duck 94
Ferruginous Pygmy Owl *147*
Ficedula hypoleuca 168
Fieldfare 40, 172
fighting 23–4
finches 8, 9, *15*, 17, 19, 20, 179–80, 181
finchlarks 162
finfoots 65, 125
Firetailed Sunbird *174*
Fish Crow 184
fish eagles 65
Flamed Minivet 163
flamingoes 63–4, *63*, 65, 84, 89, *96*
flight 12–13, 14
flight patterns 20
Flightless Wood-rail 124
Flock pigeon *51*
flower-peckers 157, 174
fly-catchers 19, 44, 54
Forbes Rail 124
Formicariidae 158
Forpus passerinus 141
francolins 108, 116
Francolinus 116
francolinus 116
Fratercula arctica *68*, 135
Fregata aquila 82
ariel 82
magnificens 82, *82*
minor 82
Fregatidae 81–2
Frigatebird *22*, 23, 81–2
frigate-birds 13, *22*, 23, 68, 81–2
Fringilla 179
coelebs 179
montifringilla 179
Fringillidae 175, 180
frogmouths 17, 147, 148
fruit pigeons 46
fruit-crows 160
Fulica 124
americana 125
atra *35*, 124, *125*
cristata *125*
Fulmar glacialis 78
glacialoides 78
fulmars 23, 68, *68*, 78, 135
Fulvous Tree Duck 91
Furnariidae 158
Furnarius rufus 158

Gadwall 92, 93
Galapagos cormorant 66, 81
Galbulidae 155
Galerida cristata 161
Galliformes 108
gallinaceous birds 108
Gallinago gallinago 129
Gallinazo 99
Gallinula chloropus *62*, 124
gallinules 124
Gallirallus australis 124
Gallus 116
gallus 116–17, *117*
Gambell's Quail 116
Game Cock 117
gannets 16, 31, 66, 68, 78–79, 80, 135
Garden Warbler 43, 169
Garganey 93
Garrulus glandarius 184, *185*
Gavia adamsi 76
arctica *75*, 76
immer 76
stellata 76
Gaviiformes 74, 76
geese 15, 18, 20, 24, *36*, 89, 90, 91–2, 94
genetics 9
Gentoo Penguin *72*, 74
Geococcyx californianus 143, *143*
Geospizinae 180
Geothlypis trichas 176
Giant Fulmar 78
Giant Humming-bird 151
Giant Kingfisher 65
gizzard 13, 15, *15*
Glareola pratincola 131
Glareolidae 131
Glaucidium brasilianum *147*
passerinum 146
Glossy Ibis 88
gnat-eaters 159
gnatcatchers 167, 169
goatsuckers 148
godwits 17, 130
Goldcrest 169, 185
Golden Eagle *16*, 50, 101–2, 106
Golden Oriole 19, 28, 181
Golden Pheasant 116, *116*
Golden Plover 127
Golden Swallow 162
Golden-breasted Waxbill *56*
Golden-crowned Kinglet 42, 169
Golden-fronted Leafbird 164
Golden-fronted Woodpecker 156
goldeneyes 94
Goldfinch *24*, 179
Goosander 94, *95*
Gorsachius 85
goisagi 85
Goshawk *31*, 41, 105
Gracula religiosa 181
Grallina bruijni 182
cyanoleuca 182, *182*
Grallinidae 182
grass-wrens 169
grassfinches 180
Grasshopper Warbler 169
Gray Jay 40–41
Great Auk *32*, *135*, 136
Great Black-backed Gull 134
Great Blue Heron 84
Great Bustard 51, 126
Great Cormorant 80
Great Crested Flycatcher 160
Great Crested Grebe 76–7, *76*
Great Curassow 111
Great Egret 64, 84
Great Frigate-bird 82
Great Grebe 76
Great Grey Owl 41, 147, *148*
Great Grey Shrike 164
Great Hornbill 154
Great Horned Owl 41, 45, 144, *144*, 147
Great Northern Diver 76
Great Razor-billed Curassow 111
Great Shearwater 21
Great Skua 132, *132*
Great Spotted Woodpecker 156, *156*
Great Tit 29, 31, 173
Great White Pelican *79*
Greater Bird of Paradise 183
Greater Flamingo 89
Greater Honey-guide 155
Greater Prairie Chicken 113
Greater Shearwater 78
Greater Spotted Kiwi 72
Greater Wood-swallow 182
Greater Yellowlegs 129
grebes 14, 16, 28, 61, 62, 74, 76–7
Green Broadbill 157–58
Green Cormorant 80
Green Heron 83–4
Green Jay 185
Green Kingfisher 153
Green Lory 141
Green Magpie 185
Green Peafowl 119
Green Plover 128
Green Sandpiper 129, *130*
Green Woodpecker 24, 27, 44, 156
Green-winged Teal 93
Greenfinch 179, *179*
Greenshank 129
Grey Butcherbird *183*
Grey Heron *61*, *82*, 83, *83*, 84
Grey (Common) Partridge 29, 114–15
Grey Phalarope 37, 131
Grey Plover 127
Grey Wagtail 163, *163*
Grey-breasted Martin 162
Grey-headed Woodpecker 156
Grey-necked Bald Crow 168
Grey-necked Rockfowl 168
Grey-necked Wood Rail *123*
Greylag Goose 91
Griffon Vulture 100
grosbeaks 41, 175
Ground Dove 129
Ground Hornbill 55, 154
ground rollers 154
ground-babblers 167
grouse 50–51, 108, 111–14
Gruidae 121–2
Gruiformes 120
Grus americana 122
canadensis *122*
grus 121–2, *122*
Guacharo 148
Guanay Cormorant *66*
Guans 108, 111
guillemots 68, 135
Guinea-fowl *51*, 55, 108, 116, 119
gulls 28, 31, 67, 68, 126, 132, 134, 135
Gurney's Pitta 33
Guttera cristata 119
Gygis alba 134
Gymnorhina dorsalis 182
hypoleuca 182
tibicen 182
Gypaetinae 99, 101
Gypaëtus barbatus *100*, 101
Gyps fulvus 100
Gyrfalcon 37–8, 106

Hadeda Ibis 88
Haematopodidae 127
Haematopus bachmani 127
fuliginosus 127
ostralegus 127
palliatus 127
Haliacetus vocifer 28, 102
Haliaëtus 101
albicilla 102
leucocephalus 102, *108*
Haliastur indus 100
Hammerhead (Hammerkop) 82, 86
Hapalodermes 153
Harlequin Quail 116
Harpactes 153
Harpia harpyja 102
Harpy Eagle 102
harriers 99, 103–5, *107*
Hawaiian Goose 91
Hawaiian honeycreepers 176
Hawfinch *16*, 17, 179
Hawk Owl 41
hawks 99, 105
Hazel Hen 113
Heath Hen 114
Hedge Sparrow (Dunnock) 31, 166–7, *167*
Heliopais personata 125
Heliornis fulica 125
Heliornithidae 125
Helmet Bird 165
helmet-shrikes 164–5
hemipodes 121
Hemiprocnidae 150
Hen Harrier 104, *104*
Hermit Thrush 172
herons 15, *15*, 16, 29, 61, 64, 65, 81, 82–6, 89
Herring Gull 132
Heteralocha acutirostris 181
Hieraëtus 101
peanatus 102
Hill Mynah 181
Himantopus himantopus *60*, 130, *131*
hirundines 65
Hirundinidae 162–3
Hirundo 162
daurica 162
rustica 162, *162*
Hoary-headed Grebe 76
Hoatzin 108, 120, *121*
Honey Buzzard 17, 28, 100
honey-eaters 174–5
honey-guides 155
Hooded Crow 184
Hooded Merganser 94
Hooded Pitta *158*
Hooded Vulture 100
Hoopoe Lark 58
hoopoes 23, 26, 153, 154, *155*

hornbills 15, 27, 152, 153, 154
Horned Grebe 76
Horned Guan 111
Horned Lark 162
Horned Screamer 89
House Crow 184, *185*
House Martin 162, 182
House Sparrow 175, 180, *180*
House Wren 166
Hudsonian Curlew 130
Hudsonian Godwit 62
Huia 181
humming-birds 12–13, 15, 18, 28, 42, 46, 48, *48*, 150–2
Hyacinth Macaw *48*
Hydrobates pelagicus 78
Hydrabatidae 78
Hydrophasianus chirurgus 126–7
Hypocoliidae 165
Hypocolius 165
ampelinus 165
Hypositta corallirostris 173
Hyposittinae 173

Ibidorhyncha struthersii 130
Ibis-bill 130
ibises 82, 85, 88
Icteria virens 176
Icteridae 157, 177–9, 181
Icterus galbula 178
Ictinia mississippiensis 100
Imperial Eagle 102
Impeyan Pheasant 116
Inca Tern 134
incubation 29
incubator birds 108
Indian Darter 81
Indian Grackle 181
Indian Skimmer *64*, 134
Indicator indicator 155
Indicatoridae 155
Indigo Bunting *19*
Irediparra gallinacea 127
Irena puella 164
Irenidae 164
Iridoprocne bicolor 162
Ithaginis cruentus 116
Ivory-billed Woodcreeper 158
Ixobrychus exilis 85
minutus 85, *85*

Jabiru mycteria 87
Jabiru Stork 64, 86, 87
jacamars 155
jacana 14, 25, 63, 126–7
Jacana spinosa 25, 126
Jacanidae 126–7
Jackdaw 130, 184, *184*
Jacksnipe 129
Jacobin pigeons 138
jaegers 132
Jamaican Tody 153
Japanese Night Heron 85
Java Sparrow 180
Javan Fowl 116
Javan Peacock 23
jays 184–5, *185*
Junco hyemalis 175
juncos 175
jungle fowls 108
Jynginae 156
Jynx ruficollis 157
torquilla *43*, 157

Kagu 125
kaka 140
kakapo 140, 141
Kalochelidon euchrysea 162
kasmalos 140
Kea 140, 141, *142*
Keel-billed Toucan *156*
Kentish Plover 128
Kestrel 52, 106–7, *107*
Killdeer 130
King Cormorant 81
King Crow 181
King Eider Duck 94, *95*
King of Saxony Bird of Paradise 183
King Penguin 26, 74, *74*
King Rail 123
King Shag *80*
King Vulture *95*, 99
kingbirds 158–61
Kingfisher 27, 62, *62*, 152, 153
kingfishers 55, 65
kinglets 169
kites 99, 100–1
Kittiwake 23, 68, 134, 135
kiwis 55, 56, 72–3
Knot 129
Koel 141
Kookaburra 55, *56*, 153
Kori Bustard 55

Lady Amherst's Pheasant 116
Lagopus 112
lagopus 111, *111*, 112
mutus *37*
Lamenting Bird 122
Lammergeier 99, *100*, 101
Land Rail 123
Laniidae 164, 183
Lanius collurio 164, *164*
excubitor 164
ludovicianus 164
senator 164
Lapland Bunting 37
Lappet-faced Vulture *57*, *99*
Lapwing 128
Laridae 132, 134
larks 50, 52, 157, 161–2, 180
Larosterna inca 134
Larus argentatus 132
atricilla 134
californicus 134
canus 134
delawarensis 134
fuscus *25*, 132
marinus 134
melanocephalus 134
minutus 134
novaehollandiae 134
ridibundus *23*, 134
Laterallus jamaicensis 124
Laughing Gull 134
Laughing Jackass 153
Laysan Albatross 78
Leach's Petrel 21, 78
leafbirds 164
Least Bittern 85
Least Flycatcher 160
Least Grebe 76
Least Kingfisher 153
Least Sandpiper 37, 129
Least Tern 134
Leghorn Fowl 128
legs 14, *14*
Leiothrix argentauris 167
Leipoa 111
Leptoptilos crumeniferus 87–88, *87*
dubius 87
Leptosomatidae 154
Lesser Adjutant 87
Lesser Black-backed Gull *25*, 132
Lesser Flamingo *7*, 63, 64, 89, *96*
Lesser Frigate-bird 82
Lesser Golden Grebe 76
Lesser Golden Plover *127*
Lesser Nighthawk 149–50
Lesser Pied Kingfisher *152*
Lesser Prairie Chicken 113
Lesser Spotted Woodpecker 156
Lesser White-fronted Goose *91*
Lesser Yellowlegs 129
Lewis' Woodpecker *29*
Lilac-breasted Roller 55
Lily-trotter *65*, *111*, 126–7
Limnodromus griseus 129
Limosa 130
Limpkin 122–3
Linnet 142, 179
Little Auk 135
Little Bittern 85, *85*
Little Blue Heron 84
Little Bunting *175*
Little Bustard 24, 126
Little Crake 124
Little Egret *83*, 84, 88
Little Grebe 76, *76*
Little Gull 134
Little Owl 16, 146
Little Ringed Plover 128
Little Spotted Kiwi 72
Little Stint 129
locust birds 131
Locustella 169
Loddige's Racket-tailed Humming-bird 152
Loddigesia mirabilis 152
Loggerhead Shrike 164
Lonchura molucca 180
Long-billed Curlew *61*, 62, 130
Long-eared Owl 26, 144, *145*, 146
Long-tailed Hermit 152
Long-tailed Nightjar 149
Long-tailed Skua (Jaeger) 36, 132
Long-tailed Tit 172, *172*
longspurs 175
loons 16, 32, 74, 76
Lophodytes cucullatus 94
Lophophorus impejanus 116
Lophortyx californicus 116
gambelii 116
Lophura nycthemera 116
loras 164
lories 139, 140
lorikeets 140
Lorius lory *141*
Lovebird 46, *47*, 140
Loxia curvirostra *40*, 179
leucoptera 179
Lullula arborea 161, *161*
Luscinia cyane 173
megarhynchos 172
svecica 172–3
Lymnocryptes minima 129
Lyrebird 113, 161
Lyrurus tetrix 113

Macaroni Penguin 74
macaws 33, 46, 139, 140
Machaerhamphinae 99
Macrodiopteryx vexillarius 18, 149
Macronectes giganteus 78
halli 78
Magellanic penguin *67*, *75*
Magnificent Frigate-bird 82, *82*
Magnolia Warbler 40, 176
Magpie 11, 29, 184
Magpie Goose 90
Magpie-lark *182*
magpies 27, 29, 184
Maguari Stork 87
Malachite Kingfisher 65
Malay Nunbabbler 167
Malay Rail-bubbler 167
Mallard 90, 92–3, *93*
Mallee Fowl *27*
Malurus 169
Man-o'-war Bird 82
manakins 22, 160
Mandarin Duck *23*, 94
Manumea Pigeon 139
Manx Shearwater 78
Marabou 37–9, *87*
Marsh Harrier 62
Marsh Hawk 52, *52*, 103–5
Marsh Sandpiper *65*, *130*
marsh tern 65
Marsh Tit 172
Marsh Warbler 169
Martial Eagle 51, *51*
martins 27, 162–3
Masked Booby *68*, 80
mating *23*, 24
Meadow Pipit 163
Meadowlark 52
Mealy Parrot 140
Mediterranean Gull 134
Megadyptes 73, 74
antipodes 74
Megapodes 108, 111
Megapodiidae 108, 111
Melanerpes aurifrons 156
erythrocephalus 156
formicivorus 156
lewis *29*
Melanocorypha calandra 161
Meleagrididae 108, 119–20
Meleagris gallopavo 120, *120*
Melierax canorus *105*
metabates *105*
Meliphaga flavescens *174*
Meliphagidae 174–5
Mellisuga helenae 151
Melopsittacus undulatus 140
Menura alberti 161
novaehollandiae *160*, 161
Menurae 157
Menuridae 161
mergansers 17, 90, 94–5
Mergini 90, 94
Mergus merganser 94, *95*
serrator 94
Merlin 106
Meropidae 153–4
Merops apiaster 153–4, *154*
mesites 120–1
Mesitornithidae 120–1
Mew Gull 132, 134
Middle Spotted Woodpecker 156
Migrant Shrike 164
migration 18–21
migratory routes 21
Military Macaw 140
Milvinae 99, 100
Milvus migrans 100, *100*
milvus 100
Mimidae 166
Mimus polyglottos 166, *167*
minivets 163
Mirafra 162
Mistle Thrush 172
Mniotilta varia 176
moas 56
Mockingbird 24, 166, *167*
Moho 175
Molothrus ater 178–9
Moluccan Mannikin 180
Momotidae 153
monias 120–1
Monias benschi 120–1
Montagu's Harrier 104
Monticola saxatilis 172
solitarius 172
Moorhen *62*, 89, 124
Motacilla alba 163, 173
cinerea 163, *163*
flava 163
Motacillidae 163
moth owls 148
Mother Carey's chicken
see Wilson's Storm Petrel
motmots 153
moult 11, 19
moundbuilders 108
Mountain Linnet 179
Mountain Quail 116
Mourning Dove *58*
mouse-birds 152
Mudlark 182
Muscicapa striata 168, *169*
thalassina 168
Muscicapidae 167
Muscicapinae 167, 168
Muscivora forficata 160
Muscovy Duck 94
Musophagidae 141
Mussel-pecker 127
Mute Swan *90*, 91
Mycteria americana 87
Myiarchus 160
crinitus 160
Myiodynastes luteiventris 18
mynahs 181
Myrtle Warbler 176

Nannopterum harrisi 81
Narina Trogon *152*
Nashville Warbler 40, 176
Nasiterna pygmaea 141
navigation 21
Nectariniidae 174
Nene Goose 91
Neodrepanis coruscans 159
hypoxantha 159
Neophron monachus 100
percnopterus *57*, 59, 100
Neosittinae 173
nesting 19, 26–9
Nestor notabilis 141, *142*
Netta rufina 93, *93*
New World Anhinga 81
New World vultures 96, 98
New Zealand Bell-bird 174
New Zealand Dabchick 76
New Zealand Dotterel 127
New Zealand Shelduck 92
Nicobar Pigeon 139
Night Heron *84*, 85
Nighthawk 17, 148, 149
Nightingale 172, 173
Nightjar 147–50, *149*
noddies 134
Noddy Tern 134
Noisy Scrub-bird 161
North African Desert-owl 144
North American Acorn Woodpecker 43
North Atlantic Gannet 80, *81*
northern forests 39–41
Northern Fulmar 78
Northern Phalarope 131
Northern Shrike 164
Notharchus macrorhynchus 155
Notornis 124
mantelli 124
Nucifraga caryocatactes 184
columbianus 184
Numenius 130

americanus *61*, 130
arquata 130
borealis *32*, 130
phaeopus 130
tahitiensis 21, 130
Numida meleagris 119
Numididae 108, 119
nuthatches 173–4
Nyctea scandiaca *37*, 147
Nyctibiidae 148
Nyctibius 148
griseus *148*
Nycticorax 85
nyctocorax *84*, 85
violaceus 85
Nycticryphes semicollaris 127
Nyctidromus albicollis 149

Oceanites oceanicus 21, 78
Oceanodroma leucorhoa 78
oceans 66–8
Ocellated Turkey 120
Oenanthe oenanthe 173
Oilbird 147, 148
Old World blackbirds 172, 181
Old World flycatchers 167, 168, 172
Old World nutcracker 184
Old World orioles 181
Old World vultures 99–101
Old World warblers 167, 169–70
Old World White Pelican 79, *79*
Olive-backed Jungle Flycatcher 167
open-bills 98
Opisthocomidae 108, 120
Opisthocomus hoazin 120, *121*
Opisthoprora 151
Orange-cheeked Warbler *56*
Orange-winged Parrot 140
Oreophasis derbianus 111
Oreortyx pictus 116
orioles 157, 178–9
Oriolidae 181
Oriolus oriolus 181
oropendolas 178
Orthotomus 169
Ortolan Bunting 175
Ortyxelos meiffrenii 121
Oscines 157, 161–2
Osprey 95, 100, 105–6, *106*
Ostrich 27, 28, *53*, 55–6, *59*, 71–2
Otididae 126
Otis tarda 126
tetrax 126
Otus 146
asio *45*, 144, 146
scops 146
Ovenbird 42, 176, *178*
ovenbirds 158
owlet-frogmouths 147, 148
owlet-nightjars 148
owls 16, 17, 26, 28, 41, 45, 143–4
oxpeckers 54–5, *55*, 181
Oxyruncidae 160
Oxyruncus cristatus 160
Oxyura jamaicensis 95
Oxyurini 90, 95
oystercatchers 126, 127

Pachycephala 168
Pachyptila 78
Padda oryzivora 180
Pagodroma nivea 78
Painted Bunting 175
Painted Snipe 25, 127
Pale Chanting Goshawk *105*
Pallas's Sandgrouse 136
Palm-chat 165
Pandion haliaëtus 105–6, *106*
Pandionidae 105–6
Pandioninae 100
Panurus biarmicus 172
Papuan Mountain Drongo 181
Paradisaea apoda 183
raggiana *183*
rudolphi *49*
Paradisaeidae 183
Paradise Tanager 176
Paradoxornithinae 168
parakeets 46, 140
Parasitic Jaeger 132
Paridae 171–2
parrot pigeons 139
parrot-finches 180
parrotbills 168
parrots 26, 27, 33, 46, 48, 139–41
Parson-bird 174
Parson finch *56*
Partridge 23, *50*, 51, 113, 114
partridges 13, 23, 27, 108
Parula Warbler 42
Parulidae 42, 176
Parus altricapillus 172
ater 172
bicolor 172
caeruleus 173–4, *174*
carolinensis 172
cristatus 172
hudsonicus 172
major 173
palustris 172
Passenger Pigeon 32, 138
Passer domesticus 180, *180*
montanus 180
Passeres 161–2
Passeriformes 157
Passerina ciris 175
cyarea *19*
Patagona gigas 151
Patagonian conure 48
Pavo 119
cristatus *118*, 119
muticus *119*
Pea Fowl 108, 116, 117, 118–9
Peacock 22, 23, 108
Pedionomidae 121
Peewit 128
Pelecanidae 79
Pelecaniformes 78
Pelecanoides 78
Pelecanoididae 78
Pelecanus crispus 79
erythrorhynchos 79
occidentalis 79
onocrotalus 79, *79*
rufescens *65*
pelicans 15, 16, 28, 63, 78, 79
Penduline Tit 28, 172
Penelope 111
penguins 8, 10, 20, 28, 67, 73–4
Pennant-winged Nightjar 18–19, 149
perching birds 157–8
perching ducks 94
Perdix perdix *50*, 114
Peregrine Falcon 28, 50, 106
Pericrocotus flammeus 163
Perninae 99, 100
Pernis apivorus 100
Peruvian Booby 80
petrels 16, 77
Petrochelidon 162
Phaëthon aethereus 78–9
lepturus *78*, 79
rubricauda 79
Phaethontidae 78–9
Phaethornis superciliosa 152
Phalacrocoracidae 80–1
Phalacrocorax albiventer *80*, 81
aristotelis 80
auritus 80
bougainvillii *66*
capensis *66*
carbo 80
pygmaeus 81
varius 83
Phalaenoptilus nuttallii 149
Phalaropes 131
Phalaropidae 131
Phalaropus
fulicarius 131
lobatus *38*, 131
tricolor 131
Phaps histrionica *51*
Pharaoh's Chicken 100
Pharomachrus mocinno *46*, 153
Phasianidae 23, 108, 114–19
Phasianus colchicus 116
Pheasant-tailed Jacana 126–7
pheasants 23, 108, 114–19
Philadelphia Vireo 177
Philepitta castanea 159
schlegeli 159
Philepittidae 159
Philesturnus carunculatus 181–2
Philippine Cockatoo *140*
Philohela minor 129
Philomachus pugnax 129
Phoebetria *77*
Phoenicomaias minor 89, *96*
Phoenicopteridae 89
Phoenicopteriformes 89
Phoenicopterus ruber 89
Phoeniculidae 154
Phoenicurus phoenicurus 173
Phylloscopus 169
sibilatrix *44*
trochilus 169
Phytotomidae 161
Pica nuttalli 184
pica 184
Picarthartes 167
gymnocephalus 168
oreas 168
Picathartinae 167–8
Picidae 156–7
Piciformes 152, 155
Picoides arcticus 157
tridactylus 156, 157
piculets 156
Picumninae 156
Picus canus 156
viridis 156
Pied Butcherbird 183
Pied Cormorant 81
Pied Flycatcher 168
Pied Kingfisher 153
Pied Wagtail 163, 173
Pied-billed Grebe 76
Pigeonhawk 106
pigeons *13*, 16, 21, 29, 136–9, 181
Pin-tailed Sandgrouse 136
Pintail 92, 93
Pine Grosbeak 38–9, 40
Pink-backed Pelican *65*
Pink-footed Goose 91
piping crows 182
pipits 52, 142, 163, 178
Pipridae 160
Piranga ludoviciana 176
olivacea 175–6
rubra 176
Pitta angolensis 159
erythrogaster 159
sordida *158*
pittas *158*, 159
Pittidae 159
Pityriasis gymnocephala 164
Plains-wanderer 121
plant-cutters 161
plantain-eaters 141
Platalea ajaja 88
leucorodia 88
Plautius alle 135
impennis 136
Plectorhyncha lanceolata 30
Plectrophenax nivalis *36*
Plegadis falcinellus 88
Ploceidae 175, 180–1
Ploceus 180–1
cucullatus *27*, *180*
plovers 17, 28, 62, 126, 127–8
plumage 11
Plush-capped Finch 176
Pluvialis 127
aegyptius 128
apricaria 127
dominica 127, *127*
obscurus 127
squatarola 127
pochards 92–3
Podargidae 148
Podargus strigoides *149*
Podica senegalensis 125
Podicipediformes 76–7
Podiceps 76
auritus 76
chilensis 76
cristatus 76, *76*
dominicus 76
grisegena 76
major 76
nigricollis 76, *77*
novaehollandiae 76
occipitalis 76
poliocephalus 76
ruficollis 76, *76*
rufopectus 76
Podilymbus podiceps 76
Poephilia cincta *56*
guttata 180
Poicephalus senegalus 140
Polemaetus bellicosus *51*
Polioptila caerulea 172
Polyborinae 108
Polysticta stelleri 94
Pomarine Skua (Jaeger) 132
Pooecetes gramineus 175
poor-will 149
Porphyrio porphyrio 124
Porphyrula martinica 124
Porzana carolina 124
parva 124
porzana 123–4
potoo 17, 147, 148
pouter pigeons 138
prairie chicken 51, 113–14
pratincoles 131
preening 10–11
Prince Albert's Lyrebird 161
Prionopidae 164–5
Prionops plumata 165
poliocephalus 165
prions 78
Procellariidae 78
Procellariiformes 77
Procnias alba 160
Progne chalybea 162
subis 162
Prosthemadera novaeseelandiae 174
Prunella modularis 166–7, *167*
Prunellidae 166–7
Pseudochelidon eurystomina 162–3
Psittacidae 139–141
Psittaciformes 139–41
Psittacula 140
Psittacus erithacus 140
Psophia crepitans 123
Psophiidae 125, 126
Ptarmigan 11, 108, 111–14
Pteridophora alberti 183
Pterocles alchata 136
Pteroclidae 136
Pterocnemia pennata 72
Pterodroma hasitata 78
Pteroglossus 155–6
Ptilogonatidae 165
Ptilonorhynchidae 183
Ptilonorhynchus violaceus *182*
puffbirds 155
Puffin 28, 31, 68, *68*, 135, *136*
Puffinus gravis 21, 78
griseus 78
puffinus 78
tenuirostris 78
Purple Gallinule 124
Purple harrier 62
Purple Heron *83*, 84
Purple Martin 162
Pycnonotidae 163–4
Pycnonotus goiavier 164
nigricans *163*
zeylanicus 164
Pygmornis rubra 151
Pygmy Cormorant 81
Pygmy Falcon 55
Pygmy Kingfisher 65, 153
Pygmy Owl 146
Pygmy Parrot 140, 141
Pygoscelis 73, 74
adeliae 74, *74*
antarctica *132*
papua *72*, 74
Pyrocephalus rubinus *159*, 160
Pyrrhocorax 184
graculus 184
pyrrhocorax 184
Pyrrhula pyrrhula 179
Pyrrhuloxiinae 175

Quail 19, 27, 51, 108, 114, 115–16
Quail-plover 121
Quelea 181
Quelea quelea 181
Quetzal *46*, 153
Quiscalus quiscula 178

Racket-tailed Drongo 181
Racket-tailed Kingfisher 153
radar tracking 20
Raggiana Bird of Paradise *183*
rails 120, 123–4
Rallicula forbesi 124
Rallidae 123–5
Rallus aquaticus 123
caerulescens 123
elegans 123
limicola 123
longirostris 123
pectoralis 123
Ramphastidae 155–6
Ramphastos 155
sulfuratus *156*
Raphidae 136
Raven 59, 184
Razor-billed Auk 135
Razorbill 31, 135–6, *135*
Recurvirostra americana *17*, 130–1
andina 130–1
novaehollandiae 131
Recurvirostridae 130
Red Crossbill 179
Red Grouse 111, 112, 113
Red Jungle Fowl 116–17, *117*

Red Kite 100
Red Lory 141
Red Ovenbird 158
Red-and-green Macaw *139*
Red-backed Shrike 164, *164*
Red-billed Gull 134
Red-billed quelea 56
Red-billed Tropic-bird 78–9
Red-breasted Merganser 94, 95
Red-breasted Nuthatch 42, 173
Red-breasted Pitta 159
Red-browed Tree Creeper 174
Red-crested Pochard 93–4, *93*
Red-eared waxbill *56*
Red-eyed Bulbul *163*
Red-eyed Vireo 18, 177, *177*
Red-footed Booby 80
Red-footed Falcon 107
Red-headed Woodpecker 156
Red-knobbed Coot *125*
Red-legged Partridge 114, 115
Red-necked Grebe 76
Red-necked Phalarope 36, 37, *38*, 131
Red-rumped Swallow 27, 162
Red-shafted Flicker 156, *157*
Red-shouldered Cuckoo-shrike 163
Red-shouldered Hawk 43
Red-tailed Hawk 41, 52, *103*
Red-tailed Tropic-bird 79
Red-throated Diver (Loon) 76
Red-vented Cockatoo *140*
Red-winged Blackbird 178, *178*
Redshank 126, 129
redstarts 172, 173, 176
Redwing 40, 172
Reed Warbler 31, *31*, 62, *142*, 169
Reeves's Pheasant 23, 116
Regulus regulus 169
sapatra 169
Reptile-bird 120
respiration 12, 14
Rhea americana 72
rheas 27, 55, 72
Rheiformes 72
Rhinoceros Auklet *135*
Rhinocryptidae 159
Rhinomyias olivacea 167
Rhipidura 168
Rhynochetidae 125
Rhynochetus jubatus 125
Rhynchops albicollis *64*
flavirostris *64*
nigra *64*
Rifleman 159
Ring Dove 137, *137*
Ring Ouzel 172
Ring-billed Gull 134
Ring-necked Pheasant 116
Ringed Kingfisher 65
Ringed Plover 128
Riparia 162
Rissa tridactyla 134
Roadrunner 59, 143, *143*
roatelos 120–1
Robin *11*, 21, 24, 43, 44, 142, 172, *173*
robins 19, 172, 173
Rock Dove 136–7, 138
Rock Partridge *114*
Rock Pipit 163
Rock Ptarmigan *37*, 38, 111, 112
Rock Wren 159
Rock-thrush 172
Rockhopper Penguin 76, *77*
rollers 56, 154, *156*
Roman pigeons 138
Rook 184
Rose Fowl 117
Rose-coloured Flamingo 89
Rose-coloured Starling 181
Roseate Spoonbill 17, 88
Rostratula 25
benghalensis 127
Rostratulidae 127
Rostrhamus sociabilis 100
Rough-legged Buzzard 38
Royal Albatross 77
Ruby-crowned Kinglet 42
Ruby-throated Humming-bird 42, 151
Ruddy Duck 95
Ruddy Shelduck 92, *92*
Ruddy Turnstone 37, 128
Ruff 22–3, 129
Ruffed Grouse 114
Rufous Humming-bird 42, 151
Rufous Scrub-bird 161
Rupicola 160
Rynchopidae 134
Rynchops albicollis 134
flavirostris 134
nigra 134, *134*
Sabine's Gull 134
Sacred Ibis 88, *88*
Saddleback 181–2
Saddlebill Stork 64, 87
Sage Grouse 113, *113*
Sagittariidae 108
Sagittarius serpentarius *55*, *99*, 108
St Helena Waxbill *56*
Saker 106
Sand Martin 162
Sanderling 18
Sandgrouse 58, 136
Sandhill Crane 51, *122*
sandpipers 126, 129–30
sapsuckers 44
Sarcorhamphus papa *95*, 99
Satin Bowerbird *182*
Satyr Tragopan 116
savanna 53–6
sawbills 17, 94
Saxicola rubetra *172*
torquata 173
Sayornis phoebe 160
saya 160
Say's Phoebe 160
Scaled Quail 115–16
Scarlet Ibis *64*, 88, *89*
Scarlet Macaw *48*, *139*, 140
Scarlet Tanager 175–6
Scarlet-backed Flowerpecker 174
Schlegel's Asity 159
Scissor-tailed Flycatcher 160
Scolopacidae 128–30
Scolopax rusticola 128–9, *129*
Scopidae 86
Scops Owl 146
Scopus umbretta 86
scoters 94
screamers 89–90
Screech Owl *45*, 144, 146
scrub-birds 161
sea ducks *see* mergansers
Sea-eagle 102
Sea-pie 127
sea-swallows 134
Secretary Bird 53, *55*, *99*
Sedge Warbler 31, 142, 169, *169*
seedsnipes 131
Seiurus 176
aurocapillus 176, *178*
Selasphorus rufus 151
Seleucidis melanoleuca 183
Semi-palmated Sandpiper 37
seriemas 125–6
Serin 179
Serinus canaria 179
serinus 179
serpent eagles 99, 102–3
Setophaga ruticilla 176
Shag 80
Sharp-shinned Hawk 41
Sharpbill 160
shearwaters 16, 66–7, 68, 77, 78
sheathbills 131–2
shelducks 17, 92
shelgeese 92
shell-storks 88
Shining Cuckoo 142–3
Shoebill 16, 82, 86
Shorelark 162
Short-billed Dowitcher 129
Short-eared owl 52, 146
Short-tailed Shearwater 78
Short-toed Eagle 102, 103
Short-toed Lark 161
Short-toed Tree-creeper 173, *173*
Short-winged Grebe 76
shortwings 173
shoveler 17, 92
shrikes 17, 20, 164
Sialia sialis 173
Siberian Blue Robin 173
Siberian White Crane 65
Sicklebird 165
silky flycatchers 165
Silver Grebe 76
Silver Gull 134
Silver Pheasant 23, 116
Silver-eared Mesia 167
Silver-grey Fulmar 78
Siskin 179
Sitta canadensis 173
carolinensis 173, *173*
europaea 173
pusilla 173–4
Sittidae 172–4
skeleton 12, *12*
skimmers 134
skuas 67, 68, 132
Skylark 27, 52, 161
Slate-breasted Water Rail 123
Slender-tailed Shearwater 78
Small-billed False Sunbird 159
small-tongued parrots 140
Smooth-billed Ani *143*
snail kites 17
Snakebird *80*, 81
Snipe 62, 126, 129
Snow Bunting *36*, 37
Snow Goose 18, *18*, 91
Snow Petrel 78
Snowy Egret 84
Snowy Owl 36, *37*, 147
Snowy Plover 128
Sociable Weaver 28
sociable weaver-birds 181
solitaires 136
Solitary Vireo 177
Somateria fischeri 94
mollisima *26*, 94, *95*
spectabilis 94, *95*
Somateriini 90, 94
song 24
song birds 161–2
Song Thrush 172
Sonnerat's Fowl 116
Sooty Oystercatcher 127
Sooty Shearwater 78
Sora 124
South American Bittern 85
South American Cattle Tyrant 54
Southern Ostrich 71
Sparrow Owl 146
Sparrowhawk 27, 41, 95, 105
sparrows 41, 52, 175, 180, 181
Spectacled Eider 94
Spectacled Shrike 165
Speotyto cunicularia 146–7, *146*
Sphenisciformes 73–4
Spheniscus 73, 74
demersus 74
magellanicus *65*, *75*
Sphyrapicus varius 156
Spizaetus 101
spoonbills 17, 82, 88, *88*
Spotted Crake 123–4
Spotted Eagle 102
Spotted Eagle Owl *145*
Spotted Flycatcher 43, 168, *169*
Spotted Redshank 129
Spotted Sandpiper 130
Sprague's Pipit 163
Spruce Grouse *24*, 40, 41
Squacco Heron 84–5, *84*
Stanley's Fowl 116
starlings 21, 157, 181
Steatornis caripensis 148
Steatornithidae 148
Steller's Eider 94
Steller's Jay *41*, 185
Stephens Island Rock Wren 159
Steppe Eagle 50
Stercorariidae 132
Stercorarius longicaudus 132
parasiticus 132
pomarinus 132
skua 132, *132*
Sterna albifrons 134
hirundo 134
nereis *26*
paradisaea *20*, 21, *133*
stiff-tailed ducks 95
stilts 130
stints 129
Stock Dove 137
Stone Curlew 131, *132*
Stonechat *172*, 173
storks *21*, 65, 82, 86–88, 89, 130
Storm Petrel 78
Strepera 182
Streptopelia decaocto *138*, 139
turtur 139
Strigidae 144, 146–7
Strigiformes 143–7
Strigops 141
habroptilus 141
Striped Button-quail 121
Strix nebulosa 147, *148*
varia 147
Struthidea cinerea 182
Struthio camelus *53*, *59*, 71
Struthioniformes 71–2
Sturnella magna *52*, 178
neglecta *52*, 178
Sturnidae 157, 181
Sturnus roseus 181
vulgaris 181
Sula abbotti 80
bassana 80, *81*
capensis 80, *81*
dactylatra *68*, 80
leucogaster *68*, 80
nebouxii 80, *81*
serrator 80
sula 80
variegata 80
Sulidae 79–80
Sulphur-bellied Flycatcher 18
Sulphur-breasted Toucan *156*
Sulphur-crested Cockatoo 140
Summer Tanager 176
sun-grebes 125
sunbirds 174
Sunbittern 125
Superb Lyrebird *160*, 161
Surfbird 128
Swallow 162, *162*
Swallow-tailed Kite 100
Swallow-tanager 176
swallows 27, 105, 130, 162
swans 24, *36*, 62, 89, 90, 91
swifts 15, 17, 150, *150*
Sylvia 169
atricapilla 169
borin 169
Sylviinae 167, 169–70
Syrmaticus reevesii 116
Syrrhaptes paradoxus 136

Tachyeres 92
Tadorna ferruginea 92
tadorna 92
variegata 92
Tadornini 90, 92
Tahitian Curlew 21
Tailor-bird 28
tailor-birds 169
Takahe 33, 124
Talking Mynah 181
Tangara chilensis 176
laviniga cara *177*
tanagers 175–6
Tantalus Ibis 88
Tanysiptera galatea 153
tapaculos 159
Tattler 130
Tawny Eagle *102*
Tawny Frogmouth *149*
Tawny Owl 146, 147, *147*
teal 17, 92, 93, 134
Teledromas fuscus 159
Temminck's Stint 129
temperate grasslands 50–52
temperate wetlands 60–63
temperate woodlands 42–5
Tennessee Warbler 176
Terathopius ecaudatus 103
terns 31, 68, 134, 135
Terpsiphone atrocaudata 168
paradisi *168*
territory 23–4
Tersina viridis 176
Tersininae 176
Tetrao urogallus 112
Tetraonidae 108, 111–14
Tetrastes bonasia 113
Thick-knee 131
Thinocoridae 131
thrashers 166
Thraupinae 175–6
Three-toed Woodpecker 156, 157
Threskiornis aethiopica 88, *88*
Threskiornithidae 88
thrushes 24, 167, 172, 181
Tichodroma muraria 173
Timaliinae 167, 168
Tinamiformes 73
tinamous 10, 73
titmice 171–2
tityras 160
Tockus flavirostris *155*
Todidae 153
todies 153
tongue 15, *43*, 44
Tooth-billed Pigeon 139
toucans 15, 46, 155–6
towhees 175
Toxostoma rufum 166
Tragopan satyra 116
treecreepers 43–44, 172–3
tree ducks 90–1
Tree Pipit 163
Tree Sparrow 175, 180
Tree Swallow 162
Treron abyssinica 139
Trichastoma abbotti 167
Trichoglossus 141
Tringa 129

erythropus 129
flavipes 129
glareola 129
hypoleucos 130
incana 130
macularia 130
melanoleuca 129
nebularia 129
ochropus 129, *130*
stagnatilis *130*
totanus 129
Trochilidae 150–2
Troglodytes aedon 166
troglodytes 166, *166*
Troglodytidae 166
Trogonidae 152
Trogoniformes 152–3
trogons 152–3
tropic birds 78–9
tropical forests 46–9
tropical wetlands 63–5
troupials 178
true warblers 169–70
Trumpeter Swan 91
trumpeters 123, 126
Tufted Duck 94
Tufted Titmouse 172
Tui 174
tundra 36–8
turacos 141
Turdinae 172–3
Turdus merula 172
migratorius 172, *173*
musicus 172
philomelos 172
pilaris 172
torquatus 172
viscivorus 172
turkey 108, 119–20, *120*
Turkey Buzzard 99
Turkey vulture 52, 99
Turnicidae 25, 121
Turnix 121
sylvatica 121
turnstones 128
Turtle Dove 15, 139
Twelve-wired Bird of Paradise 183
Twite 179
Two-barred Crossbill 39, 179
Tympanuchus cupido 113
pallidicinctus 113
Tyranni 157, 158
Tyrannidae 159–60
Tyrannus tyrannus 160
tyrant flycatchers 159–60
Tyto alba 144, *144*
Tytonidae 144, 146

Umbrella-bird 160
Upland Sandpiper 51–2, 56, 130
Upupa epops 154, *155*
Upupidae 154
Uria aalge 135
Urubu 99

Vanellus 128
armatus 128
tricolor 128, *128*
vanellus 128
vanga-shrikes 165
Vangidae 165
Variegated Tinamou 73
Veery 172
Veery's thrush 42
Velvet Asity 159
Verditer Flycatcher 168
Vermilion Flycatcher *159*, 160
Vermivora peregrina 176
ruficapilla 176
Vesper Sparrow 175
Vireo flavifrons 177
gilvus 177
griseus 177
olivaceus 177, *177*
philadelphicus 177
solitarius 177
Vireonidae 176–7
vireos 176–7
Virginia Rail 123
Vultur californianus 32, *96*, 99
gryphus 96, *96*
vultures 13, 59, 95
Vulturine Guinea-fowl 119, *119*

waders 126, 130
wagtails 21, 58, 105, 163
Wall Creeper 173
Wandering Albatross *67*, 77, *77*
warblers *15*, 24, 40, 41, 42, 181
Warbling Vireo 177
water-ouzels 165–6
Water-rail 123, 124
water-thrushes 176
Wattled Crow 181
Wattled False Sunbird 159
Waved Albatross *25*
Waxbill 56, *56*
waxbills 180
Waxwing *40*, 165, *165*
weaver-birds 28, *54*, 55, 180–1
Weka 124
Western Bell-magpie 182
Western Grebe 76
Western Meadowlark *52*, 178
Western Tanager 176
Western Wood Pewee 160
Whale-headed Stork 86
Wheatear 142, 172, 173
Whimbrel 130
Whinchat *172*
Whip-poor-will 149
whistlers 168
whistling ducks 90–1
Whistling Swan 91
White Bellbird 160
White Gooney 78
White Helmet-shrike 165
White Owl 144
White Peacock 119
White Pelican 63
White Spoonbill 88, *88*
White Stork 86–7, *86*
White Wagtail 163, 173
White-backed Bell-magpie 182
White-bellied Sandgrouse 136
White-billed Diver 76
White-breasted Nuthatch 173, *173*
White-crowned Forktail 173
White-eyed Pochard 94
White-eyed Vireo 177
white-eyes 174
White-flippered Penguin 74
White-fronted Goose 91, *91*
White-necked Bald Crow 168
White-necked Nighthawk 149
White-necked Puffbird 155
White-necked Rockfowl 168
White-rumped Shama 173
White-tailed Eagle 33, 102
White-tailed Ptarmigan 111
White-tailed Tropic Bird *78*, 79
White-throated Tree Creeper 174
White-winged Chough 182
Whooper Swan 91
Whooping Crane 122
whydahs 31, 180
Wigeon 17, 92, 93
Wild Duck 92
Wild Goose 91
Wild Swan 91
Willet 130
Willow Hen 11
Willow Ptarmigan 111, *111*, 112
Willow Tit 172
Willow Warbler 142, 169
Wilson's Phalarope 131
Wilson's Snipe 129
Wilson's Storm Petrel 21, 66, 78
wings 12–13, *12*
Winter Wren 166
wood hoopoes 154
Wood Owl 147
Wood Pigeon 26, 137, *137*
Wood Rail *123*
Wood Sandpiper 65, 129
Wood Stork 87
Wood Thrush 42, 172
Wood Warbler 43, *44*
Wood-grouse 112, 113
wood-nightjars 148
wood-swallows 182
wood warblers 176
Woodchat Shrike 164
Woodcock 14, 126, 128–29, *129*
woodcreepers 158
woodhewers 158
Woodland Kingfisher 55
Woodlark 161, *161*
woodpeckers 15, 19, 27, *43*, 44–5, 46, 152, 155, 156–7
Woodpecker-Finch *179*
wrens 19, 43, 44, 142, 166, *166*
Wren-thrush 170
Wren-tit 168
Wrybill 128
Wryneck *43*, 44, 156, 157

Xema sabini 134
Xenicidae 159
Xenicus gilviventris 159
logipes 159
lyalli 159
Xiphorhynchus flavigaster 158

Yellow Bunting 175
Yellow Wagtail 62, 163
Yellow Warbler 42, 176
Yellow-backed Sunbird 174
Yellow-bellied Sapsucker 42, 156
Yellow-bellied Waxbill *56*
Yellow-billed Cuckoo 143
Yellow-billed Loon 76
Yellow-billed Magpie 184
Yellow-billed Sheathbill *132*
Yellow-billed Tropic-bird 79
Yellow-breasted Chat 176
Yellow-crowned Bulbul 164
Yellow-crowned Night Heron 85
Yellow-eyed Penguin 74
Yellow-headed Amazon 140
Yellow-horned Hornbill *155*
Yellow-rumped Warbler 40
Yellow-shafted Flicker 156, *157*
Yellow-throat 176
Yellow-throated Vireo 177
Yellow-throated Warbler 176
Yellow-tinted Honeyeater *174*
Yellow-vented Bulbul 164
Yellowhammer 175
You-you 140
young birds 30–31
Ypecaha Wood-rail 124

Zebra Finch 56, 180
Zeledonia coronata 172
Zeledoniinae 172
Zenaida macroura *58*
Zosteropidae 174